RUSSIANS
IN SPACE

RUSSIANS

IN SPACE

BY

Evgeny Riabchikov

EDITED BY *Colonel General Nikolai P. Kamanin*

TRANSLATED BY *Guy Daniels*

PREPARED BY
THE NOVOSTI PRESS AGENCY PUBLISHING HOUSE, *Moscow*

DOUBLEDAY & COMPANY, INC.
Garden City, New York *1971*

Library of Congress Catalog Card Number 70–144291
Copyright © 1971 by Novosti Press Agency Publishing House
Translation Copyright © 1971 by Doubleday & Company, Inc.
All Rights Reserved
Printed in the United States of America

Contents

RUSSIANS
IN SPACE

The First Manned

Spaceship

The rocket was waiting . . .

Silvery gray and one hundred twenty-five feet tall, it stood there like a piece of sculpture, ready to surge into the sky. The rocket seemed to breathe like a living being, exuding wisps of vapor. The metal clamps of the green work tower were holding it in a tight embrace.

A gray-green bus was speeding toward the space vehicle along a paved road that ran through the springtime wilderness of the steppe.[1] Among those riding in the big bus were two men in bright orange spacesuits. This, and the fact that both of them occupied specially built seats, set them off from their companions.

At the time, the names of these two men were unknown to the public. From their external appearance they might have been twins: both were short and stocky, and they wore identical spacesuits, apparently cut to the same measure. On their heads they wore identical white helmets with the letters CCCP (USSR) in-

[1] The Baikonur (or Tyuratom) launch complex, northeast of the Aral Sea, is surrounded by semi-arid desert.—Translator

scribed on the front. Each of them had a small mirror sewn into the
orange sleeve of his spacesuit, and each wore black boots. They were
Yuri Gagarin and Gherman Titov.

They lifted the transparent face-plates of their white helmets,
revealing two faces which, far from being identical, were totally
unalike. Gagarin's expression amazed the physicians on the bus.
Scarcely leaning back in his seat, he looked cheerfully at his companions and joked with them to raise their spirits. There was so
much in Gagarin's smile: easy affection, magnanimity, tenderness
(almost like that of a child), and a serenity that was unforgettable.

Yuri Gagarin was on his way to be launched in a spaceship.
He would be the first man in the world to make a flight into the
unknown and to discover whether man could exist in space. He
was about to become a cosmonaut.

In those days, space was a complete enigma. People were
frightened by its mysteries: by the treachery of weightlessness, the
danger of deadly radiation, and the G-loads during the powered
ascent of the vehicle. Looking at Gagarin, however, one had the
impression that he was not about to make a space flight but was
merely along for the ride and was concerned about the morale
of the others.

"How do you feel, boys?" he asked. Then he suggested, "Let's
sing!" And they all sang.

Gherman Titov's expression, as he looked at his companions, was
calmer and somewhat more stern, although he too joined in.

In those days the ritual for seeing a man off to space had not
yet been worked out. The people in the bus tried to talk about
anything at all—just so it had nothing to do with space or the
impending flight—in order not to put an unnecessary strain on
the nerves of the cosmonauts.

Only Gagarin was to make the flight, but Titov was also in
the bus.

Why?

All the precautions and strict adherence to preventive measures
could not rule out the possibility of an awkward accident. For
example, the cosmonaut might become depressed; he might catch
a cold just before the launch; he might sprain his ankle on the
athletic field; or he might even get a piece of grit in his eye,
and because of just such a trifle, he might be disqualified for a

certain length of time. Therefore, a backup was provided for the cosmonaut so that a vast scientific-engineering operation of unprecedented scope would not be postponed because of an unforeseen accident. The supernumerary was always ready to take Number One's place if necessary.

Titov knew that he was merely serving as a backup.

At a recent session of the State Commission the results of the technical preparations had been reviewed, and a decision had been made as to which cosmonaut would be the first to make a flight.

The chairman of the State Commission had first given the floor to Chief Designer Sergei Pavlovich Korolev. Korolev, a rather stout, thickset man, whose face was at once expressive of idealism and a strong will, announced in a calm and businesslike tone of voice: "The spaceship is ready. The entire apparatus and equipment has been tested and functions impeccably. I request the Commission's authorization to proceed with the world's first manned space flight."

The commission unanimously approved the resolution: "We approve Comrade Korolev's proposal for the world's first manned space flight on the spaceship *Vostok* for 12 April 1961."

The Soviet Government had made the USSR Air Force responsible for training the cosmonauts. At this session of the State Commission, the Air Force was represented by Lieutenant General Nikolai Petrovich Kamanin. The general—a man with a high forehead and a handsome face—took the floor and made a detailed report on the flight-readiness of the cosmonauts, especially Yuri Gagarin and Gherman Titov. Then he introduced Gagarin and Titov to the members of the commission.

Gagarin rose to his feet, looked calmly at everyone about him, and smiled. The scientists, design engineers, doctors, and generals were already acquainted with Gagarin: they had been with him in the workshops of the space industry, in the laboratories, at the training sessions, and at lectures in the auditoriums. But at this tense moment they felt something special and heart-warming in the smile he gave them.

Gherman Titov—curly haired, with a high forehead and lively eyes—leaped to his feet and stood at attention.

Yuri Gagarin and Gherman Titov were standing shoulder to

shoulder. Both cosmonauts were trained to perfection. Both were first-class pilots. Both were popular with their friends, and both had families. Which one would be chosen?

The decision would be made by the members of the State Commission seated at the table—the scientists and designers, the doctors and engineers. Each of them understood his responsibility, and each would discharge it as he thought best, trying to avoid subjectivism and be as fair as was humanly possible.

They were waiting to hear the remarks of General Kamanin, who was to inform them of the recommendations of the Soviet Air Force.

At this point, a few words about Kamanin are in order.

In 1934 the steamer *Chelyuskin* was icebound in the Arctic. The Soviet Government sent a number of pilots to rescue the passengers and crew of the *Chelyuskin*. The youngest of the pilots was Nikolai Kamanin. He and his comrades displayed unprecedented courage and boldness, making flights over unmapped areas of the Arctic, far from any base. The crew and passengers of the *Chelyuskin* were rescued. The Soviet Government, as a mark of its high esteem for the feat performed by the pilots, established the highest honorary title in the country: Hero of the Soviet Union, accompanied by investiture with the Order of Lenin and a five-pointed gold star.

Later on Nikolai Kamanin was graduated from the military academy and became commander of an air division, then of an air corps. During the Great Patriotic War General Kamanin was at the front with his whole family: his wife, Mariya Mikhailovna, served with him at advance posts as a radio operator; and his son, Arkady, flew in his father's corps in a PO-2 plane, carrying messages, wounded, and ammunition.

After the war General Kamanin was assigned to responsible duties in connection with training amateur pilots. When the space age dawned, he took an active part in training the team of cosmonauts: in their development, their academic instruction, and their training for space flights.

"The Air Force recommends Senior Lieutenant Yuri Alekseyevich Gagarin for the flight," Kamanin calmly announced.

Yuri Gagarin again gracefully rose to his feet, looked happily at everyone present, and said a few words by way of thanks.

Later, after completion of the first manned space flight, I asked General Kamanin why, when the final choice was made, Yuri Gagarin had been selected.

"A real man," Kamanin told me, "is characterized by at least five traits: courage, sober judgment, a strong will, diligence, and dedication to his objectives. All these traits are abundantly represented in Gagarin's character. But in addition to character, medical and psychological fitness must be taken into account. A man may be perfect; but if he is subject to even slight dizziness, there can be no question of his making a flight. In all these respects, both Gagarin and Titov were fine specimens."

Kamanin went over to a file cabinet and removed a thick file from it. He leafed through the dossier and found a description of Yuri Gagarin. Here is what I read:

Throughout the period of training for flight, Yu. A. Gagarin displayed great accuracy in the performance of various experimental psychological tests. He manifested great equanimity when subjected to sudden and powerful stimuli. His reaction to "novelties" (the state of weightlessness, prolonged sessions in the isolation chamber, parachute jumps, and other procedures) were always positive: he evinced the ability quickly to orient himself in new circumstances and skill in maintaining self-control in various unexpected situations.

Observations made during his confinement in the isolation chamber revealed a highly developed capacity to relax, during even the brief pauses provided for rest: to drop off to sleep quickly, and to awaken on his own at the scheduled time.

Noteworthy among his character traits was his sense of humor —his good nature and fondness for joking.

Then my attention was caught by the following:

His sessions in the trainer were characterized by a calm, self-confident performance, with clear, concise reports after the completion of each procedure. His self-confidence, presence

of mind, curiosity, and cheerfulness made for a distinct originality in the elaboration of professional skills.

Kamanin took the document, put it back in the file, and looked
at me expectantly. "Are you convinced?"
I nodded.
"We had to give thought not only to the first flight but to
the second as well. Titov was a more likely choice for the second
flight."
"Were there any other factors influencing the choice of candidates?" I asked Kamanin.
"With regard strictly to their merits as human beings," Kamanin
said, "the two were evenly matched. Each of them is a fine Soviet
man. Gagarin is from a kolkhoz [collective farm] family. Titov
comes from a hard-working Siberian family: his father is a teacher, a
truck driver, a mechanic—a jack-of-all-trades. As for the purely
professional aspect, both are first-rate pilots. For example, here is
the official report on Gagarin from his flying school." Kamanin
handed me another document.

During his period of training at the school [I read] Yu. A.
Gagarin showed himself to be a disciplined student . . . His performance in drill and physical training was good; in academic
work it was excellent. He did very well in the flight-training
program, and his acquired skills were firmly retained. He loves
to fly and handles a plane boldly and confidently. In the state
examinations in flying techniques and combat application, he
received a rating of "Excellent." He is well-versed in working
with the material components of an aircraft and was graduated
from the school in the first rank.

I put down the report and looked expectantly at Kamanin.
"Another thing that counted a lot," he remarked, "was the fact
that Sergei Pavlovich Korolev, himself a former pilot, has a high
opinion of Gagarin's flying style. Moreover, Korolev maintains that
if Gagarin receives a higher education—as he will at the academy
—he will become a top scientist. Gagarin has a great capacity
for analyzing everything that interests him. He is a born investigator. And for the first flight it was very important that the cosmonaut

be able to see a lot in a short time, and analyze what he had seen."

There was a brief interruption while Kamanin took some phone calls, and then he continued his account. "The chief designer of our space vehicles[2] has a very high regard for Gagarin's talents as an investigator and believes he will make an excellent designer. The opinion of Professor Yazdovsky, a medical specialist, is also important. He says Gagarin could serve as the model of a man whose organism possesses tremendous reserves."

Kamanin fell silent, apparently going over in his mind everything connected with the choice of Gagarin. Then he said, in a rush of enthusiasm: "The other cosmonauts unanimously recognized Gagarin's right to be first. Titov himself thought Gagarin was the most likely candidate. All this, considered together with Gagarin's unusual gifts and rare personal charm, prompted the Air Force command to recommend him for the first manned space flight. Does this satisfy you?"

I was perfectly satisfied with this answer. And yet I must confess that even after some years had gone by, I was still somewhat anxious about the psychological aspect of the events. What were Gherman Titov's feelings when General Kamanin announced that Gagarin was recommended as Number One?

In the course of working on my full-length films dealing with the lives and flights of Yuri Gagarin and Gherman Titov, I often viewed the clips of that historic session of the State Commission. But not once did I detect, in Titov's facial expression, any trace of bitterness, dismay, or disappointment. His behavior was fine display of objectivity and genuine comradeship.

When, after Gagarin's flight, I queried Titov, he told me: "Yuri was trained to perfection. He was the worthiest one among us. The choice was absolutely right."

And Gagarin said: "What did I feel at that session of the commission, standing beside my friend and backup? Everything was clear and yet unclear—maybe even very complex. I was thinking of Gherman. He's a very good flier. He's an intelligent man and a wonderful friend. He should make the flight too. I felt rather awkward. Why me? Why not him? Of course the com-

[2] S. P. Korolev.—Translator

mission's decision explained everything. But it would have been better to make the flight together."

As the bus neared the launching complex, the cosmonauts were singing. One of Gagarin's friends went over to him and stuck a caramel in his mouth, explaining: "When airliners take off and land, the stewardesses hand out candy. I'll be your steward . . ."

Gagarin, in his white space helmet, nodded by way of thanks and began to munch the candy.

There is a widespread belief that in his last—or most critical —moments, a person mentally reviews his entire life. I don't know whether Gagarin's own life passed before his mind's eye in just that way, but this is the right time to tell about it.

Yuri Gagarin was born on 9 March 1934 in the village of Klushino, in the woods and marshlands of the Smolensk region. His parents worked on a kolkhoz. There were four children in the family, Yuri being the third. His father, Aleksei Ivanovich Gagarin, was a cabinetmaker, a carpenter, and a bricklayer. He taught Yuri how to plow, how to hitch up a team of horses, and how to handle an ax. Aleksei had very little education (he had gone through only two grades at a parochial school); but both he and the boy's mother, Anna, wanted very badly for Yuri to become an educated man.

Yuri started school in the trying times of the Great Patriotic War. The children had neither notebooks nor textbooks, and two classes were crowded into a single room. They used old newspapers to write on, and when learning to add and subtract they used rifle cartridges in lieu of the usual modern counters.

The Nazi forces driving toward Moscow seized the area around Smolensk, and Hitler's soldiers appeared in the villages. They threw the Gagarin family out of their home, and the children had to help Aleksei and Anna dig a dugout as quickly as possible. They lived in that dark and crowded hole, expecting the worst at any moment.

The German soldier who had taken over the Gagarins' house was a fat Bavarian named Albert. One day he seized Yuri's little brother, Borya, and—laughing—hanged him with his scarf from the branch of an apple tree. The boy's fear-crazed mother and

Yuri, who was in a frenzy of rage, ran up and just managed to rescue Borya.

But even worse was to come. Some SS troops dragged the two older children—Yuri's brother Valentin and his sister, Zoya—out of the dugout and, together with other young men and girls, herded them out of the village toward the west—toward Germany. Yuri's mother and the other women of the village ran after the column of prisoners. They followed them for a long time. But at length the SS troops drove the women off, striking them with their rifle butts and setting attack dogs on them.

After the war the family moved to Gzhatsk, where Yuri completed six grades of secondary school. Then he went to Lyubertsy, near Moscow, to continue his education at a trade school attached to a plant manufacturing agricultural machinery. Here he worked as a foundry hand. Eager to learn more, he next went to Saratov on the Volga, where he entered an industrial technical school, continuing in his specialty as a foundryman. But he never became an iron puddler, because in Saratov all his life plans changed: he conceived an overwhelming desire to fly. He had seen airplanes before, especially during the war, but without any notion of becoming a pilot. In Saratov, however, when he and the other students from the technical school visited a flying club, he felt the lure of the skies. Upon application, he was accepted into the flying club. He completed the course there in his spare time and became an amateur pilot.

The flying instructor, Dmitry Pavlovich Martyanov, took notice of the talented student. He frequently praised him for his ability to handle a plane, and was delighted by his skill in making smooth landings. "He'll make a wonderful pilot," he told his fellow instructors.

Martyanov suggested to Yuri that he go into aviation and become a professional pilot. Gagarin followed his mentor's advice and entered the Orenburg Aviation School. It was there, at a dance held at the school, that he met Valentina Ivanovna Goryacheva. Valya was a rather shy girl who since graduation from the tenth grade, had been working at the Orenburg telegraph office. Her father, Ivan Stepanovich, was a cook, and her mother, Varvara Semenovna, was a housewife. Theirs was a large family —three brothers and three sisters—and Valya was the youngest child.

Yuri and Valya were soon drawn to each other: they were both fond of reading, skating, and theatergoing. They could spend hours together discussing a book they had read or a movie or play they had seen. Yuri was very much taken with Valya's modesty, her straightforwardness, and her clear view of things. They soon fell in love.

On 9 March 1957, Yuri's birthday, Valya gave him her photograph with an inscription in a hand much like his own: "Remember, Yuri, that we ourselves must create our own happiness. Don't bow your head before Fate. Remember that knowing how to wait is a great art. Safeguard that feeling for the moment of greatest happiness."

That autumn, on 4 October, Yuri and Valya lived through an event that shook the entire world: the launching of the first artificial earth satellite. Yuri was at the airfield about to take off on a flight, when he heard that the Sputnik had been launched. His friend and classmate, Yuri Dergunov, came running up all out of breath and shouted: "Sputnik! Our Sputnik is in the sky!"

After the flight, all of the student pilots listened to radio reports of the orbiting of the worlds' first artificial earth satellite. They discussed its shape: why was it a sphere? And its weight of 184 pounds—although small by today's standards—impressed them. Of course it wasn't an aircraft, but it still meant a good deal.

That evening Yuri and Valya talked about how space could be further explored. He gave her his impressions of the friendly debate that had been stirred up at the barracks. Some of the student pilots maintained that men would soon be making space flights; others declared that it wouldn't be done for another twenty years. When someone asked who would go up first, the argument grew heated. Some said it would be a scientist, others an engineer, and still others a submariner or an alpinist.

Later, recalling that day, Yuri Gagarin wrote:

> For my part, I wanted it to be a test pilot. Of course if it was a pilot, he would have to be well-versed in many branches of science and engineering. After all, a spacecraft—whose design it was difficult to imagine—would naturally be more complex than all known types of aircraft. And it would be considerably more difficult to fly such a craft.

That same evening, settling himself beside Valya, Gagarin took up pad and pencil and tried to sketch the future spacecraft. At various times he imagined it in the shape of a rocket, a sphere, a disk, and a rhomboid. As he was making these sketches, Yuri felt a strange, almost painful yearning—an urge toward space. But he was afraid to admit it, not only to Valya but to himself.

Other important events were in the making for the student pilots. On 7 November 1957, at an evening ceremony, Yuri Gagarin was graduated with high distinction from the flying school and given the rank of lieutenant. After a celebration with his classmates, Gagarin donned his new officer's greatcoat and went to see Valya: the day before she had accepted his proposal of marriage. They were to be married today.

Valya met him, wearing a white wedding dress. For the first time, the young couple kissed each other in the presence of all and declared themselves to be man and wife.

The wedding went off splendidly. Valya's father made a brilliant show of his culinary skill. He was an excellent cook, and the table was laden with food and drink. In short, everything was just as it should be at a good Russian wedding. The guests gave forth with the traditional shout of "Bitter!" and made the young couple (to their own satisfaction) kiss each other again and again.[3] Then everyone sang and danced.

As a top-ranking graduate of the flying school, Yuri Gagarin had the right to make his own choice of a billet. He was offered a strong inducement to remain in Orenburg at the school. But Gagarin wanted to go to a post in the Far North—in the Arctic. It was hard for Valya to leave her home in Orenburg and go off to an unknown region. But she understood: Yuri wanted to go to a post offering greater challenges . . .

Gagarin's first flights as a fighter pilot were made in the light of the aurora borealis, over the cliffs and ice fields of the Arctic. He flew very well, earned the respect of his new friends, and was pleased with everything. But after the launching of *Luna*-3, which flew around the moon and photographed its far side for the first time, Gagarin thought: "I mustn't delay any longer. A

[3] The idea behind this ritual at Russian weddings—explicated *ad nauseam* by scholars and commentators—is that the guests' vodka is bitter until made sweet by the bridegroom's kissing the bride.—Translator

manned space flight will be made before long!" And he submitted through channels a request to be put on the list of prospective cosmonauts.

His request was approved, and shortly thereafter he appeared before the Selection Commission, which assigned him to the cosmonaut team.

At that time a hot debate was still going on among the scientists: From what profession should prospective cosmonauts be chosen, and what was the most effective method of selection? Today, of course, such questions may seem absurd; but at that time a great deal depended on how they were answered. What the debate boiled down to was this: Who would be capable, after a relatively brief training period, of making a space flight?

In the opinion of some scientists, the simplest thing would be to choose the future cosmonauts from among the men of the submarine fleet. Of necessity, only the boldest and most rugged men were selected for submarine crews—men who, moreover, could bear up under the inconvenience of living and working in the very confining, enclosed space of a submarine. It was precisely this fact, maintained the advocates of choosing cosmonauts from among the submariners, that would be decisive in space flight, since the man would be in the confining and enclosed space of the pilot's compartment of a spacecraft.

Others were opposed to this view: "Of course there are some very fine men among the submariners. But they have no notion of altitude. And the ability to live and work at an extreme altitude will be the decisive factor in space flight. Consequently, it is obvious that there is every good reason for selecting the candidates only from among the alpinists and parachutists: they are born for high altitudes and are conditioned to living under conditions of oxygen deprivation."

And yet it was the aviators who stated their case with the greatest vigor. Nikolai Kamanin and his colleagues affirmed: "There is no doubt but what aviation is the best profession in which to seek candidates for the team of cosmonauts. The cosmonaut must act as a pilot in controlling the spacecraft. In flight, he may encounter difficulties that only an experienced flier can overcome."

In the course of the debate, a general "opposition party" was also formed. Certain scientists, designers, and engineers firmly maintained that it was a mistake to play up the complexity of space flight; and that such being the case, it was merely a matter of selecting healthy, rugged scientists and engineers.

But the aviators won. They convincingly showed that astronautics was an extension of aviation and that, consequently, a flight could not be made successfully without an experienced pilot in command of the spaceship. All this was quite apart from the fact that, once they had become cosmonauts, the pilots would have to master new disciplines. In particular, they would have to acquire a thorough understanding of celestial mechanics, rocketry, medicobiological and other disciplines, since they would participate in scientific experiments and observations.

Evgeny Anatolevich Karpov was chosen as the first director of the team. It was this broad-shouldered, powerfully built, and imperturbable-looking man who first greeted Gagarin and the other pilots who hoped to become cosmonauts, when they arrived in Moscow from their air bases.

For six weeks Karpov observed the pilots and supervised the screening tests and investigations. He was particularly impressed by Yuri Gagarin.

That April morning in 1961, before the launch, Karpov made some notations in a little, pocket-sized notebook. In it, I read the following:

> Preflight weight of Yuri Gagarin: 68.5 kilograms. Body temperature: 97.3 F. Pulse rate: 88. Respiration: 14. Arterial pressure: 120/70. Vital capacity of lungs: 4.600 cm.

In Karpov's notebook I also found earlier notations:

> Both at home and at the hospital, Yuri felt calm, confident, cheerful, and optimistic. Valya is wonderful! In helping Yuri get ready to leave, and in seeing him off, she displayed extraordinary self-control and courage—like a genuine cosmonaut's wife.

Later, Gagarin told me about those preflight hours: "Before flying off to the cosmodrome, I was at home. Valya had gone out shopping, and I began to get my things together. Valya knew everything, of course, and was very brave about my departure. (As soon as the cosmonaut team was formed, our wives set up their own women's council, and Valya took an active part in it.) In general, she was used to my going off on missions; but this was a special case.

"Well, she went shopping and left me to look after Lenochka and Galinka. I looked at my daughters and began to dandle Lenochka. Galinka was just a tiny baby. Lenochka understood that her daddy was going away and wanted to be of some help. But then Galinka began to cry, and I started to change her diaper. In a joking tone I told her: "What a thoughtless child! Her daddy is about to go up into space, and she dirties her diaper!" Then Valya came back and took over caring for the girls, while I hurried up to get my things ready."

At the end of the asphalt road cutting through the green of the steppe, Gagarin saw the silvery-gray space rocket, embraced by the green work towers. He looked at it through the window of the bus, and said: "You've waited a long time, sweetheart!"

He recalled the first time he had visited the cosmodrome with his fellow cosmonauts. A rocket had been standing there, ready to be launched with a capsule carrying a dog into space.

Gagarin now stepped out of the bus, walked along the concrete slab to the rocket, and stopped. Before him was a piece of metal sculpture, symbolizing the twentieth century.

"Beautiful!" he murmured.

Later, when he told me of his first impressions of the rocket and the spaceship, Yuri Gagarin said that the space vehicle struck him as more beautiful than a locomotive or steamship, than an airplane or the most extraordinary bridges, palaces, and statues all taken together. He said he felt this was the new beauty of a new age, in its own way as perfect as the Acropolis, and would remain so for the people of all countries in the future.

The day when they first saw the *Vostok* booster, the cosmonauts were shown the mongrel dog that was being readied for launching.

"What's her name?" they asked.

"Dymka [Haze] or Tuchka [Little Cloud]," the technician answered.

"What a name!" Gagarin said. "She's a heroic dog, and you call her Dymka. It doesn't fit."

When the scientist had introduced the cosmonauts to the dog that was about to be tested, he suggested that they give her another nickname. The suggestions came in bursts: Kosmicheskaya. Svetlaya. Laskovaya. Geroiskaya.

"Zvezdochka [Little Star]!" said Gagarin.

This pleased everyone. And it was under the name of Zvezdochka that the dog made her flight into space.

Now, as he reached the cosmodrome, Gagarin remembered his first impression of the space vehicle and the episode with the dog. And he smiled. But he instantly grew serious again. The memories, jokes, and songs had come to an end. It was time for a grueling test.

Although it was not necessary, Gagarin and Titov were helped out of their seats. Walking awkwardly, Gagarin went to the door of the bus and stepped down. When his feet touched the concrete slab, he exclaimed: "What a glorious sun!"

Gagarin was optimistic and delighted by everything. He took pleasure in the sunrise and the freshness of the morning, in the orderliness of the launching site, in his sweatsuit under the orange spacesuit, and in the jokes of his friends. To the others, he seemed radiant. One had the feeling that Gagarin wanted to carry into the eternal and infinite universe beyond the earth only the finest and best that exists in man.

Spring is a harbinger of warmth and light—a renewal of nature. The spring of 1961 augured the opening of a new era.

This was the advent of that "stellar hour" of mankind that Stefan Zweig had described:

> Every step in an era [the writer noted] demands preparation; every significant event matures gradually . . . Out of millions of vainly spent hours, only one becomes genuinely historic—the stellar hour of mankind . . . If the stellar hour strikes, it predetermines future years and centuries. That hour predetermines the fate of hundreds of generations, directs the lives of individual humans, of an entire people, or even of all mankind.

The "stellar hour" was untheatrical, with everything seeming as usual. Doubtless, all was "as usual" on the deck of Columbus' caravel when he approached the shores of America, and under

the bleachers of the stadium in Chicago where Fermi switched
on the world's first atomic reactor.

Near the bus, Gagarin was met by General Kamanin, who embraced him and said: "I'll see you again in the Kuybyshev area
a few hours from now."

Recalling those historic minutes, Kamanin said later: "When they
got out of the bus, Yuri and his friends were stirred by emotion
and began to exchange embraces and kisses on the cheek. I very
nearly had to use force to disengage the cosmonaut from the
embraces of his companions. But order was quickly restored, and
then Gagarin went up to Titov. They touched—you might say
"clinked"—space helmets, making a ringing metallic sound, and
each raised his hand in greeting. Then they quickly separated."

Academician Mstislav Vsevolodovich Keldysh, president of the
USSR Academy of Sciences, gave Gagarin a hearty handshake and
embraced him. Then Gagarin went over to Academician Korolev.
Korolev had passed a sleepless night, and the traces of fatigue
were etched on his face.

The evening before, Korolev had visited the cosmonauts' cottage
(where Gagarin was to spend the night before the launch) and
invited Gagarin and Titov to come out for a walk with him. As
they strolled along the path, their three silhouettes were visible
against the background of the afterglow on the steppe.

Korolev talked to the cosmonauts about the earth and the sky,
speculating aloud, and jokingly remarked: "Five years from now
people will be making space flights on their holidays."

Gagarin and Titov laughed, and Korolev was pleased by the
heartiness of their laughter. He left them and went off to the space
vehicle.

At 9:50 P.M. the doctors checked the cosmonauts' blood pressure,
temperature, and pulse rate. Everything was normal.

"Now to bed!" Kamanin told them, just as a father might have.

The doctors were quartered in the room next to the cosmonauts'
bedroom. They were apprehensive that Gagarin might not be able
to go to sleep—particularly because of the sensors attached to his
body. Yet a half hour later, when Korolev cautiously tiptoed into
the bedroom, Gagarin was lying on his back with one side of
his face cupped, like a child's, in his hand, sleeping soundly.

The next morning, at ten minutes of five, Kamanin and Karpov awoke as though on command. Kamanin looked at his watch, then glanced into the bedroom: Gagarin and Titov were still sleeping.

"Reveille is at five-thirty," he reminded Karpov.

At five-thirty Karpov went into the bedroom, tapped Gagarin on the shoulder, and said in a calm, matter-of-fact tone, "Time to get up."

Gagarin immediately sat up. And when asked, "How did you sleep?" he replied with a smile, "The way I was taught to."

Next came the physical exercises, then the unusual cosmonauts' breakfast. For several days, Gagarin had been taking his nourishment in a manner other than the earthly one: sucking nutritious, high-calorie food into his mouth from a tube.

Korolev came in. He was delighted by the way the cosmonauts looked: freshly shaven, pink-cheeked from a sound sleep, cheerful, and lively. Korolev himself was care-ridden: one could see how fatigue had taken its toll on "the Chief," as Korolev was called at the cosmodrome and at the design bureau. (He was also commonly known as S.P., the initial letters of his first name and patronymic: Sergei Pavlovich.)

"Everything will be fine. Everything will be normal," Gagarin said.

They loved S.P. They understood his state of mind and were trying to reassure a man in whom they had great faith.

A session of the State Commission was held at six o'clock. Each of the reports consisted of a single sentence or phrase: "No irregularities—everything is ready." "No questions." "Go for launch."

After the session, Kamanin signed the flight orders and went to the cosmonauts who were suiting up. The assistants were helping Gagarin put on a warm, sky-blue undergarment and, over it, his bright orange spacesuit. The latter would keep the cosmonaut alive if the cabin were to become depressurized. The bright orange color of the spacesuit was for maximum visibility after the landing.

Now Gagarin and Korolev were standing at the base of the rocket. Korolev's eyes were sparkling, his dark brows arched up, and the determined set of his chin became even sterner. S.P. was a taciturn, resolute man. A powerful, indomitable will seemed to emanate from him—a will that everyone at the cosmodrome obeyed.

A month after the launch of 12 April 1961, I asked Sergei

Korolev to tell me what he felt on the day of Yuri Gagarin's flight. What was he thinking about?

Korolev shrugged. "We had complete confidence in the successful accomplishment of the flight, because of the thorough preparedness of all services, all organizations. You must bear in mind that we had already put up five spaceships, some of them with dogs and one with a dummy pilot. Yuri had met his predecessor, the dummy pilot, and by way of a friendly gesture had jokingly offered him a cigarette. All of the launches had gone off normally. That was why our group was fully confident of success. We wanted to convey this feeling to Gagarin."

Korolev paused briefly to reflect, then continued: "What can I tell you about Yuri? I liked him the very first time I met him. He is a born cosmonaut. In the course of my life, I've seen some very interesting people. Gagarin is a very considerable person. During the days of preparation for the launch, when everyone had more than his share of concerns, apprehensions, and anxieties, he alone seemed to keep calm. More than that: he was full of good spirits and beamed like the sun. 'Why are you always smiling?' I asked him. 'I don't know. I guess I'm just not a serious person,' he said. And I thought to myself: 'We could use more such "unserious" persons on this earth.'

"On the morning of the flight, when Yuri was being suited up, I glanced into the dressing room and asked: 'How do you feel?' 'Fine,' Yuri answered. And then, as usual, he asked with a kindly smile: 'And you?' He gazed intently at my grayish, tired face (I had not slept the night before the launch) and his smile vanished. 'Don't worry, Sergei Pavlovich,' he told me quietly. 'Everything will be all right.' And I thought: 'Here is a man about to make an unprecedented and—let's face it—dangerous flight. But *he* reassures *me*—a man who's going to remain on earth.'"

Yuri Gagarin reported to the chairman of the State Commission that he was ready for the flight. Then the sports commissioner, V. A. Plaksin, came up to Gagarin and asked him for his flight certificate. (The Code of the International Astronautics Federation requires that the sports commissioner verify the certificate before the launch.) Gagarin took the certificate from the breast pocket of his spacesuit and handed it to the sports commissioner. The latter verified the document and made a notation in the record.

Then Gagarin was asked to make a statement to the press and radio services. He went up to the microphone.

"Dear friends, you who are close to me, and you whom I do not know, fellow Russians, and people of all countries and continents," he began. He spoke simply and sincerely, with no signs of anxiety. "In a few minutes a powerful space vehicle will carry me into the distant realm of space. What can I tell you in these last minutes before the launch? My whole life now appears to me as one beautiful moment. All that I previously lived through and did, was lived through and done for the sake of this moment."

He was silent for a moment, gathering his thoughts; then he went on. "You can understand that it is difficult for me to analyze my feelings right now, when the critical moment is close at hand: that moment for which we have long—and passionately—been preparing ourselves. I wonder whether it is worthwhile to tell you of the feelings I experienced when I was offered the chance to make this flight? Joy? No, it was not merely joy. Pride? No, it was not merely pride. I felt a great happiness. To be the first man in space—to meet nature face to face in an unprecedented encounter—could one dream of anything greater? But immediately after that I thought of the tremendous responsibility I bore: to be the first to do what generations of people had dreamed of; to be the first to pave the way into space for mankind . . . Just tell me if there is any more complex task than the one that has fallen to my lot! This responsibility is not toward one person, not toward a few dozen, not toward a group. It is a responsibility toward all mankind—toward its present and its future . . ."

He paused, and all was silent except for the sound of the April wind blowing across the steppe.

"Am I happy as I set off on this space flight?" As he asked the question, he smiled. "Of course I'm happy. After all, taking part in new discoveries has brought the greatest happiness to people of all times and all ages."

Gagarin looked around him at the faces of Korolev, Keldysh, Kamanin, Karpov, and Gherman Titov, who was standing next to them in his orange-colored spacesuit. Korolev stole a glance at his watch. Gagarin noticed it and began to conclude his talk.

"There are not many minutes left, now, before liftoff. Dear friends, I say to you, 'Until we meet again'—as people always say to others when leaving on a long trip. How I would like to embrace all of you—both those I know and those I have never met; both those who are far away and those who are near."

The green elevator quickly carried Yuri Gagarin up to the top of the space vehicle. From there, the people standing around below looked noticeably smaller. They waved excitedly and shouted something, but he could no longer hear their voices. The silence was broken only by the cry of a bird that flew by him.

When he stepped out of the elevator onto the top deck, Gagarin looked at the steppe, glittering in the April sun, and at the sky, full of puffy white clouds. Taking a deep breath of the fresh air, he went to the railing and waved at those who were remaining on earth.

Helped by his assistants, wearing dark sweatsuits with red armbands, Gagarin got into his seat in the cabin of the spaceship *Vostok*-1. The leader of the design group gave him last-minute instructions and helped him into the contour seat.

In the course of preparations for the launch, there had been a slight malfunction in the closing of No. 1 hatch. It had been closed; but there was no contact, so it had to be opened again to correct the trifling defect. The whole thing was done so rapidly that Gagarin didn't even notice it.

Now the launch pad was empty. The last one to leave it was Korolev. Absorbed in his own thoughts and anxieties, he went slowly down the narrow stone stairway to the underground concrete blockhouse—the Launch Control Center. Turning abruptly to the chairman of the State Commission, he remarked: "What Gagarin said was intelligent. Very intelligent!"

On the long bank of monitoring instruments, colored lights pulsed and flashed. Operators wearing blue coveralls and black headphones sat at their consoles, waiting for the command. In the Launch Control Center with Korolev was his deputy, Leonid Aleksandrovich Voskresensky. The latter, a man with a high forehead and a look of imperturbability, glued his gray eyes to a periscope through which he could observe the rocket.

The liftoff was not scheduled to take place as soon as Gagarin was seated in the cabin of the spacecraft. Such was the complexity of the launch, that another ninety minutes of preparations had been scheduled. Ninety minutes of tests. Ninety minutes of tense waiting for the cosmonaut and the entire launch crew . . .

Korolev cut in his telephone: "This is Zarya [Dawn]. Give me Number One."

The voice of Number One immediately replied from the operations room of the CDPC (Co-ordinating Data-Processing Center): "I hear you, Sergei Pavlovich."

They engaged in a conversation over a distance of thousands of kilometers. The CDPC was located at a great distance from the launch complex and co-ordinated the work of the tracking stations, communications systems, computers, and the cosmodrome.

When he was through talking to the CDPC, Korolev turned to Voskresensky, who was standing at the periscope. "How are you feeling, Leonid Aleksandrovich?"

"Just fine."

"No heart palpitations?"

"At a time like this, can anyone's heart be quiet?"

Having had his joke, Korolev listened to Voskresensky's report. All systems of the booster rocket were being checked out. Voskresensky, who had received reports from the launch crew, knew everything that was taking place outside the blockhouse—up there, on that launch pad, that "table" on which the heavy metallic body of the rocket was resting.

When he had heard Voskresensky's report, Korolev smiled slyly and said: "I have some validol pills in my pocket. Would you like one?"

Each of them took a pill and sucked on it; then both got back to work.

After sitting in his chair for a short time, Korolev got up and paced about the room. Then he went to the microphone and asked: "How do you hear me?"

"Loud and clear," answered Gagarin. "Testing of communications has been completed. Initial position of tumbler switches on control panel as prescribed. Globe on dividing line. Pressure in cabin: one atmosphere. Humidity: 65 per cent. Temperature: 66 degrees. Pressure in the instrument compartment: 1.2. Pressure in the orientation-control systems: normal. I feel fine. Am ready for liftoff. How do you hear me?"

Before the actual liftoff, Korolev, Kamanin, and the first future cosmonauts gathered around the communications station to talk with Gagarin. "CapCom" Pavel Popovich—lively, cheerful, and bursting with health—borrowed the call-sign "Zarya."

> *Zarya:* Well, everything is normal. It's all going according to
> schedule. On the machine, everything is going fine.
> *Gagarin:* How about the medical data? Is my heart beating?
> *Zarya:* Your pulse rate is 64, and your respiration is 24.
> Everything is normal.
> *Gagarin:* Roger. So my heart is beating.

Korolev took the microphone.

> *Korolev:* How are you feeling?
> *Gagarin:* I'm not worried. I feel fine. How are you feeling?
> Tell the doctors that my pulse is normal.

The cosmonauts, gathered around the communications station,
clapped their hands. They took pleasure in the fact that during
these tense minutes Gagarin's behavior was calm, confident, and
even gay-spirited.

At the same time Voskresensky, in the concrete blockhouse near
the launch site, was gazing intently into the eye-piece of the
periscope, like a submarine skipper. The dull gray tube of the
periscope was turned by means of cranks. Voskresensky became
all tension. To the beat of the chronometer, he called out the orders:
"Bleed-off . . . Hold . . . Ignition . . . Switch to 'launch' . . ."

And then the final command: "Liftoff!"

At 9:07 A.M. Gagarin heard a whine and a growing roar; and
he felt the spacecraft quiver all over. Then, over the loudspeaker,
his triumphant voice was heard: "We're off!"

He did not say "We are airborne." Or "We are launched." He
said "We're off!"

This typically Russian (or peasant) exclamation of Gagarin's
showed his sympathetic relationship with the space vehicle as a living being. It was similar to the way one felt toward a favorite horse
in the old days.

The Man and
the Planet

Yuri Gagarin spent 108 minutes in flight.

Yes, only 108 minutes. But what minutes they were!

In the course of Gagarin's 108 minutes, a unique revolution occurred in the minds of men. That which had been fantasy had become a reality; that which had been shrouded in secrecy and had inspired dread had become a new milieu for human habitation.

"The roar was loud," Gagarin said later, "but not really any louder than what you usually hear in the cockpit of a jet plane. Another interesting thing is that a great many new musical nuances and timbres can be heard in that roar. I have never heard anything like it on earth. I got the impression that the powerful rocket engines were creating the music of the future—perhaps more moving than the music of our time."

During the first seconds, summoning up all his strength, will, and flying experience, Gagarin patiently bore up under the constantly increasing G-forces. They pressed him hard against his contour seat, and he could not so much as move an arm or a leg. There was nothing unexpected in all this; and Gagarin knew that the G-forces would act on him only briefly—during the boost phase of the flight. But he nonetheless had the impression that time had come to a stop.

The canine explorers who had gone into space before Gagarin had revealed, by means of instruments, the G-forces they had experienced. And Gagarin himself, in the course of training for the flight, had often been whirled around in the cabin of the centrifuge and at moments of fiendish whirling had experienced repeated G-loads. This experience enabled him to remain calm when he encountered them on the powered ascent of *Vostok-1*.

"Sixty seconds after liftoff," Gagarin heard Korolev's voice saying.

S.P. was standing at the microphone watching the hand of the chronometer. He was wiping his forehead with his handkerchief, vicariously living what Gagarin was experiencing at that moment.

"Sixty?" Gagarin repeated in astonishment. Obviously he had the impression that he had already been airborne for quite a few minutes.

Overcoming the leaden heaviness of his jaw and tongue, he went on: "Roger. Sixty. I feel fine. Am continuing the flight. G-forces are increasing. Everything is all right."

He had said "Everything is all right," knowing that Korolev, Keldysh, Kamanin, and all the others in Launch Control were waiting for some encouraging words from him.

Again Korolev asked: "How do you feel?"

This time, Gagarin's answer was a bit sly. "I feel good. How do you feel?"

Korolev smiled. "Well done! He's joking . . ."

Gagarin's joke put everyone in a good mood.

Gagarin could hear clearly the voice of Korolev, of the chairman of the State Commission, of Kamanin, and of Pavel Popovich, acting as capsule commander—liaison between Gagarin and the other cosmonauts. He heard the voices of the radio operators as well. It seemed to him that the ether was full of businesslike noise, music, and the clicking to telegraph keys.

As soon as *Vostok* emerged from the dense strata of the earth's atmosphere, the nose cone was automatically jettisoned. Down below were feathery clouds, and the light blue and green of the earth.

Yuri Gagarin had often looked down at the earth from the cockpit of a jet plane; but now he was seeing it from a height never before reached by a human being. Gagarin was entranced by the view displayed before him. He poured out his feelings, exclaiming: "It sure is beautiful!" Then, realizing that this was no time for lyricism, he adopted a businesslike tone.

But for Korolev, Gagarin's spontaneous delight at the beauty of the earth was especially significant. It showed that no matter how complex the conditions of space flight, they could not repress what was obviously irrepressibly human in man.

The psychologists, who had heard every word Gagarin spoke, were delighted: space had no deadening effect on the emotions!

Gagarin reported: "I can see the earth through the viewport. The cloud cover is increasing."

Then, after a pause: "I am observing the earth. The visibility is good. I can see everything."

Now it was the meteorologists' turn to cheer—along with the geodesists and cartographers. They now knew that from that great altitude one could clearly discern the beds of rivers, the contours of mountain peaks, the storm centers of typhoons and seismic sea waves . . .

Korolev, during those same minutes, was interested in the technical aspects of the flight: how were things going with the separation of the booster-rocket stages?

A carrier rocket consists of a set of rockets joined together. In his day (making a theoretical analysis of such a combination) Konstantin Tsiolkovsky called it a "rocket train." This gives an accurate notion of the whole system.

The carrier rocket of *Vostok,* whose engines had an over-all capacity of 20 million horsepower, consisted of three stages. The first lifted the space vehicle off the launch pad and was then automatically jettisoned, so as not to interfere with the further flights of the vehicle. Then the second stage fired. When it had done its work, it too was jettisoned, and the third stage started its burn. Finally, the third stage likewise disappeared. Boosted by the three stages of the rocket and having attained the "first cosmic speed,"[1] the spaceship *Vostok* went into its orbital flight.

The spaceship *Vostok* consisted of two basic parts. The first was the re-entry compartment (pilot's cabin) which accommo-

[1] Tsiolkovsky's term for earth-orbiting velocity: about 5 miles per second.—Translator

dated Gagarin, the equipment assuring the vital functioning of his organism during the flight, the instrumentation for guidance, communications, control, and the landing system. The second was the instrument compartment, in which were mounted the instruments for guiding the spacecraft during orbital flight, for communications, telemetric measurements, orbital control, and *Vostok's* braking engine installation.

After the satellite-spaceship was injected into orbit, it was separated from the last stage of the carrier rocket—a process that Gagarin observed through his viewports.

"Separation from the carrier rocket completed . . ."

This meant that the spacecraft, now freed of the last rocket stage, had broken into the infinite expanse of space. *Vostok's* period of revolution around the earth was 89.34 minutes. Its minimal distance from the earth, or perigee, was 181 kilometers, and its maximum distance, or apogee, was 327 kilometers.

As the G-forces which had held Gagarin fast in his contour seat disappeared, they were replaced by another condition unknown on earth: weightlessness. After the deafening roar came silence.

On earth, it is possible to get at least a notion of the ideal silence of space. Many people have experienced the quiet of deep caves or ancient, underground vaults, in the quiet depths of a forest, or on mountain peaks; or they have found it by going down deep into the sea. But it is extremely difficult to understand what weightlessness is like.

All life on earth has developed under the action of our planet's powerful forces of gravitation.

In order to leave the earth and go into space, man must overcome those powerful forces of gravitation. At the present stage in the development of applied science, this can be done only by means of rockets. When the thrust of the rocket's engines is struggling against the forces of gravitation, any living thing in the space vehicle is subject to extreme G-loads. These loads are so great that a man's blood becomes as heavy as mercury, moving only sluggishly in the peripheral parts of his body; and his eyelids are incredibly weighted down. After the ordeal of the G-loads comes a moment when gravitational force disappears, and the cosmonaut experiences weightlessness.

One question that perturbed the scientists was this: Wouldn't the sudden absence of gravitational force affect the cosmonaut's circulation? His hearing, his tactile sense, and his vision? To a great extent, the outcome of the first space flight depended upon how the cosmonaut withstood weightlessness.

Gagarin had been specially trained for his encounter with weightlessness—a stage people on earth were virtually unacquainted with. True, a person riding in an elevator can sometimes experience, for the briefest of moments, something resembling weightlessness. Thus in Italy, a special tower with a "falling cabin" was constructed for purposes of studying weightlessness, and that state was achieved in the cabin for a few seconds. In other countries, different procedures were used. People wearing diving suits were placed in vats full of a liquid whose specific gravity corresponded to that of the human being. These persons floated about in the tanks as though they were weightless. But this did not solve the problem, because the blood and internal organs of the person in the tank had not lost their weight. Furthermore, there was no change in the otolithic mechanism of the person's vestibular apparatus, a mechanism which reacts to all changes in a man's spatial position. Finally, when a person was immersed in such a tank for a long period of time, it had a harmful effect on his organism: he became sluggish and weak and did not bear up well under the subsequent G-forces.

What could be done?

The scientists proposed that the sensation of weightlessness be created with the help of an aircraft. When a plane is flying in an elliptical or parabolic trajectory, weightlessness occurs—although for a very brief time, measurable in tenths of seconds.

Professor Vladimir Ivanovich Yazdovsky attributed special importance to surmounting the barrier of weighlessness. Many experiments and training flights were devoted to this end.

And so one day, wearing a leather jacket and leather flying helmet, Gagarin climbed into the cockpit of a jet plane—a familiar experience for him. He tightened the straps on his shoulders and waist and switched on the radio. When he had received clearance from the tower, he taxied to the takeoff strip.

For him, every flight was sheer pleasure: he loved to fly. But on this particular day he felt as if he were once again a student back at the flying school in Saratov, on the Volga, making his first flight. On that occasion he was Number Two man in the cockpit, taking orders from the flying instructor. And this time he was experiencing something like that long-ago flight in Saratov: again he was Number Two man in the cockpit.

The plane—a two-seater with dual controls—was a kind of special-purpose flying laboratory. Back on the ground, the instructor had shown Gagarin a white plastic sphere hanging in the cockpit and told him to keep a close eye on it. Then Gagarin was given a flask of water. He was to open it while in a state of weightlessness and take a few swallows.

The sphere beside him was swinging back and forth on its string. There was nothing unusual in its behavior—it just hung there and swayed back and forth.

The plane climbed. The earth, far below, was obscured by a haze. Bright sunlight flooded the cockpit, and the white sphere suddenly became golden. Gagarin was thinking: "Here I am, a grown man and a prospective cosmonaut, playing with a golden ball and holding a little flask of water to drink from. If only my little girl could see her daddy with these toys."

"Get ready!" came the instructor's command over the voice radio, and Gagarin looked at the little sphere. They went into a dive.

When the jet fighter pulled out of its dive into a steep climb, an unusual thing happened—Gagarin suddenly lost the sensation of his own weight and began to float. As for the little sphere, it was no longer dangling and swaying, but teasingly floated in the air near Gagarin's face.

With a quick motion, Gagarin opened the flask and tilted it. To his surprise he saw that no stream of water came from the neck of the flask. Instead, bright globules—droplets of water—spilled out. And they wouldn't fall into his mouth; they insisted on floating about in the cockpit. He could even catch them in his hand, like butterflies.

Gagarin had never seen anything like it before, although he had made many long dives and executed the most complex figures of aerobatics. During those vertiginous flights, he had of course experienced something like weightlessness. But since he was concentrating on flying, he had paid little attention to the scarcely noticeable loss of his own weight. Now, however, during weightless phase of the flight, Gagarin had the impression that the old fairy tale of the man who had lost his own weight had been revived.

But the fairy tale came to a quick end: the plane leveled out, and the white sphere again dangled on its string. The bright drops of water formed into a stream, mischievously dousing the cosmonaut's chin and chest.

"Shall we try it again?" the instructor asked.

"Let's try it again!" Gagarin replied.

And they repeated the experiment.

When the plane returned to the base, an entire council of doctors in various specialties were waiting, along with the other cosmonauts.

Then Gherman Titov made a similar flight.

In a condition of weightlessness, the person freed of his own weight seems to become a different being—he can fly and swim in the air. Titov swam and felt he could soar up from the cockpit into the air and over the whole planet. When he opened the flask, he, too, saw a handful of strange droplets. The water had formed into beads and the glittering globules floated about near his mouth without falling into it. Titov tried to use his arms and legs, but in the same second when he began to experiment, his weightlessness vanished.

On the next run, Titov grasped the dual control stick, and the plane responded. Man could function in a condition of weightlessness.

Back at the airfield, Titov was met by a film technician who had prepared the automatic camera before the flight. "Cherman," he said, "let's go right now and take a look at how you and Gagarin flew. Kamanin has been bugging us, wanting to know when the film will be developed."

The viewing of the film made with the automatic camera was attended by Kamanin, Goreglyad, Professors Yazdovsky and Gazenko, plus various physicians and staff scientists.

Gagarin smiled from the screen. Under the G-forces, his expression changed. The screen showed the unusual antics of the golden sphere. Then Titov's face appeared. His eyes—their expression serious and concerned—were fixed on the sphere. The stream of water spilled out in the form of glittering beads, as they had in front of Gagarin. But the vital thing was that both Gagarin and Titov had functioned. Keeping their presence of mind under conditions they had never experienced before, they had communicated via voice radio and given intelligent answers to questions from the ground. And Titov had even flown the aircraft.

When the viewing was over, Yazdovsky observed thoughtfully:

"A remarkable experiment! Weightlessness, which has caused us so much anxiety—and, to tell the truth, has even frightened us— can be overcome."

After long and complex training sessions in a weightless condition in special aircraft, Gagarin was now launched on his flight. All fears of whatever kind turned out to have been groundless—Gagarin felt fine when weightless. He was in good spirits, energetic, delighted by the astonishing views afforded by space, and eager to share that delight with the CDPC.

Gagarin maintained two-way radio communications with earth via three channels. The frequencies of the spaceship's short-wave transmitters were 9.019 and 20.006 megacycles, and in the ultra-short-wave band it was 143.625 megacycles. Gagarin noted that reception was very good. The signal transmitter provided telemetric information to earth on the functioning of various systems on the spaceship and the functioning of the cosmonaut himself. From earth, *Vostok* received commands controlling the systems of the spacecraft. Since he was maintaining two-way communication on all of the channels, Gagarin barely managed to transmit all the information so important to the scientists.

Gagarin was keeping an eye on the instruments in the spaceship, observing the earth and the sky through the viewports, making notations in the log, determining *Vostok*'s position relative to earth from the miniaturized globe on the instrument panel, transmitting information, and receiving advice, instructions, and the good wishes of friends from the ground.

There were no doubts as to the pressurization of the pilot's compartment. But by way of a safeguard against anything unexpected, Gagarin made his flight in a spacesuit. The cosmonaut did not feel the weight of his spacesuit, nor did he feel the weight of the big, white space helmet encasing his head.

Gagarin was using an ordinary graphite pencil for making notations in his log. A fountain pen would have leaked, as sometimes happens during the flight of conventional aircraft. He found it easy to write in his weightless condition and had filled several pages of the log, when something unexpected occurred—weightlessness played a trick on him. After jotting down one of his notations, Gagarin forgot for a moment that he was in a condition of zero gravity and laid the pencil down. The pencil took wing and, together with the writing board, went floating about the cabin. He tried to retrieve it, but the string with which he had secured it became untied; a moment later it had disappeared under his contour seat. Not wanting to waste time looking for it, he notified the Control Center of what had happened and switched over to tape recording. The words he dictated into the microphone were recorded on tape, and then transmitted by radio to the Control Center.

Except for this trifling incident, nothing unforeseen took place during the flight. Gagarin carried out his work assignments, and from liftoff to re-entry everything went virtually as planned. He was constantly answering queries from the ground.

"What does the hydrosphere look like?"

"Dark blue, faintly glittering patches," Gagarin immediately replied.

"Is the earth's roundness apparent?"

"Yes, of course."

The cosmonaut was delighted with the rich variety of colors displayed by the earth. He could see that it was ringed by a marvelous halo of light blue, which gradually darkened—first to turquoise, then to dark blue, violet, and deep black.

Vostok was entering the shadow of the earth. Traveling at a speed of 28,000 kilometers per hour, the spaceship seemed to burst from daylight into dark. All was silent. At that moment, *Vostok* was passing over the ocean. The light reflected by the mirror of the sea was reminiscent of moonlight, but brighter and purer. Bright stars shone everywhere in the heavens. No one on earth had ever seen such stars.

After the flight, Yuri Gagarin told me: "Of all the nights I had seen in my lifetime, none was remotely comparable to night in space. I have never forgotten it. What was so different about it? It was most unusual to see night fall so swiftly, and dawn follow it so quickly afterward. During that brief night, the stars were so clearly visible—blindingly bright and full-bodied. The sky was blacker than it ever appears from the earth, with the real, slate-blackness of space. At times I had the impression that everything around me was happening in a kind of gigantic planetarium where one can turn night into day and day into night. After the darkness, the horizon began to brighten. But it was not the same kind of thing I had seen in the forest or on the open plain, when

the sun rises slowly and even majestically, still hidden from view
as the first predawn rays reach the earth, and the woods, meadows,
and streams are suffused with light. In space, everything happened
differently—the sun abruptly shot up over the horizon, and its
fierce light stabbed into my eyes. The cosmic dawn is instantaneous;
and in space the hues of beginning day, both soft and brilliant,
thrill you with a kind of magic."

Yuri Gagarin had learned in school that three fourths of the
earth's surface is ocean, that the earth is, by and large, a watery
globe. But to Gagarin, as to most people, this notion had seemed
rather abstract. Once he found himself high above the earth,
however, its roundness and wateriness were abundantly plain to
see. Water, water—everywhere water . . . Our planet, he realized,
is indeed a planet of oceans—a "watery planet."

As he passed over the Western Hemisphere, Gagarin thought of
Columbus and his sailing across the ocean in search of the Indies.
Gagarin had long been interested in Columbus. He had read
many articles on the question of who discovered America. And he
had been thrilled by the report that the first discoverers of America
had been primitive Europeans and Mongoloids from Asia, who,
more than 30,000 years ago, had settled in North and South America
and become its indigenous inhabitants.

Seas, oceans, continents, islands flashed past far below as the
cosmonaut looked down. For the very first time, a human being
was circling his own planet in space; and a strong, joyous feeling
filled him. He thought of the earth, and of mankind. His thoughts
took on greater scope, in an attempt to encompass both past and
future. And he wanted, at one and the same moment, to think
of what was happening back home: in Gzhatsk and Saratov, in
Orenburg, in Star Town, and, of course, in Moscow.

At 9:51 when the spacecraft emerged from the earth's shadow,
the automatic orientation system went into action. It sought
out the sun and "locked on" it to orient the ship. As the sun's
rays came through the earth's atmosphere, the horizon turned
bright orange, then gradually shaded through all the hues of the
rainbow, to light blue, dark blue, violet, and even black. Gagarin
asked himself: "Where have I seen such a combination of colors?"
And then he remembered: on the canvases of Nicholas Roerich
and Rockwell Kent.

At 9:52, as he was passing over Cape Horn, Gagarin reported: "The flight is proceeding normally."

The spacecraft *Vostok*, moving at a velocity of about 28,000 kilometers per hour, was keeping strictly to the timetable.

According to his schedule, Gagarin was to eat and drink some water at a specified time. He had no desire either to eat or drink, not wanting to waste time on such things. But a schedule is a schedule.

During the period when the first five unmanned *Vostok* spacecrafts were being launched, one after another, to perfect their systems before a manned flight was made, the Academy of Medical Science had worked out a diet for the cosmonaut and a system whereby he could take food and water while weightless. Also, Gagarin had tried to take water from a special apparatus during a flight in a jet plane. Now, he was to test for the first time whether a man could eat and drink in the weightlessness of space.

He took the tube, unscrewed its cap, squeezed it, and ate with pleasure. He discovered he could eat just as he could on earth. But there was one little hitch: he couldn't open his mouth at all wide. And if you took the water tube away from your lips, the drops of water would float freely about in the cabin.

From time to time, Gagarin listened to his own heart beating. It was functioning normally. His respiration was also normal. He felt well, and his capacity for work and thought was in no way diminished. All this, Gagarin thought, was as it should be. He felt no giddiness from his success—nor from the shouts of joy, greetings, and congratulations that came pouring in to him over his radio. He was not affected by feelings of loneliness or monotony in flight, nor by a crowding of impressions. He was totally absorbed in his work, a discipline familiar to him as a pilot.

In this connection, Korolev once told me: "A good pilot is one who, in one minute of flight, can make enough observations, and draw enough conclusions, to keep an entire institute busy with them for a whole year. A bad pilot can fly for a whole week but only obtain enough information for an hour's work. What pleased us so much about Gagarin was that in 108 minutes he was able to see a great deal and enrich science with valuable information and conclusions."

In the astounding world of space in which he found himself, Gagarin began thinking of his mother. She had known nothing of his impending flight, and he tried to imagine where and when she had heard the news of the launch. Valya, his wife, had seen him off for the launch, calm and collected—which had given him confidence. But how was she taking the news of the flight now? And what about his daughters . . . ?

Far below him, aquamarine in appearance, was beloved earth. Since the birth of mankind, thousands of generations had inhabited her surface, one after another. Man had always dreamed of flying up into the sky. Now, for the first time, an earthling was looking down at his own planet from an immense height, seeing it with his eyes, appreciating its beauty, and experiencing that poignant feeling: "How small our planet is in the vast infinity of the universe! A tiny, blue-green dot in the dark wasteland of space."

Gagarin glanced at his instrument panel. Affixed to it was a little blue globe. Its purpose was to show the position of the spacecraft in relation to the earth's surface. A tiny, miniature planet in the cabin . . . The globe was constantly in motion. By looking at it, Gagarin could tell what part of the earth *Vostok* was passing over. According to the globe, he was nearing the end of the pass over the ocean. Africa was ahead.

He made his scheduled report: "The flight is proceeding normally. I am having no trouble with weightlessness."

He was going into the final phase, perhaps more critical than the injection into orbit and the orbital flight.

At 10:15, as Gagarin was passing over the continent of Africa, a computer programming unit instructed the spacecraft's apparatus fire the retrorockets.

Earlier, as he was accompanying Gagarin to the cosmonauts' cottage at the cosmodrome, Korolev cautioned him: "It is very important to make thorough preparations for re-entry and landing. A human organism accustomed to weightlessness will be particularly sensitive to the G-forces that will necessarily be felt upon returning to earth." Then Korolev advised: "More physical exercises!"

Gagarin was well aware that gradually, because of the natural braking effect in the upper layers of the atmosphere, the spacecraft —consisting of two basic compartments: the pilot's cabin (constructed in the form of a sphere) and the instrument compartment —would lose its initial velocity, and the parameters of its orbit would change. To a great extent, the parameters of the orbit depended upon the work of the guidance systems and the rocket engines during the boost phase of the flight. In this case, everything had gone off perfectly. *Vostok* had been injected into orbit with great accuracy; the flight had gone strictly as scheduled; and apparently the re-entry and landing would also go well.

But in aviation, as is generally known, many consider takeoff and flight less hazardous than landing.

On *Vostok*, after the command for re-entry had been received, the cosmonaut could either make the landing himself—manually— or cut in the automatic system. In the latter case, the special solar sensor would lock on to the sun, and special mechanisms would orient the spacecraft so that the braking engine would be aligned against the vector of velocity. When the retrorockets had fired, the spacecraft would re-enter on a trajectory intersecting the thick strata of the atmosphere.

Later, Gagarin said: "During the space flight, everything had happened pretty much the same way it had been worked out in Star Town. But how would things go during the last phase of the flight? Even if all systems began functioning normally, might there not be some unforeseen danger lying in wait for me? Automation is all very well, but I still used the globe to keep track of the spacecraft's position. And I was ready to use manual control, just in case it was necessary to re-enter and land on my own."

But Gagarin had not been instructed to effect a manual landing (this task was later assigned to another cosmonaut); he was directed to depend on automatic control. Needless to say, as a pilot, Gagarin wanted to land the spaceship himself.

Gagarin made himself as comfortable as possible in the ejection seat and got ready to re-enter and land automatically. He imagined how, after the burn of the retrorockets, the spherical capsule would separate from the instrument compartment, and the little ball in which he was seated would plunge into the dense layers of the atmosphere.

At 10:25 the retrorockets were fired automatically, and *Vostok* began to lose velocity and de-orbit into a transitional ellipse. In the dense layers of the atmosphere, the heat-resistant covering of the metallic sphere quickly became red hot. Through the heat-proof shutters of the viewports, Gagarin could see the frightening crimson reflection of the flames. On the outside, the temperature reached tens of thousands of degrees. But within the cabin it remained normal: 68 degrees Fahrenheit.

Gagarin found himself pushed back against the contour seat—after weightlessness had come the G-forces. During re-entry they were even greater than during the boost phase. His arms and legs felt like lead. It was very hard to speak . . .

The earth loomed up in the viewports, filling them with green and dark blue. Clouds came into view. Beneath them sparkled the Volga, and Gagarin saw the white houses of Saratov. It was there that he had studied at the technical school. And it was there that he had made his first flight—in a Yak trainer.

At 10:55—108 minutes after the launch—the spacecraft *Vostok*, after having orbited the earth in space, came down in a plowed field near the Leninsky Put kolkhoz. This site—not far from the village of Smelovka, southwest of the town of Engels, across from Saratov—has become historic.

Gagarin landed by parachute a few dozen yards from a deep ravine through which the April freshets were happily babbling. Not far away, the cosmonaut saw a woman and her little girl. They were standing beside a spotted calf and gazing in disbelief at the strangely dressed man. In his orange spacesuit and white space helmet Gagarin would of course have amazed anyone.

Removing his space helmet, he shouted joyously to the woman: "I'm one of your own people, comrades! One of your own!"

On that particular day Anna Akimovna Takhtarova, the wife of a forester, was planting potatoes. With her was her six-year-old granddaughter, Rita. The little girl was the first to notice Gagarin.

The old woman and her granddaughter ran up to the man in the spacesuit. Gagarin asked them the name of the village near which his spacecraft had landed. And he added: "I must immediately report my safe return to earth."

"Have you really come from space?" Anna asked incredulously.

"Just imagine—I have!" Gagarin said.

"Would you like a bit to eat? Or some milk?"

"Thanks very much," Gagarin replied, "but I'm in a great hurry."

Just then, the tractor drivers from the first tractor brigade of the collective farm came rushing up. After a night of planting wheat, they had been resting in the machine operator's cottage. That morning they had heard the TASS announcement of the first manned space flight, which had stated that the first cosmonaut was Yuri Alekseyevich Gagarin, a citizen of the USSR.

The tractor drivers had been wondering: What was a spaceship like? Would it fly very long?

Naturally, they all wanted to find out more about Gagarin. Just as they were talking about him, someone shouted: "A spaceship!"

All six of the tractor drivers rushed out of the cottage toward the spacecraft. Near the blackened, metallic sphere they came to a halt. The capsule was still red hot and giving off heat. White spots could be seen on the scorched, heat-resistant skin. Nearby, in his orange spacesuit, stood Gagarin.

"Is it really him?" asked one of the tractor drivers.

With the air of a person who is the first to learn of something very important, Anna said: "The cosmonaut Gagarin has landed."

"Hello, boys!" Gagarin shouted to the tractor drivers.

With every minute, more and more people crowded around the spaceship. Soon the search party arrived, with a roar of helicopters and other aircraft. The doctors examined Gagarin; and the sports commissioner, I. Borisenko, made his landing a matter of record.

Yuri Gagarin had taken off his orange spacesuit. In his sky-blue undergarment, facing into the warm spring sun, he looked up at the sky where he had recently been.

Presently, Titov landed his plane at the spot where Gagarin had just come down. Overcome with emotion, the two of them embraced for a long time. At length Titov gave Gagarin a searching look and asked: "Are you satisfied?"

"Very much!" Gagarin exclaimed emphatically. He had not yet recovered from the impressions of his return to earth and this meeting with his friend. With his whole being he felt like shouting and singing.

"Very much!" he repeated. "And you'll be just as satisfied next time!"

From that moment on, he was engulfed by a great, unprecedented wave of fame. The teletypes clattered. The ether hummed. In headlines of newspapers all over the world was the name GAGARIN! Radio and television commentators reported the most "staggering," "sensational," "amazing" event of the century—a human being had lived and worked in space!

Thousands of people wanted Gagarin's autograph. He was constantly being asked to put his signature on sheets of paper, books, and even cigarette packages. People were eager to get a look at him, to exchange greetings with him, to hear him say even so much as a word. Understanding this, he generously gave out autographs and willingly talked about his flight.

In those days, almost everyone identified himself with the feat of a man in whom he could see something of himself—the realization of his own dreams. Gagarin became a hero to mankind and the embodiment of humaneness.

Gagarin wrote:

> The constant repetition of my name in radio broadcasts and the appearance in newspapers of my photograph and articles about my space flight only marked the beginning of that thrilling excitement which possessed me for a long time. Ahead of me were great experiences of which the most fertile imagination could give no notion, and which I did not even surmise in advance.

Along the Road
to Fame

After the flight, Gagarin rested and underwent a thorough medical examination. Accompanied by doctors, commissioners, cameramen, and reporters, Gagarin flew to a picturesque spot in the Zhiguli Hills on the Volga. There, at the comfortable little house where he was to stay, he found other doctors, his cosmonaut friends, and a crowd of reporters waiting for him.

Nikolai Kamanin has this to say about what happened at the dacha in the Zhiguli Hills: "The dacha assigned to the cosmonaut for his rest period was situated on a high bank of the Volga. The second-floor balcony offered a beautiful view of the river and the wooded heights on the other bank.

"Yuri went into the bedroom and was helped out of the warm undergarment he had worn beneath his spacesuit. He was smiling, but looked very tired. The doctors immediately went to work on him. From time to time one of the photographers would slip into the room and shoot off a blinding flash bulb.

"At nine o'clock in the evening, everyone at the dacha gathered around the dinner table. The guests included members of the State Commission, cosmonauts, Yazdovsky, Karpov, and the officials of the Kuybyshevskaya Oblast. The tone of the speeches was joyous. But there was very little drinking—you could feel how tired everyone was. By eleven the dinner party was over, and Gagarin and Titov went to bed."

April on the Volga, in the Zhiguli Hills, is a marvelous time of year. Gagarin and Titov took a ride in a motor launch along the broad river. They went for walks in the park, during which they had long talks. Cosmonaut Number Two heard about all the details of the flight. He was especially interested in how Gagarin felt while weightless, and how he bore up during re-entry. Also in the appearance of the flames that raged around the spacecraft at that time.

Gagarin would keep saying: "Gherman, that's something you must take into account . . ." "When you make your flight, Gherman, pay attention to . . ." "Gherman, remember . . ."

But the two friends soon had to part. On 14 April, Gagarin was to fly to Moscow for the ceremonies in the capital.

At 10:40 on 14 April an IL-18 turbojet airliner with Gagarin on board took off for Moscow. Gagarin was accompanied by Kamanin, doctors, cameramen, and reporters. Not a one of them took his eyes off him. They all wanted to see for themselves how a man looked after making a space flight. Would he not show the effects of weightlessness and radiation? Would there not be some traces, however slight, from the G-forces?

The plane's crew brought Gagarin souvenirs; the captain made a speech; and the pretty stewardesses prepared a splendid breakfast for the cosmonaut. The cameramen and newspaper photographers were busy shooting, and the radio newsmen pleaded with Gagarin to say something into their microphones—if only a few words. Patiently, Gagarin posed, and answered questions.

With apologies to the reporters, Kamanin snatched Gagarin away from them and found a seat for him next to a window. "You have to gather your thoughts and get ready to make your report," Kamanin told him. "Moscow is waiting. There will be a ceremony at Vnukovo Airport and in Red Square."

As the airliner approached the capital it was met by seven jet fighters which acted as an honor escort, two flying on either side of the IL-18 and three behind it. When Gagarin looked out of the plane window and saw he was being escorted by the jet fighters, he was greatly excited. Could there be any greater honor for a

1. Nikolai Kibalchich (1853–81), a Russian revolutionary and inventor. He was the first to propose a project of a manned flying machine with an engine powered by compressed-powder candles.

$$\frac{V}{V_1} = \mathcal{L}_{naf}\left\{1 + \frac{M_2}{M_1}\right\}$$

2. In 1903 Konstantin Tsiolkovsky expounded the theory of rocket flight and proposed the use of rockets for interplanetary travel. Advancing the hypothesis of the constant velocity of ejected reaction particles, he worked out and thoroughly investigated the equation for rocket propulsion. With it he established what we now call the Tsiolkovsky formula: the mathematical relationships between rocket mass and fuel mass. From this formula a highly important deduction was drawn: that rocket velocity depends on the relative weight of the rocket.

3. Konstantin Tsiolkovsky in his garden and his model of a rigid dirigible.

4. Konstantin Tsiolkovsky in his study in Kaluga.

5. Tsiolkovsky's sketch of a space rocket for "traveling . . . in an absolute vacuum." (1883).

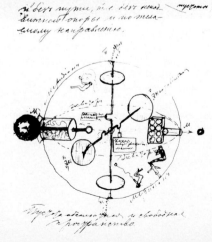

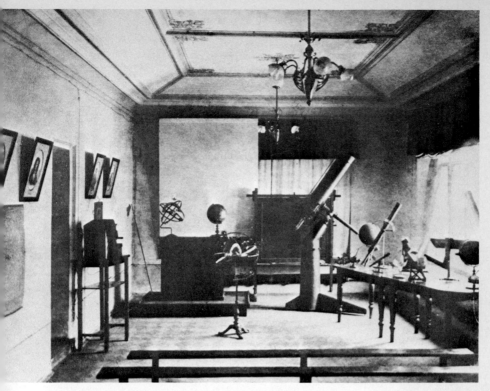

6. The lecture hall of the Moscow Astronomical Observatory where the
first conference of the Society for the Study of Interplanetary Communications
was held on June 20, 1924.

7. Tsiolkovsky's drawing of the original compound rocket
which he called "rocket train" (1929).

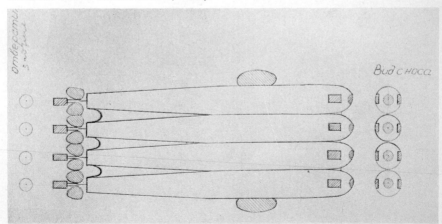

8. Tsiolkovsky's house in Kaluga where the scientist lived and worked. The desk in his study.

9. Sergei Korolev's one-horsepower rocket, national gliding contests in Koktebel, the Crimea (1929). (PUBLISHED FOR THE FIRST TIME IN 1971.)

10. In 1930–31 Dudakov, a scientist at the Gas Dynamics Laboratory in Leningrad, tested solid-fuel accelerators on the TB-1 heavy bomber. The use of rockets during the bomber's takeoff cuts the length of the takeoff run and makes it possible to increase the flying weight.

11. Boris Cheranovsky, designer of the glider RP-1, and test pilot Sergei Korolev, after a flight.

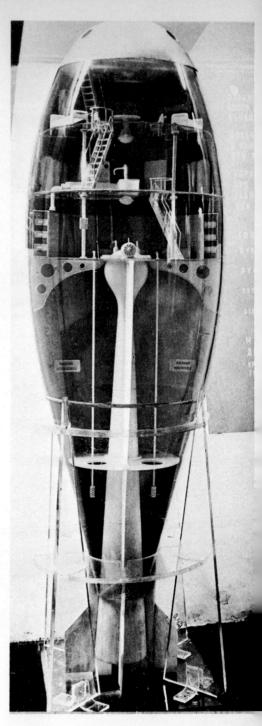

12. Kaluga. The K. E. Tsiolkovsky State Museum of Cosmonautics. The mock-up of the rocket spaceship based on Tsiolkovsky's drawing (1915).

13. The first Soviet liquid-fuel 09 rocket designed by engineer Mikhail Tikhonravov. It was elaborated by the Group for the Study of Reactive Propulsion (GIRD) headed by Sergei Korolev. The engine of this rocket operated on liquid oxygen and compressed gasoline (a jellylike solution of rosin in gasoline).
On 17 August 1933 the 09 rocket was launched from a firing ground in the outskirts of Moscow.

14. The 09 rocket being fueled with liquid oxygen. From left to right: Sergei Korolev, GIRD head, Nikolai Efremov, senior engineer of the second team, and Yuri Pobedonostsev, head of the third team.

15. Experimental launching of the 09 rocket engine on the bench.

16. A model of the 07 rocket designed by the GIRD team in 1933. It had a rather unusual form with its engine placed above its center of gravity and the fuel tanks (two for alcohol and two for oxygen) housed in the stabilizers. The reason for this was the search for better aerodynamic characteristics. Its first launching tests were held on 17 November 1934.

pilot? He spoke to them over the voice radio: "My warmest greetings to my friends in the fighter planes. Yuri Gagarin."

The fighter pilots wagged their wings in thanks for the greeting.

"Moscow!" Gagarin heard Kamanin call out, and he glanced through the window. Spread out below him was Moscow, with its squares and broad streets, its sparkling, winding river, the golden domes of the ancient cathedrals of the Kremlin, and the gray tops of the tall buildings. The streets and the public squares were jammed with people. One had the impression that all the inhabitants of Moscow were looking up at the airliner flying overhead, escorted by the fighter planes.

After making a triumphal flight over the main thoroughfares of Moscow, the silver-gray airliner, still accompanied by the fighter planes, headed for Vnukovo Airport. As they neared the airport the fighters flew off, wagging their wings again, and disappeared. Clearly visible down below, now, were the gray concrete runways and taxi strips. The parking aprons for the airliners came into view, and one could glimpse the festive colors of the decorations on the reviewing stand. Farther away, Gagarin saw the artillery pieces ready to fire a salute in his honor.

When the IL-18 had landed, Kamanin gave Gagarin a quick inspection. In his new officer's greatcoat with the shoulder straps of a major, Gagarin stood at attention, self-possessed yet radiant with joy. Kamanin offered his last words of advice and carefully took Gagarin by the arm, as if apprehensive that he might step out of the plane too soon.

The airliner rolled up toward the high ramp that was waiting for it. Its engines were switched off at precisely 1300 hours, and the white door was opened.

The whole great airport resounded with ecstatic shouts. Thousands of people chanted "Ga-ga-rin! Ga-ga-rin!"

Even at such a time, Gagarin remained himself. Using the window as a mirror, he gave himself a quick once-over. Then he heaved a deep sigh, straightened his shoulders, smoothed out his sleeves, and mentally rehearsed his report.

The IL-18 stopped near the silvery passenger ramp. A reddish orange carpet had been carefully spread out on its steps. The strip of carpet seemed to flow down the gangway like a red stream. It ran across the gray concrete of the field, then up the steps to the official reviewing stand.

Gagarin stepped out of the plane and onto the carpet with a firm step. Concentrating hard, he kept his eyes fixed straight ahead.

He saw the smooth red pathway formed by the carpet and, at its end, the reviewing stand, the microphones, the faces of government officials, and the faces of his mother and Valya.

He could not let himself be distracted by anything. He simply must not! He, a pilot, had to march along this ceremonial carpet as smartly as a well-drilled infantryman.

Of his experience at Vnukovo, Gagarin wrote:

> Never—not even in the spacecraft—had I been so nervous as I was at that moment. The path seemed to stretch on for ever and ever. But while I was walking along it, I managed to keep my presence of mind. I knew that all eyes were on me.

At that particular time, I too was watching Gagarin. But I was watching him from a press box, being one of those in charge of the television broadcast of the ceremonies. With a fast-beating heart, I followed each step the cosmonaut took. Suddenly I saw something that gave me a start. On one of Gagarin's new black boots, the tight bootlace had become untied. The lace was winding itself around his leg like a thin black snake, ready to bite him at any moment . . .

I glanced around at my two television colleagues, but apparently neither of them had noticed anything. Like everyone else, they were fascinated by the unusual nature of the occasion and with how smartly Gagarin was pacing along—he seemed not to be walking but gliding along the carpeted pathway. Meantime, the perfidious bootlace kept unwinding itself, growing longer and longer, and I became very uneasy. What if Gagarin, not noticing what had happened, should stumble because of that unruly bootlace? And —most dreadful of all—what if he should fall flat on his face?

Fortunately, Gagarin noticed the trouble. Later he wrote:

> . . . suddenly I felt that my bootlace had become untied. At any moment I might step on it and go sprawling in the red carpet in the presence of all those honorable people. Just imagine the embarrassment and the laughs. Up in space, he didn't fall. But on level ground he took a pratfall . . .

If the same thing had happened to someone else, he would most likely have become confused, got out of step, and stumbled. But Gagarin kept on pacing along as smoothly as before, in strict time. He swung his arms smartly, shoulders well back, and the crowd admired his graceful movements, not suspecting that all the while he was thinking of the bootlace and pacing evenly so as not to step on it.

"Fifteen paces more . . . Now only ten . . ." Gagarin was counting them off to himself. "I'll soon reach the reviewing stand and make my report."

The red pathway was behind him. The steps led upward. He was on the reviewing stand. Then came the report to the Party leaders and the Government. The report to the people.

"Our dream has come true, Yuri!" Valya whispered in his ear. Then she quickly turned away, wiping happy tears from her eyes.

Gagarin embraced her. "You're my smart girl. Thank you!"

Then the procession of gaily decorated automobiles set out from Vnukovo along Lenin Prospekt toward the center of Moscow—Red Square. Bedecked with wreaths and garlands, the cars moved slowly along between ranks of thousands of people. At that time Gherman Titov and his friends on the cosmonaut team were fighting their way through the crowd on Red Square. The cosmonauts had got out of their bus, its way blocked by the crowd, and were proceeding on foot. Even they were stopped on Kirov Street.

Pavel Popovich implored the crowd: "Comrades, let us through! We're cosmonauts."

"Today we're all cosmonauts!" shouted a husky young man who was determinedly elbowing his way through the crowd. "Is there anybody who doesn't want to be on Red Square today?"

Another cosmonaut shouted: "But we have official papers and invitations—honestly!" And he called to Pavel Popovich, caught in the press of the crowd: "Show them!"

Popovich laughed. "Right now official papers won't help—they won't let us through anyway. Let's make haste slowly, friends . . . We have time enough before it begins. This training won't hurt us." And Popovich pushed so hard with his shoulders that he quickly made his way through the crowd.

By the time the ceremonies were about to begin, the cosmonauts were standing at the foot of Lenin's mausoleum. A great many people had gathered in Red Square, and all of them were in high spirits. The moment Yuri Gagarin appeared atop the mausoleum, a joyful noise filled the square. Applause broke out; people shouted "Hurrah!" and called out "Hurray for Gagarin!" "Hurrah!" "Greetings, Yuri!"

Gherman Titov stood on tiptoe and watched intently as Gagarin mounted the mausoleum and took his place at the microphone. Next to him were the leaders of the Party, the Government, and the State. Titov thought: "Will the time really come when I too will have to stand up like that before this sea of humanity? And what about Yuri? Won't he lose his self-possession? Won't his voice tremble? He's not a professional speaker; he's just a cosmonaut . . ."

It was Gagarin's turn to speak. There was prolonged applause from Red Square. Gagarin looked into the eyes of thousands of people and smiled. Then he raised his hand, and there was silence.

Titov was moved by the sincerity that could be felt in the first words of Gagarin's speech—by his simple manner of speaking. A short time later, moving slightly forward, Gagarin looked around for his friends at the foot of the mausoleum, and when he found them, he beamed. "I'm sure," he said, "that my fellow cosmonauts are also ready at any time to make a flight around our planet."

Titov flushed. It seemed to him that his name had been singled out, and he was embarrassed. But when he looked out of the corner of his eye at those around him, he saw it was not true—everyone was still gazing up at Gagarin.

After pausing until the crowd in Red Square had quieted down, Gagarin continued: "I can assure you that we shall make even longer trips in our Soviet spaceships."

From the top of the mausoleum, Gagarin saw his cosmonaut friends moving past and called the ministers' attention to them. He waved excitedly and shouted. At that moment, Gagarin and Titov exchanged glances. Seeing each other, they smiled.

This was what Kamanin had anticipated. They will inevitably see each other, he had thought. They can't help trading glances. But how will Titov take it? He, the backup, is mingling with the crowd—an unknown understudy. But actually it might have turned out the other way. Titov might have been standing on the mausoleum, while Gagarin was mingling with the crowd . . .

Kamanin was relieved; the two cosmonauts exchanged friendly smiles and waved at each other.

The golden domes of the ancient cathedrals glittered, and the lawns were the fresh green of springtime. In Ivanovskaya Square stood the black limousines of government officials. The cosmonauts went on a bit farther and found themselves in front of the majestic entrance of the Great Kremlin Palace.

In the white marble St. George Hall and in the vaulted, gold-painted Hall of Facets, ministers and marshals, famous scientists and ambassadors, actors and writers, priests and public delegations from various countries had gathered for the state reception. Titov had never been at a reception of this kind, and he was dazzled by the sight of so many celebrities. He had grown up in distant Siberia, where he had helped his father build their own house from logs. He was used to simplicity and frugal living, and the novel experience of the reception left him slightly stunned.

But he was reassured by the sight of Korolev, standing modestly off to one side. He was wearing a severe, dark suit draped neatly over his stout frame and he had the look of a person who had nothing to do with the festivities taking place in the hall.

Korolev was surrounded by a group of design engineers and scientists—the top specialists in the field of space technology—who were also known to Titov. Noticing Titov, Korolev raised his hand in greeting and invited him to join them. Cosmonaut Number Two went up to Korolev and once again congratulated him on the great success. Korolev gave him a close look—one might even say a searching one—and a gentle pat on the shoulder. "This is my wife, Nina Ivanovna," he said, introducing a tall, beautiful woman.

Nina pressed Titov's hand gently and whispered to him: "You'll get used to it."

Titov reddened and said to Korolev: "You deserve credit for this. It's for you . . ."

But Korolev frowned, and his expression became stern. With a sigh, he said: "The sooner these festivities are over, the better. It's time for you, Gherman, to get started on some serious training. We've made a beginning. We've learned a lot . . ."

Kamanin came up to Korolev. As usual, he was reserved and somewhat lacking in warmth; but he was beaming with pleasure nonetheless. For the second time, he congratulated Korolev. Then, after shaking hands with the other design engineers and scientists and offering them a few compliments, he took Titov by the arm. "Well, Gherman, we'll have to put your training program into high gear now."

The group was joined by Professor Vladimir Yazdovsky, the leading light in space medicine. His shaven head shone under the chandeliers. He embraced Titov and felt his biceps in a demonstrative gesture. "A stout fellow! He'll hold up for a full day's flight!"

Yazdovsky whispered a joke into Korolev's ear, and the latter burst out laughing.

A waiter came up, carrying a tray with glasses and a decanter of cognac.

Kamanin proposed a toast: "To another success!"

His toast was more than usually appreciated, since everyone knew that Kamanin did not drink.

Korolev raised his glass, studied the light through it, then slowly shifted his glance to Titov: "Are you ready?"

Titov was slightly embarrassed: "Everything will go just as you taught us."

Looking over the heads of the distinguished gathering, Titov saw Gagarin. He was radiant and captivated the ministers, scientists, actors, and diplomats who came up to make his acquaintance. He had a gracious word for each of them. He was happy and made everyone else happy.

Titov decided he would not speak to Gagarin right away. He did not want to make a show of his direct involvement in the space program. In a casual way, he poured some cognac into his glass, warmed it between the palms of his hands, and looked around with curiosity. He felt an urge for impetuous behavior, he wanted to recite poetry and sing, to laugh and embrace his friends. But rather than make any such boisterous display of his feelings he finished his cognac, left the glass on a table, crossed his arms on his chest and, his eyes half-closed, recalled the day when he had first seen Gagarin, the day when everything began.

Titov

Remembers

They met at the hospital—not an ordinary hospital, but a special institution on a quiet street on the outskirts of Moscow where, at the time, prospective cosmonauts were quartered while undergoing screening tests. Titov had just reported in. At the gatehouse a short-haired woman in a light dress checked his papers. Then she picked up the phone and called the doctor on duty, informing him who the latest arrival was. When she had hung up, she explained to Titov in detail where he was to report.

Having thanked the receptionist, he set out along an asphalt walk leading toward the park. He soon found himself in front of the green columns of the entrance to the main building. Going on past this entrance, he rounded the corner of the building. Here, under a frosted light, was the doorway into the Emergency Ward.

He opened the door and went in. A nurse in white uniform greeted him with a smile, calling him by his first name and patronymic. Titov was startled. He had only just arrived, and they already knew all about him!

The nurse signed him in and told him to go into the doctor's examining room and undress. As he was starting to take off his

uniform, Evgeny Alekseyevich Fyodorov came in. He was the
doctor who had interviewed Titov at the air base where he was
stationed, asking him about his life history, his plans, and his attitude toward a possible manned space flight.

When he saw Fyodorov, Titov smiled happily. Here at last was
someone he knew! Fyodorov greeted him warmly and asked how his
trip had been.

"Just fine," replied Titov, who by this time was stark naked.

When he had completed his examination of Titov, Fyodorov
told him: "Now take a shower, change clothes, and go into the
ward. Later I'll tell you when we'll begin your tests."

"Yes, sir! I'll get ready!" Titov said. But his heart skipped a beat.
As he looked at Fyodorov—at his blue eyes (half-concealed by
dark glasses) and his impassive face, with features that seemed to
have been sculptured—he felt a slight chill. Plainly, the tests were
not going to be easy . . .

Titov remembered, in great detail, his shower, changing into the
dark hospital garb, following the nurse through several corridors,
up a narrow stairway on the first floor, and then through the door
into the ward. It proved to be less a ward than a kind of hotel
room, with two varnished-oak beds.

Titov was eager to familiarize himself with his surroundings.
Thanking the nurse who had conducted him to the ward, he went
to the window. Raising the shade, he found that he had a fine view
of the park. Beyond the trees, among clumps of lilac and false
acacia, he could glimpse the roofs of a few buildings whose appearance was strange and mysterious. Were the simulator trainers
housed in there? He pulled down the shade, turned, and saw
Fyodorov standing in the doorway.

Fyodorov offered him a cigarette: "Have one."

"Thanks, I don't smoke."

"That's to your credit. You shouldn't smoke. Now, before you
meet the director of the hospital, let's take a walk around the main
building and the park, and I'll try to brief you."

When they had walked around the squat building, they strolled
into the park and along a path. The profound, almost palpable
silence was not conducive to chatting.

"Our hospital," Fyodorov said at length and unhurriedly, "is a
unique medical institution. As aviation has developed, we have
studied the physical condition of pilots under increasing G-forces

and after accidents. Now we shall shift our attention to space. The dog Laika did not return from space; but she proved that a living being can exist in space. Have you thought about that?"

"The first Sputnik really shook me up!" Titov exclaimed. "I kept thinking: When would a human being go up. I wanted very badly to make a space flight. Very."

Fyodorov slowly took off his glasses. "Very?"

"Very!"

Fyodorov put his glasses back on and set off again along the path, plucking down yellow maple leaves as he went. "What awaits man up there in space?" he asked, as though thinking aloud. "Great G-forces during the powered ascent. Weightlessness . . . G-forces again during re-entry . . . Please don't think I'm trying to scare you. I'm merely sharing my thoughts with you."

"But you're *not* scaring me!" Titov exclaimed. "I'm healthy, I feel fine, and I want to make a space flight. I'm not frightened by G-loads and weightlessness."

"How does your wife feel about it?"

"Tamara will agree—I'm sure of that." Titov's tone was firm. "I admit it's not easy for her, because she's about to become a mother. And it isn't easy for me. But I'm willing, and I'm sure she'll be willing."

"All right, now," Fyodorov said thoughtfully. "Since we've already had such a frank conversation, tell me: Why is it that you— a first-rate pilot with a loving wife and a good reputation among his fellow fliers—are so eager to go into space? What motivates you? Could it be that you are looking for money and fame?"

"*What?* What do you mean?" Titov protested. "What does money have to do with it? Or fame? No," he said simply and firmly, after a moment's reflection, "I want to be of some use to our country and . . ." He paused again, running his hands through his curly hair. "I want to be of some use to mankind. I realize what kind of era is coming; man will go into space. And I'm willing to give all my strength—and, if necessary, my life—to the cause of exploring space for the sake of all human beings."

"Thoughts of death are not to the purpose!" Fyodorov said sharply and quickly returned to the original topic. "I hope you will pass all the tests successfully and become a cosmonaut; that is, a man on whom—I'll tell you frankly—we'll make many experiments. We are already witnessing the birth of space medicine

and space biology—the indispensable handmaidens of space technology. I think you'll find it interesting to become acquainted with
the problems of space medicine."

At this point, having touched upon his favorite subject, Fyodorov became animated, throwing off his usual reserve and aloofness.
He began to talk of how, in its time, aerostatics had placed entirely
new demands upon human perception; how aviation had done the
same thing as regards psychodynamics; and how space flight would
impose special demands on a person's thought processes and test
his best qualities.

Carried away by his thought, he said with considerable feeling:
"The intelligence, skill, knowledge, high ideals, and high motivation
with which he will oppose his realization of danger will assure
protective emotional excitation and guard the cosmonaut against
emotional-sensory and emotional-motor disturbances of his activity."

When he had blurted out all this, Fyodorov suddenly paused
and unashamedly burst out laughing. "I really got off on a tangent!
But for that matter, a person thinks most about his own concerns.
You, for example, have a different problem to deal with. I have done
research on polar winters and the voyages of submarine crews and
ascertained how important it is to break in upon isolation, if only
with the sound from a radio, with the feeling of live contact with
the great outside world. And so when you, a cosmonaut, find yourself in a small, enclosed space and experience estrangement and
isolation, it will be very important . . ."

Fyodorov broke off his speech in midsentence. "I've let myself
get carried away. And I gather that you think you've already been
accepted as a cosmonaut. Let's not be in a hurry. You will be subject
to complex and let's face it—difficult tests. Frankly, you have a
great many competitors. We get thousands of letters from all over
the country from men expressing a desire to fly to the moon, to
Mars, and to Venus. Really! In fact, everyone wants to go at least
as far as the moon. And you too, I suppose, are looking forward to
a flight to the moon?"

"I'm ready for any flight," Titov replied seriously.

"Now I'll show you what we have here." With these words,
Fyodorov conducted the neophyte to the laboratory where the
massive, steel, battleship-gray decompression chambers were lo-

cated. Next they visited the psychologist's laboratory and glanced into the room housing the "devil's wheel"—the centrifuge.

"Now you must get some rest," said Fyodorov in a friendly tone. After telling Titov that he hoped he would sleep well, he added that if he wanted to strike up an acquaintance, he should keep an eye out for Yuri Gagarin. "He's a fine man and very likable. I like him, and I'm sure you will."

A short time later Yuri Gagarin met Cosmonaut Number Two. Titov, standing there before him, was a curly-headed, sinewy, very well-built young man. Holding out his hand, he said: "Gherman. My father gave me that name in honor of the character created by Pushkin. And he named my sister Zemfira—likewise in honor of Pushkin."[1]

Yuri and Gherman soon became friends. Gagarin was much impressed by the fact that his new acquaintance recited poems very well and knew a great many of them by heart. Not only that, but he was a remarkable athlete, as he soon demonstrated on the gymnastic apparatus. On one occasion, unbeknown to the director of the hospital, he performed such acrobatic feats that Gagarin, applauding excitedly, said, "Gherman, you should join the circus right now!"

During their free time, after the medical examinations, Gagarin and Titov would go off to a remote area of the park and stroll along the paths.

Titov was amazed by Gagarin's cheerful freedom from anxiety, by his rare equanimity, by his ability to bear up with a smile under complex and trying tests, and then to behave as if nothing had happened.

The men and women in white coats were preparing the fliers for the unusual and seemingly fantastic profession of cosmonauts. No one knew exactly what traits the future pilots of spaceships should possess; and all of the medical scientists conducting the screening tests subjected the prospective cosmonauts, simultaneously, to their own experiments. Then the scientists studied the data from their instruments, analyzed their personal observations, and asked themselves: Would it be better to make the experiments more complex? Or should they reduce the workload?

[1] Gherman is the protagonist of Pushkin's story "The Queen of Spades," and Zemfira is the tragic heroine of his narrative poem, *The Gypsies.*—Translator

Quite unaware of how much anxiety they were causing the scientists, the two friends wandered through the park, went into the pergola, and sat down there. Sometimes they never exchanged a word; they just sat there in silence and thought.

If the weather was bad, they would find a place to sit in the waiting room of the hospital, near the fish tank. Gherman never tired of watching the goldfish slowly swimming about in the illuminated aquarium. With a swish of the tail, they would disappear into the slender green seaweed or into the tiny cliffs made of cockleshells. Striped or spotted fish with gorgeous tails would appear like a vision from a fairy tale, and tiny creatures could be glimpsed among the growths. Then the goldfish would emerge again.

"I love nature, I love birds, and animals," Titov confided to Gagarin. "I'm from the Altay. There, in the taiga—or on the steppes or unplowed fields—you can see wolves and hares, and squirrels climbing the trunks of cedar trees."

An area near the fish tank, like a club, was the place where one made the acquaintance of the pilots who had come from various parts of the country as prospective cosmonauts. The newcomers were quick to ask the veterans how the tests were going and whether they had any chance of becoming cosmonauts. When would the flight be made? And who would be the first?

There were many pilots who wanted to become cosmonauts. They arrived from various air bases, having first been screened locally by medical teams. All of them were young pilots—strong, healthy, and daring. Some of them were openly boastful; others were frankly afraid of the tests. Each one went through the experience in his own way.

One day a powerfully built pilot showed up. He was a man of imposing stature, and agile. Titov never forgot his big head, covered with dark hair, his broad shoulders, and his muscular arms. At the sight of him, Titov said to Gagarin: "There is a genuine cosmonaut."

A few days later, this Paul Bunyan came into Titov's room and announced in a voice loud enough to be heard on all floors of the hospital: "Well, they worked me over today! They spinned and whirled me around—enough to scare anybody! But they won't scare me! I gave the doctors something to work on. It'll be quite a while before they recover!"

Titov gazed at him in admiration and sighed: "There's a man

who's afraid of nothing! No doubt about it: he'll become a cosmonaut. And he'll probably be the first to go into space."

"Just look at him—what a fine specimen!" Gagarin whispered to Titov. "He'll be the first!"

Yet after a few days, he was seen collecting his belongings. Frowning, he shoved them into his suitcase, hoisted it up on his broad shoulders, and then waved his hand in farewell. "The devil only knows what is going on! I've flown jet bombers, and the medical board gave me an okay. But I wasn't the right size for space. 'You're a giant,' they said. 'You're too big for the capsule.' Well, good luck, boys! I'll go on with the old routine of flying airplanes."

His departure had a depressing effect on Titov.

It was a winter evening, and a snowstorm was raging. The light suspended above the side entrance to the hospital swayed in the wind, and the flickering glow that came through the window sometimes danced on the ceiling, sometimes on the wall, and sometimes on Gherman Titov's face.

Gherman watched the play of the dim, wavering light. Because of it—or perhaps because the blizzard was howling so loudly—he could not sleep. And he began to think of his native village, snowbound in the distant Altay.

In his mind's eye was a hut with its windows iced over—the hut he had helped his father build. They had used their axes to hew thick pine logs for the walls. Later, Titov had seen many different cities and buildings of the most varied architecture; but the family hut had always seemed to him the most beautiful building in the world.

Remembering these things, he smiled, tucked his arms under the blanket, and settled into a more comfortable position on his side. Once again, his thoughts returned to his native village. At this moment, his father was probably getting out his fiddle and wiping it with a cloth. Then he would test the strings with the bow, nod his head, and start playing.

A good many things in Titov's life were associated with his father's violin. He had watched while his father had selected the dried pieces of wood, carved the parts out of them, and had gone searching for horsehair to make the bow. When he had finished all the parts and put them together, the result was a real violin. Once in his father's hands, it was like a bird arrested in flight—

held down by the player's chin. A sweep of the bow, and everything in the room would begin to dance.

As Gherman's mother listened, tears would glisten in her eyes. Carried away by emotion, she would stroke the boy's head with her work-hardened hand, and he would feel its warmth.

Gherman's relationship with his father, Stepan Pavlovich, had been far from simple. He was both his father's son and his pupil—attending class under him at the local school and taking exams given by him.

Stepan was unusually modest and fair-minded: he could not bear the thought that someone might reproach him for favoring his son. Consequently, he demanded more of Gherman than of the other students. He assigned him more homework and punished him harshly whenever he played a prank. This sometimes gave rise to a quarrel between the boy's mother and father. Aleksandra Mikhailovna reproached her husband with being too exacting of his son and pupil and even with "tormenting" him. But Stepan remained unswayed. Fortunately, Gherman found schoolwork to his liking and learned everything quickly, so that he didn't even notice his father's nagging.

He loved his father and regarded him as an exceptional man. Stepan was a teacher and a truck driver. He also knew how to hitch up a team of horses, how to drive a tractor, and how to draw. He was that kind of educated Russian who has spent much of his life bringing enlightenment, knowledge, and a love of the beautiful to those living in rural areas.

When the war broke out, the young men went into the army. Then it was their fathers' turn. One day the local school superintendent, Ivan Andreyevich Bely, asked Stepan to come to his office. After turning over to him the keys to the school, the seal, the accounts, and various documents, he asked him to sit down at the desk.

For a long time, the two of them sat there, recalling how they had worked together. At length the superintendent heaved a sigh and said: "I wish you luck as the new superintendent. As long as you're here, I won't have to worry about the school. Well, good-by, Stepan!"

The war was a period that Gherman would never forget. He remembers how his father presided over the ceremonies for the beginning of the school year. Neatly dressed, Stepan took his place in front of the ranks of students, looked them over with a kindly expression, and offered them his best wishes. Then he told the children the bitter truth about the war. He spoke of the hardships and said that by studying they were doing their part in the war—in the struggle for victory.

Everyone talked about the war from morning till night—at school and at home, on the streets, everywhere. The grief of those who received "funeral telegrams"—notices that a son, a nephew, a brother, or a father had been killed at the front—was shared by all.

Like his schoolmates, Gherman Titov each day became more serious, more stern in his outlook, and more purposeful. It was a moving experience for him when the first wounded were brought back to Polkovnikovo and described the enemy atrocities and the deaths of their comrades.

It tormented Stepan, who was strong and rugged, to think that while he was living a life of peace and quiet in Siberia, other men his age were fighting. Several times he asked to be sent to the front as a volunteer. But since his wife had given birth to a daughter, Zemfira, he had to remain temporarily in Polkovnikovo. Later, however, he went to the front.

When the time came for him to go, his wife kept her eyes dry like a true Siberian. Gherman, frowning, said nothing. The only weeping came from little Zemfira, in her homemade cradle.

Stepan kept his spirits up and tried to joke. But when bidding his family good-by, he said to Gherman with a slight quaver in his voice: "Well, Gherman, you're the man in charge here now. Don't let anyone harm our womenfolk."

"I won't!" Gherman replied firmly.

Everyone in the village came to see Stepan off. He was a man they had all loved as a teacher, and they wished him good luck as a soldier. Then he set out from Polkovnikovo on his way to the war.

At one time, Stepan had been tractor foreman on a collective farm, and later he had worked on tractors and trucks, since he was fond of machines. With this background, he was sent to the front as a truck driver.

Before getting his own truck, however, he was sent to the city of Gorky on the Volga, where he worked on the production line in an automobile plant and helped to assemble his own truck, which he then drove to the front. Once there, he hauled ammunition to advance posts, rescued wounded men who were under fire, and transported troops . . . When the war ended, he was in East Prussia.

During the three years while his father was away, Gherman was the man of the house. He diligently helped his mother, took care of the little girl, chopped wood, and fetched water.

In the wintertime, he and the other boys built snow cities and stormed strongholds made of ice and snow. In the summer they made excursions into the taiga. (From his earliest years, Gherman had come to know the forest well. He could identify the voices of birds and animals, and was not frightened by the darkness and underbrush. Siberia, with its taiga, its mountains, and its fast-flowing rivers, had endowed the boy with a rugged, manly character.)

Titov took leave of his memories. Outside the hospital windows, in the park, the blizzard was still raging and howling. It was like the snowstorms in the taiga—except that out there in Siberia they were much more terrible.

That morning, Titov was to undergo testing in the decompression chamber. He walked into the laboratory and took a look at the gray steel monster, which seemed to be lying in wait for him. Then he stepped into the decompression chamber, took his seat, put his hands on his knees, and looked through the round porthole at the doctor. The latter's dark eyes stared fixedly at Gherman's face. Nothing escaped them: they kept track of everything, and analyzed it.

From the movement of the doctor's lips, Gherman understood the command: "Liftoff!" A loud hum was heard; and in the room next to the decompression chamber pumps went into action, sucking the air from the steel chamber. As soon as they had drawn out some of the oxygen, arrows began to tremble on the dials, then slowly moved, marking off the gradations.

The idea behind the design of the decompression chamber was to reproduce on earth, in a laboratory, the conditions obtaining at high altitudes. Pumps suck out the air, creating a rarefied atmosphere in the chamber; and the man seated inside the thick metal shell begins to experience pretty much the same thing he will find at high altitude: oxygen starvation, rapid heartbeat, dark and blinding spots before the eyes, suffocation . . . If the walls of the decompression chamber could tell what they had witnessed, they would tell how strong, sturdy young men had unexpectedly lost consciousness, fainted, and later frankly admitted: "It's too much for me. I can't take the altitude . . ."

Gherman had been in decompression chambers before, and he calmly observed the altimeter. It showed that the chamber had "ascended" to a height of 10,000 feet. Gherman had flown at this altitude in a fighter plane, quite without anxiety and did not really consider it very high. He smiled pleasantly at the doctor and even made a comic grimace. But to his astonishment, the doctor did not respond to the joke: he remained stern and aloof.

The indicator crawled up to 13,000 feet, but Gherman had been at that height as well. Soon the hand on the dial showed 18,000 feet—the height of the summit of Mount Elbrus. The doctor's eyes betrayed some anxiety. Gherman noticed the change; but he smiled again and, unable to restrain himself, he winked.

But why was his vision failing? Feeling a chill in his heart, he wondered: Can I really be getting sick? But he rejected the notion immediately and turned his head, trying to find out why such a thing had happened. So that was it! With the increase in altitude, a light, chilly mist had entered the chamber. It had fogged over the porthole and the instrument dials, and, needless to say, Gherman had seen the doctor's anxious eyes as if through tears.

Next came the order to put on the oxygen mask. Unhurriedly, Gherman picked up the black oxygen mask from the table, straightened out the leather straps, put it on, cut in the oxygen, and inhaled it with pleasure. (It is only at great altitudes that a person begins to appreciate the air we breathe.)

The fog in the decompression chamber grew thicker. The altimeter showed a height of more than 39,360 feet. Gherman swallowed his saliva and thought it would be good to suck on a piece of candy, because his mouth felt rather dry. He smiled at the thought. The doctor, who had been watching him intently, noticed his smile and was amazed. Time after time, he had seen men lose their strength, grow limp, and even lose consciousness. But this fellow was playful at high altitudes!

The test was over. The doctor looked at Gherman and, with a sigh of relief, issued the order: "Descent!"

The technician spun the control wheel in the opposite direction, and the motors which had started the pumps working, now stopped.

Silence descended upon the laboratory. The fog in the decompression chamber was dissipated. The white indicator on the dial moved rapidly—in the opposite direction this time—showing a drop of thousands of feet in altitude.

The door opened. Taking off his oxygen mask, Titov stretched. Then, smiling—satisfied with the "flight"—he bent down agilely, ducked through the door, and stood before the doctor, beaming.

"Let's check your pulse and blood pressure," the doctor said in a businesslike tone.

Everything was normal. Picking up his book (he was never without one), Titov took his leave of the doctors and left the laboratory. The next man to be tested was Yuri Gagarin. He waved at Titov and vanished into the decompression chamber.

Gagarin and Titov took advantage of any opportunity to be together—to share their daydreams and memories. They would stroll along the paths in the park and always felt good when they were together.

Yet it was some time before Titov decided to confide his secret to Gagarin. One day, however, he led his friend off to a secluded corner of the park, stopped near an old oak, and looked intently into Gagarin's face. The latter did not flinch under this unexpectedly stern scrutiny. "Get it off your chest," he said.

"How can I tell you as frankly and clearly as possible?" Titov said hesitatingly.

"Get to the point!" Gagarin embraced his friend and patted him on the back. Then, mimicking a doctor, he asked: "Where does it hurt? Stick your tongue out."

Titov laughed and stuck out his tongue.

"Well, what's the matter?"

"I'm worried," Titov began, rather confused. "And here's what's worrying me. I've already told you that I'm from the Altay. I've always liked to ride a bike. I was very good at it. Once, when I was going very fast, I took a fall that almost cost me my arm. The doctors patched it up, but they told me: 'Gherman, you used to have notions about flying, but now you can forget it.' I was grateful to the doctors for healing me, but that pronouncement made me furious. I was determined to fly! I followed my father's advice and took up athletic exercises. I conditioned my arm. I followed a regimen. When I was called up before the medical board, no one noticed that I had broken my arm. Not only that, but I was recommended for the Air Force."

Gagarin grew more serious. As a sympathetic and sensitive person, he understood that Titov was entrusting him with his fate—that he was looking to him for advice and support.

"And nobody here has noticed anything?"

Titov shook his head in the negative.

"And you haven't said anything?"

"If I said anything, they'd drop me like a hot potato."

"Well, then, let's see your arm." Gagarin rolled up the sleeve of Titov's sweatshirt and began to knead, pull, and bend his arm so vigorously that his friend almost cried out in pain.

When he had completed his amateur medical examination, Gagarin roughly jerked the sleeve of his sweatshirt down again and said almost angrily: "You don't have a break in your arm, and you never did have. Are you playing tricks on me? Testing me out?"

"What do you mean, Yuri?" Titov asked, quite upset. "I told you the truth. It's all healed now. But what should I do?"

The two of them laughed and walked out of the park. Gagarin was sure that Titov had merely been joking, and Titov felt offended that he had not been able to share his secret with anyone.

The time passed quickly, given over to various tests. One day Gherman encountered Fyodorov, who invited him for a stroll around the park. Titov took great pleasure in these moments particularly when Fyodorov talked about future space flights.

This time the topic was the psychological tests for which Gagarin and Titov were preparing. Fyodorov said that in the past, when men rode on horseback and a trip in a carriage was considered to be the fastest kind of travel, the coachmen was expected to be skillful in handling the carriage, driving the horses, and stopping the carriage when necessary. But then man invented the "iron horse"—the steam locomotive—which was followed by the electric locomotive, and both of them pulled railroad cars at a speed in excess of 150 kilometers per hour. Much more alertness, skill, and quick reactions are demanded of today's locomotive engineer than of a coachman driving a carriage. Not to mention the pilot of a supersonic aircraft, who must possess incredible alertness and lightninglike reactions. And a cosmonaut? After all, a cosmonaut's flight velocity will be 28,000 kilometers per hour.

In modern science, it has become the practice to measure very small intervals of time in hitherto-unknown units: milliseconds and microseconds. We have reached an era of ultrahigh speeds, both in atomic physics and in cosmonautics, which requires the construction of ultrasensitive instruments and apparatuses that react to ultrasmall intervals of time. But it is even more important to train cosmonauts to react to very brief time intervals.

As he listened to Fyodorov, Titov remembered occasions in his flying experience when he and his fellow pilots in the aviation regiment had been required to solve difficult problems in flight, literally in segments of seconds. Then, however, he was flying in a supersonic fighter plane at a speed somewhat more than 1,300 kilometers per hour, whereas space flight would be twenty times faster.

While Gherman was talking to Fyodorov about developing hyper-reactivity in cosmonauts, Gagarin walked into a small office where a woman doctor with curly dark hair was waiting for him. Gagarin sat down in a chair in front of an ordinary desk on which multi-colored charts were displayed. On one of them, black and white numbers were scattered in chaotic disorder; on the other were little rings of various colors.

"Yuri," the woman doctor said, "we are going to work with the polychromic charts designed by Professor Rabkin. Our tests—that is, our systems of questions and instructions—boil down to the fact that you must make calculations very rapidly." The doctor directed a narrow beam of light at a large cardboard rectangle. "On this chart are black and white numbers that you are supposed to add up so that they total twenty-four. In other words, when I indicate a white number, you must immediately find the black number which, added to the white one, makes twenty-four. Is that clear?"

Gagarin laughed. "Quite clear—twenty-four every time. But they used to say, 'Twenty-five again!'[2] And another number that used to be in style was twenty-one. Blackjack!"

"Enough of your jokes," the lady doctor said rather ill-humoredly. "Let's begin. And remember that everything will be recorded on tape, and on a special apparatus."

With her pointer, she indicated the number three. Wiping the smile from his face, Gagarin glanced at the brightly-illuminated

[2] *Opyat dvadtsat pyat:* a rhyming phrase meaning "The same old thing."—Translator

chart, found a black 21, put his finger on it, and calmly said: "Twenty-four!"

"Good!" said the doctor, and then pointed to the figure 18. At almost the same moment, Gagarin found a black 6 and said, not without malice: "Twenty-four!"

Faster and faster, the pointer darted here and there on the chart. Then suddenly, urgent, confusing voices boomed out from hidden loudspeakers. As Gagarin went on locating the right numbers, the male and female voices from the loudspeakers flooded the room, each one trying to drown out the other, and all of them trying to confuse the person being tested. "Nine . . . fifteen . . . twenty-three . . . seven . . . eleven . . ."

Gagarin was caught up in the excitement. He listened to the urgent voices contradicting one another, and the varicolored figures and circles swam before his eyes. But amid all this chaos he went on finding the right answer, quickly and calmly.

"Twenty-four . . . twenty-four . . . ," he kept saying, in a rather mocking tone of voice.

"Excellent!" the doctor said. "That's fine!"

"Thank you," Gagarin said mischievously. "But I can do better than that. What else do you have to offer?"

They went into the next office, which was dark and small. "Sit down!" said the psychiatrist. He was bald, with a stern, gloomy expression.

Still feeling the effects of the high rating he received on the last test, Gagarin sat down before the psychiatrist. His relaxed and gracious manner expressed his readiness for anything. It was as though he were saying, "Do with me what you will—it's all the same to me!"

Rather stiffly, the psychiatrist told him: "In that black box, against a background of frosted glass, light bulbs of different colors will flash on. You are to watch its left side, where a band of colored light will appear. Remember its color. Then to the right, on the same screen, lights of various colors will appear. The moment you see a light of the same color as that on your left, you are to react immediately and squeeze this handle here. Is that clear?"

"Quite clear," sighed Gagarin. "I just hope I don't break this thing."

The room was blacked out, and at the same instant strange sounds could be heard: pounding, rattling, sighs, moans—they could have been anything. Suddenly the screen lit up, and three dim colored spots appeared on it: red, green, and white. Gagarin squeezed the rubber, pear-shaped bulb—the same kind that is found on the sprayers used in beauty parlors.

The screen went dark and lighted up again. Sounds flooded the office. They became sharp and piercing, seeming to penetrate into one's head—befuddling and brain-splitting. To the left, white spots again appeared. To the right, flashing by in a continuous flow, were circles, squares, and triangles of dark blue, violet, and yellow . . . It seemed that at any moment the specified colors—red, green, and white—would appear. But no. Differently colored spots, with tormenting intensity, danced and did somersaults before Gagarin's eyes. But just as he was relaxing his attention, a red circle appeared on the screen. It quickly expanded, then suddenly vanished. Just as quickly, a scarcely discernible white spot appeared. Gagarin squeezed the rubber bulb. A second later, when three asterisks— red, green, and white—simultaneously appeared among the throng of dancing spots, asterisks, and triangles, he squeezed the bulb three times with lightninglike rapidity. Then the light came on in the room.

"Who's this?" It was the familiar, cheerful voice of Yazdovsky, whose bald head had appeared in the doorway. "Ah, it's Yuri! Congratulations! Well done! You're a sharpshooter! But where is Titov?"

Yazdovsky looked through the door and beckoned to Titov with his finger.

That same day, Gagarin informed Titov that some pilots from Titov's own fighter unit were reporting in to the hospital. Gherman rushed off in search of them. Not finding them in the office, he dashed over to the cafeteria, then to the lounge. On the way, he met them in the corridor and greeted them with a shout. These were his old friends, Oleg and Volodya.

They embraced and exchanged slaps on the back. "How are things back there?" "How are they here?" "How is Tamara? When did you see her last?"

When he and his friends had had their fill of chatting, Titov showed them through the hospital. They visited the cafeteria and the lounge, then went out to the waiting room. There, Gherman asked his friends to sit down in the armchairs arranged in a semi-circle before the big fish tank. Behind the thick glass walls, in the bright light from the electric bulbs, the goldfish silently darted about, while bubbles of water rose up in a silver garland.

Pointing to the fish tank, Gherman announced in a guide's tone of voice: "The greatest medical discovery of the century! It turns out that the fish, the algae, and the water have a soothing effect on the nervous system."

Oleg laughed. "But that's not for us! Even if they were gorillas, our nerves would be all right."

"But that's not the idea!" exclaimed Titov, refusing to joke.

He went up to the fish tank and tapped on the thick glass. Behind it, the fish darted about rapidly. "I laughed too—at first. But later on, when I'd been jammed into various kinds of chambers and whirled around, I got into the habit of coming here to watch the fish."

"Did they give you a rough time?" Oleg asked seriously.

"Uh-*huh!* Those tests and examinations the flight surgeons gave us back in the fighter unit were child's play!" Once again, Titov tapped on the glass side of the fish tank and watched the goldfish. "My friend Yuri Gagarin and I have often said that if things go any further here, they'll wash us all out."

He paused and looked up at the ceiling. "Nobody has been up there yet, and nobody knows anything about it . . . So the screening is very strict."

The friends stood around the fish tank, watching the goldfish, and each of them was given over to his own thoughts. The mysterious fish swam out from the green murk of the algae, wiggled their bright-colored tails, and vanished into the grottoes of the aquarium.

Oleg's friends did not know at the time that the centrifuge would soon "break" him. Reluctantly, with mixed feelings, as though sensing a catastrophe, he entered the squat stone building whose gloomy look had bewildered him on the day he reported in.

"Don't be afraid of anything," Titov had told him, to ease his anxiety. "You're rugged. You're a daring pilot. You fly like a god in supersonic jets. And this is nothing—just a lousy centrifuge!"

But the thing that seemed most unlikely of all was what happened. This first-class fighter pilot, who had performed perfectly on the most complex flights and amazed the whole fighter group with his daring aerobatics, came very near fainting in the centrifuge.

In the ward, Oleg's friends gathered around his bed, sighing. All of them were downcast. Then Yuri Gagarin appeared in the doorway. "Don't panic," he said, coming in and sitting down at the foot of the bed. "These things happen . . . But you'll go on flying—the doctors won't try to stop you. And as for space flight—you can do that later."

Two days afterward, Oleg's friends saw him off. A light snow was falling, and it glittered on the trees. Oleg, who had changed from his hospital garb into his officer's uniform, stepped out of the door looking calm and collected, shoulders thrown back, without a trace of dejection in his face. Swinging his suitcase, he walked ahead of the friends who were seeing him off.

They told him good-by and watched him as he went out to the street, hailed a cab, climbed in, and went off without so much as turning his head to look at them.

"Whose turn is it now?" sighed Volodya. "Whose?"

"'Whose! Whose!'" Nelyubov, another candidate, mimicked him angrily. "Things are sad enough as it is, and you're making sounds like an owl."

"Take it easy!" Volodya told him. "Maybe it's a portent of my own bad luck."

He was not mistaken. A week later, the same group marched out to the green front gate. Volodya was carrying his suitcase. From time to time he would put it down in the snow, sit down on it, and look about with a puzzled expression at the snow-silvered linden trees. "Me too?" he asked incredulously. "*Me too?* What about my dreams of space? Remember how we all used to talk about the stars?"

"We'll get there!" Titov said. "The main thing is will power, purpose, and determination."

Volodya looked at Gagarin: "For you, the centrifuge is a snap. But for me . . . Well, enough of that! Good-by and good luck!"

Titov slipped a letter for Tamara into Volodya's pocket, and the two friends embraced, almost on the point of tears. Then Volodya hurried out to the street, with a last wave to his friends. As they stood there at the gate watching him, he stepped into the street, suitcase swinging in his hand, hailed a cab, and got in. But a

17. In 1939 the Rocket Research Institute staff completed the work on RS-82 and RS-132 rockets for use on bomber planes.

In photo: The rocket projector on a bomber (photographed in 1933).

18. A model of the first 212 winged rocket designed by Sergei Korolev. It made its first sucessful flight with an 09 engine in 1939. The 212 rocket is the direct prototype of jet projectiles.

19. A rocket built by a team of the Stratospheric Committee of the USSR Osoaviakhim Central Council. A. Polyarny is holding the rocket. Moscow, 1935.

20. Center: Yuri Pobedonostsev (standing), Sergei Korolev (sitting). Extreme right: Friedrich Tsander. All founders of the Central Group for the Study of Reactive Propulsion.

21. A group of GIRD scientists and technicians who launched the GIRD-10 rocket. Last, on the left, is Sergei Korolev, head of GIRD.

22. On 28 February 1940 the first Soviet RP-318-1 rocket glider was tested in the air. It was designed by Sergei Korolev and equipped with an RDA-1-150 liquid-fuel rocket engine (a modified version of the DRN-68 engine designed by Valentin Glushko). The rocket glider was flown by glider pilot Vladimir Fyodorov.

23. The first free flight of the Soviet RP-318-1 rocket glider occurred on 28 February 1940. It was flown by Vladimir Fyodorov, one of the best glider pilots of the time who later became a well-known test pilot. The rocket glider was carried into the air by an R-5 tug plane. At an altitude of approximately 8,200 feet, after uncoupling, the pilot fired the rocket engine and in five or six seconds increased the speed from 80 to 140 kilometers an hour.

24. The geophysical V2A rocket on the launching pad. It was designed for exploration of the upper atmospheric layers. In May 1957 it raised the 4,850 pounds of equipment to the height of 212 kilometers.

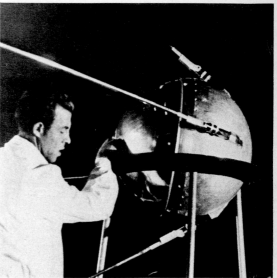

25. The world's first artificial earth satellite on a rigging truck in the assembly shop.

26. The Soviet meteorological RM-1 rocket being prepared for launching (1954). It carried temperature and air pressure measuring devices, cameras and radiotelemetric equipment. Its altitude was up to 100 kilometers.

27. Takeoff of the first Soviet meteorological RM-1 rocket (1954).

28,29 On 30 January 1964
the *Electron*-1 (**ABOVE**) and
Electron-2 (**RIGHT**) satellites
were launched for simultaneous
exploration of the inner and
outer zones of the radiation belt
at different heights. For the first
time in the world a single carrier
rocket placed two scientific
stations in different orbits.

moment later he climbed out of it and, not even noticing his friends, took one last look at the hospital.

That night before going to sleep, Titov was sitting on the bed of his roommate, Ivan Anikeyev. "It's too bad to lose a good man like Volodya," he was saying. "Do you suppose you and I will be going out the gate like that some day, with our suitcases? I couldn't take it!"

There was a light knock at the door, and Nelyubov stepped quietly in, looking worried. "Not sleeping?" he whispered.

"Come here." Titov got up to greet Nelyubov, and then flopped back on Ivan Anikeyev's bed. "I was saying that Volodya was a great loss. Do you suppose they're driving us so hard for no good reason?" He ran a hand through his curly hair. "The time will come when we'll remember this evening and all our fears and anxieties . . . you know?"

He looked at Nelyubov and went on: "When I close my eyes I can see a spacecraft. Just what kind I don't know, but I visualize something unusual. Then I see the stars. I'm flying! Tsiolkovsky wrote something like this: 'Man will not always remain on the earth. In his pursuit of light and space, he will first timidly probe beyond the limits of the atmosphere, then ultimately he will conquer all of circumsolar space.' Right?"

"Right! Quite right. But let me get some sleep!" said Ivan Anikeyev, twisting around in the bed so that Titov almost fell off it. "Don't go on tearing your heart to pieces!"

Titov stood up. "See you tomorrow, boys. We'll make it to the stars!"

The "Devil's Merry-Go-Round"

They were always talking about the centrifuge. It frightened them and at the same time fascinated them.

This complex installation was housed in a simple brick building which, from the outside, looked in no way unusual. Inside, in the center of a large room, stood a metal shaft from which a tubular arm extended horizontally. At the end of the latter was a small, blue-black cabin. Around the entire structure was a silvery, latticed enclosure.

The day came when Titov reported to the centrifuge building for the last of his tests. Before the whirling began, the shades were drawn tightly over the windows, the lights were turned on, and engineers and mechanics checked out the centrifuge. The medical team examined Titov. They checked his pulse, temperature, blood pressure. At Fyodorov's request, Titov stuck out his tongue. "A nice, pink tongue!" said Fyodorov.

Then, stripped to the waist, Titov stood before a nurse. When she had swabbed his tanned, muscular torso with cotton soaked in alcohol and ether, she attached the sensors with their leads of fine wire. Rubberized strips and "tourniquets" were used to fasten the electrodes more firmly to his body.

Titov next put on a dark sweatshirt and white pants and, holding the leads from the sensors, his black helmet, and his goggles, stepped up on the scales. Having weighed in, he entered the round room and took his seat in the little cabin of the centrifuge, in a half-supine position. He looked on with a smile as the assistants strapped him into the seat and plugged the sensors into the instruments. He put on his helmet and big goggles and began to study the panel of lights in front of him. Against the black of the panel, figures and luminous symbols stood out.

The centrifuge engineers and mechanics completed their checkout of the cabin, the instruments, and the cable tracks. The recording instruments had previously been loaded with rolls of paper, and the hollow glass styluses filled with ink. Everything was ready.

Yazdovsky came into the room, accompanied by Fyodorov and another doctor, Pavel Mikhailovich. This taciturn individual, wearing a white jacket and surgical cap, climbed into Titov's cabin and checked to make sure the electrodes were firmly attached. Then Yazdovsky and Fyodorov took their places outside the silvery, latticed enclosure, where they were required to remain while the centrifuge was in operation.

The lights were switched off. The entire room was dark except for a few bulbs throwing their light on white jackets, instruments, and equipment in the instrument compartment beyond the enclosure and near the centrifuge shaft itself.

The instruments went into operation, and the strips of paper began to unroll. The wavy, meandering lines recorded on them by the styluses told how Titov was feeling.

Yazdovsky looked at Titov and smiled. The latter responded with such a cheerful, lively grin that the scientist was touched. Intelligence sparkled in the eyes of this man sitting in the dark cabin who was about to undergo everything he would feel during the launch of a spacecraft.

Titov squinted and looked to see what the doctors in the instrument compartment were doing. One might have gathered from his expression that it was not he but someone else who was making the flight.

Titov's tanned face was illuminated by the beam from a reflector

light in the cabin. His helmet covered his curly hair, and over his
eyes were the protective goggles.

I witnessed this test and saw how the metallic arm—as though
reluctantly—set the cabin in motion and swung it about in a circle.
At first one could still discern Titov's face in the cabin—his rather
sharp nose and the strong lines of his mouth and eyebrows. But
within a few seconds the cabin was whirling about so fast that his
features could not be distinguished.

Nor could my eyes follow the point of white light in the cabin:
now it was to the left, now to the right of me; then again to the
left and once more to the right. As I tried to follow the light, my
head began to whirl. But what about Titov? How was he feeling?

Strips of printing paper, unrolling from the reels, were spreading
out across the floor. On them one could see the fantastic wavy lines
made by the styluses.

The speed was stepped up, and the roaring sound became louder.
The little cabin was flashing by with dizzying speed.

On the panel in front of Titov, figures flashed up. He could see
them clearly, although he was already feeling the deformation of
his face and the leaden heaviness of his body. He had not only to
make out the figures but add, subtract, and report the answers to
Yazdovsky over the voice radio.

He mentally added some figures, then tried to open his mouth,
but a strange force was keeping his lips close together. His jaw
felt like iron, and it was hard for him to function. By sheer strength
of will, however, he managed to open his mouth and say: "Eighteen . . ."

Around him, everything was whirling, rushing about, roaring,
and raging. The whole world seemed to be collapsing and headed
for destruction . . . But then more figures flashed up on the panel:
Yazdovsky was continuing the experiment and required a clear
answer from Titov.

By this time, the cosmonaut weighed a ton. He was tempest-
tossed and could scarcely move his lips. But he opened them and
shouted into the microphone: "Forty-six . . ."

Titov realized that it was not simply a matter of enduring the
avalanche of weight, the roaring and rumbling, and the oppressive
darkness of the room. The important thing was to act, make decisions, and communicate via the radio. So, summoning up all his will

power, he kept on thinking, calculating, and conversing while being furiously spun about by the devil's merry-go-round.

At length, however, the metallic arm, which only moments before had been whirling him about in the light-blue cabin with the dark seat, seemed to grow tired and slowed to a stop. Silence descended.

The doctors and nurses in their white uniforms gathered around the cabin. Titov was smiling. He stretched as if after a good night's sleep, reached forward, and placed his hands on the edge of the light panel.

The results were excellent, and everything seemed in order. But then came a calamity: Gherman had caught a cold. He sneezed. This sort of thing simply didn't happen to him! From out of nowhere appeared a doctor and a nurse with a thermometer. Gherman's temperature, it turned out, was 99.7 degrees F. Bed rest was prescribed.

Very much upset, he walked slowly along the corridor, climbed the stairway to his own ward, into which the winter sun was now shining, and glumly sat down in an armchair. "Could this really mean the end?" he asked himself sorrowfully. Everything had been going so well, and then suddenly . . . But perhaps the whole thing had been done on purpose. Perhaps the real reason was his broken arm . . .

Outside, a December snow was falling. Slowly, the snowflakes came to rest on the branches of the birches and lindens. The wind was howling, and far off beyond the darkness of the park he could see the flashing blue lights of the electric railway.

The door opened almost noiselessly, and Gagarin came in. "Don't let it get you down," he began with a kindly smile. "I was talking with Fyodorov, and he says there's nothing to worry about. Just a cold that won't last."

Gherman shrugged. "Remember when that big, rugged character left? Now it's my turn to pack up my things."

"Oh, come on! Just sniffle, take some pills, flop into bed, and that'll be all there is to it."

Gherman's heart was warmed by his friend's words. Coming up to Gagarin, he said: "If only you were right, Yuri! But life is a hard thing sometimes. I'll have to lie there in bed and wait for my sentencing." After a pause, he went on spiritedly: "I grew up in the Altay, where the winters are the kind you get only in Siberia— very cold, with blizzards. In winters like that, we'd run the three kilometers to school. Sometimes we'd fall into a snowdrift or lose our way in a blizzard. Or we'd chase after the girls and push them into the drifts. We were always in the snow, with red faces and our clothes soaking wet. But nobody ever had so much as a sniffle. In the summer, you know, we'd go into the forests and to the lakes. (We have beautiful lakes back home!) We'd swim in the cold water, sleep out in the rain—and it was literally like water off a duck's back. But now I've got a cold! And because of the cold, I've got a high sedimentation rate! And when does it happen? At the most critical point in the tests! . . . But it's not the cold that matters. I've got a premonition . . ."

"Everything will be all right," Gagarin assured him.

Titov had to stay in bed and take bitter medicines. He soon recovered, thanks to his strong constitution and good medical care; and he walked out of the ward confident he could make up for lost time. Instead, however, he was called to the main office of the hospital, where his papers were handed back to him. He was ordered to return to duty with his fighter unit.

"Back to the regiment? But what about my space training?"

The doctor on duty looked at Titov impassively. "A decision will be made later. Go back to your unit and your flying. You are fully fit for flight duty."

Titov went directly to Fyodorov. As usual, Dr. Fyodorov was wearing his dark glasses, and his expression was calm but a bit aloof. Yet his voice was full of friendly sympathy. "I'm sure the commission will give you the nod. But in the meantime you'll have to go back to your post. It's a matter of following orders."

Titov sighed, chagrined. Then he thanked Fyodorov for his solicitude and their friendly talks and said good-by.

In the ward, his friends were awaiting him.

"Well?" asked Gagarin.

"I invite you to see me off . . ."

"But what did he tell you?"

"I have to leave . . ." Titov was trying to speak unconstrainedly. But somewhere deep in his heart he felt a chill and—along with it— humiliation and disappointment.

"Did he hold out any hopes?" Gagarin persisted.

"It's easy to hold out hopes," said Titov, with a deprecating wave of the hand. And taking off his hospital garments, he got into his officer's field shirt.

Gagarin was pensive. "But don't you think this might be another kind of test? That they want to find out how badly you want to become a cosmonaut? How you'll bear up under these hardships, and whether you've got what it takes to get through them?"

With no attempt at concealing his irriation, Titov replied: "Today we're all becoming professors of medicine and developing various theories. But there's an old saying: 'Out of sight, out of mind.' I'll go away, and the people here will forget all about me."

"Don't blow your top!" Gagarin said, trying to calm his friend down. "I'll look into everything here, and let you know what I find out."

When the formalities were over, Titov threw his greatcoat over his shoulders, picked up his suitcase, and, accompanied by his friends, walked along the snow-covered path toward the gatehouse. It was painful to take leave of the columns at the hospital's main entrance—of the snow-covered fountain where plaster urchins in light-blue swimming trunks were still trying to catch plaster fish. Titov's heart was wrenched as he walked past the tall wooden pergola where he and Gagarin had had so many talks about space flight . . .

The short-haired woman in the light dress was on duty in the gatehouse. When she saw Titov with his suitcase, she threw out her arms in a gesture of amazement. "So you've been washed out, too, Curly! What's going on? This screening is getting really tough!"

Titov laughed and shook hands with her. She had shown him real sympathy. He said good-by to Gagarin, Nikolayev, Popovich, Anikeyev, Nelyubov, and other new friends. Then suddenly growing serious, he added: "I'll come back here again. Just remember that: I'll be back!"

When Gherman Titov once again saw, through a flurry of snow-flakes, the buildings of the air base, and when he again heard the roar and screaming of the jet planes, he was overcome with mixed feelings. He was gladdened by the thought that he would soon see his wife and friends again; and he was eager to climb into the cockpit of his jet fighter and zoom up into the sky toward the night stars. But he was still plagued by a kind of embarrassment—perhaps a feeling of guilt. What would he say to his commanding officer, Podosinov, who had recommended him for the cosmonaut team? Just what would he tell him? And what would be the reaction of the flight surgeons at the air base, who had always been proud of him and considered him a model of good health and well-rounded development? Finally, what would he say to Tamara?

When he reached his own quarters, he saw some children who had made a snowman near the entrance. The little scamps were tumbling in the snowdrifts and chasing each other. When they noticed Titov, they shouted excitedly. He had often performed tricks and acrobatic stunts for them and was their idol.

When at length he had torn himself away from their clutching, wet-mittened hands, he went inside the building. He could feel his heart pound as he opened his own door and stood on the threshold, so covered with snow that he himself looked like a snowman.

"Gherman!" Tamara shouted joyously and threw herself into her husband's arms. He held her close, feeling the warmth of her breath and her tears on his cheek. "Now, there, my funny girl . . ."

He felt guilty towards his wife. No doubt she had been worried —waking up in the middle of the night to wonder how her Gherman was. And the child?

Titov remembered that evening long ago when he had met her. A dance was being held at the officers' club, but he had become engrossed in a book by H. G. Wells and had arrived late. The regimental band was playing a waltz, and the other officers were whirling about the floor with their wives, fiancées, or girls they knew. But Gherman was alone and bored. He was on the point of leaving when he noticed a slender, dark-haired girl with pretty, sparkling eyes. He was struck by the look in those eyes—at once gentle and intelligent. Prompted by a suddenly aroused feeling, with a toss of his curly head, he went straight over to the girl and asked her to dance.

Both of them seemed to understand instantly what a strange, happy surprise it was that had brought them together, and they danced in a kind of rapture. They danced all evening, unwilling to leave each other. Old waltz tunes, which had sent more than one generation awhirl, set them awhirl, too.

The better they got to know each other, the stronger their mutual attraction grew; and in snatches and half-spoken phrases, by means of smiles and gestures, they opened their hearts to each other. They talked of their earlier lives and their secret dreams. Gherman told Tamara about the distant Altay, about the raging rivers of Siberia, which came rushing down from the mountain heights; about his boyhood dreams of becoming a flier. And she told him, rather shyly, that she was from the Luganskaya Oblast; that she had come to visit her sister, and stayed on to work as a cook in the mess hall at the air base.

These first meetings and confidences were still fresh in his memory . . . And now Tamara was weeping in his arms, and her tears stirred his deepest feelings.

"And how . . . how is the child?" he asked.

She put her hands on his shoulders and looked intently into his eyes. "Soon . . . It will be here soon."

He picked her up in his arms and danced around the room with her, squeezing her hard against him in his excitement. Then, still holding her, he sat down and began to talk to her in a jumble of words—the way a man does when he is so happy that he loses the thread of his thought and jumps from one idea to another. He wondered aloud whether it would be a boy or a girl. He talked about where it would be best to get the crib and the layette.

The next morning Titov reported for duty with the air group. His commanding officer, Nikolai Stepanovich Podosinov, who had recommended him for the cosmonaut team, greeted him as if nothing had happened—as if Titov had never been away. Podosinov talked about fuel and engines, about new equipment and new air zones. In this way he spared Titov the necessity of launching immediately into an unpleasant conversation about being sent back from the hospital. Deeply appreciative of Podosinov's tact, Titov himself brought up the subject of what had happened at the hospital. But from his CO's look and slight smile, Titov realized that none of this was new to him. Apparently, he knew all—even more than Titov himself.

"I'm convinced," said Podosinov emphatically, "that the commission will decide in your favor. Otherwise, what kind of situation would we have? Three of our boys went there, and all three were sent back. That won't wash!

"You have splendid abilities. Forget the high sedimentation rate and the cold—you'll get over that. Our flight surgeons consider you perfectly fit to master the new hardware," Podosinov said. "In the meantime, you'll fly here with us."

After being away from the air base, it was a pleasure to walk along the parking apron, swept clean of snow, past the row of planes. The mechanics had taken off the tarpaulins, displaying the silvery fuselages, the swept-back wings, and the snub tails with the bright red, blue, and yellow numbers painted on them. The smell of kerosene, the growling of the huge fueling rigs, the prolonged scream and howl of the jet engines, and the voices of the pilots and mechanics—all these things went to make up that milieu Titov was so fond of, and which was so familiar to him.

With undisguised pleasure he put on his pressure suit and helmet and climbed into the cockpit of his MIG. The microphone and the instruments on the panel in front of him seemed to have been waiting for him. In the earphones he could hear voices from the control tower; then came the command to taxi to the strip and take off.

The earth, with the concrete runways of the airfield, the parking aprons, the buildings of the air base, and the snow-covered flatlands around them, disappeared beneath a film of clouds. For another few moments he could make out the hazy Baltic Sea extending along the horizon. But then it was lost from view, along with the layers of clouds, and through the transparent canopy the sunlight flooded the cockpit. The silvery flashing of the wings was unbearably bright. Above him and all around him was the winter sky, reflected in the cockpit as well. And the sky was in his soul, possessing his thoughts and feelings.

Other jets were flying beside him in formation. Like Titov, their pilots were feeling the joy of flight—that state of exhilaration when the plane seems to float through the blue of the heavens.

Titov surrendered himself wholly to the job of flying. He was all attention, concentrating—ready at any moment to engage the "enemy." Because it was quite possible that an "air battle" might come up (if that was what the training plan called for), and he had to be on the ready to find the "enemy" first and attack him.

Gherman loved the exciting moments of searching out the "enemy." Since childhood, the Siberian's instinct for hunting had been so fully developed in him that it sometimes seemed he was again experiencing that passion for tracking down game that his father had inculcated in him.

First the contact, then the attack, and the "air battle." You had to see everything at once—the enemy plane in the cross hairs of the gunsight, the instruments on the panel, the radar screen, the friendly planes, the earth, and the sky. But the sky, the earth, the planes—everything whirled about, loomed up, turned cartwheels, fell away, shot up, and tumbled above your head.

Titov took particular pleasure in this combat test. He felt relaxed and free, and his movements were especially accurate. Later on, back at the air base, he realized what had prompted him to such ardor in performing, shortly before, those figures of aerobatics. It was his eagerness to test his strength and will power, to convince himself that everything he had gone through back there at the hospital had been due to misfortune and misunderstanding, that he was vigorous, healthy, and ready to undergo much harder tests.

'I'll take the commission by storm!" he told himself with firm conviction. "I'll storm the specialists, and I'll make a space flight."

But he didn't have to take the commission by storm. He was called back to Moscow.

With pounding heart, he once again went in through the familiar gate with the green stone columns. The short-haired woman, wearing a fluffy kerchief on her head, was again on duty in the gatehouse. He greeted her as an old acquaintance, and she exclaimed: "Glad to see you back, Curly! What a stubborn one you are—you got what you wanted!"

Titov paid his respects to the wooden pergola and walked past the main entrance and the fountain facing it. (The fountain was mute, and the plaster figures of the urchins pursuing the fish were covered with snow.) Then he went into the Emergency Ward.

The doctor on duty—ordinarily aloof to the point of severity— gave him an approving smile. And the nurses greeted him with particular respect. It was easy for Titov to gather that something very much in his favor had happened.

Once again he was wearing hospital garb: the dark sweatshirt and the equally dark, rough woolen pants. Once again he was quartered on the floor above, in the familiar ward. But now his neighbors were an entirely different lot. The old hands had vanished from the scene—gone back to their air bases scattered throughout the country—and their places had been taken by newcomers. Obviously, the cosmonauts were still being screened with the old intensity and exigency.

Titov found out that he had been definitely assigned to the cosmonaut team. And he also found out that Fyodorov had shown a particular interest in his case. It turned out that that calm individual with the aloof expression could defend his own point of view heatedly. He had conclusively shown that according to all the evidence, Titov was a very fit candidate for the cosmonaut team. His arguments had been so persuasive, and his insistence so strong, that the members of the commission (the nation's leading medical scientists and biologists) had reviewed the documentation and raised the question: Should the fact that Titov had long ago broken his arm be taken into consideration? They asked the flight surgeons at the air base to ascertain how Titov felt after his return to his unit—what his state of mind was. And when the answers came back, they decided to approve Gherman Stepanovich Titov for the cosmonaut team.

Titov hurried off to find Fyodorov. He located him in the main office and nearly threw himself on the doctor's neck out of gratitude. But Fyodorov's only reaction was to smile with his eyes and greet Titov with some reserve.

"Congratulations!" he said, concealing his own great pleasure and closely scrutinizing Titov as usual. "I'm glad for you. I believe in your future in the space program. The cosmonaut team had already been selected, basically. It includes your friend Gagarin, along with Andriyan Nikolayev, Leonov, and Popovich . . . They have already gone back—temporarily—to the air bases where they were stationed. You too, when you've gone through the official procedures here, can go back to your post, wind up your duties, and then report to your new unit—bringing your wife along with you."

"To a new unit?" Titov repeated. "A new unit?" And right then and there he told Fyodorov the joyful news: he would soon be a father!

"Congratulations!" the doctor said, in a tone which left no doubt that he already knew everything. "It follows logically that with you, a unique chain reaction of joys and successes is already starting. But how does Tamara Vasilevna feel?"

"So you remember my wife's patronymic?" Titov asked, greatly pleased. "Well, she's nervous . . . And I understand why. We're about to have a child, and I'm making ready for a space flight . . . But she understands me, too. She once said that my dream is her dream."

This conversation was taking place in the main office of the hospital—a room containing a few desks and chairs, plus a safe painted a dark brown. Fyodorov, who was standing next to the wall—a wall covered with charts, instructions, and personnel schedules—was obviously pleased with Titov. "Remember how you and I used to stroll through the park? In those days everything seemed so far in the future—but now you're already a cosmonaut. The training and the conditioning flights will soon begin. And then—the first launch."

Fyodorov was gratified by this talk with Titov. He may even have been waiting for him—waiting to have a heart-to-heart talk with him about Tamara, the child to come, the flight ino space, and the psychological stress that the flier had gone through after leaving the hospital.

It was hot and stuffy in the office, so Fyodorov suggested to Titov that they step outside. Putting on their overcoats, they left the office. The park had been snowed in that evening, and only the pathways cut through the drifts. The two of them walked along the path where they had strolled after their first meeting. Fyodorov brushed his shoulder against the branch of a lilac bush, dislodging clumps of snow.

As though thinking aloud, the medical scientist began in a confidential tone: "We are initiating a series of flights with animals— with dogs. We'll also send up various plants. We still need a good deal of time to study thoroughly the state of a living organism in space. And then . . ." Fyodorov looked at Titov. "Then there'll be a manned flight. I very much wish you would inform Tamara Vasilevna that before we send a man into space, all safety measures will have been taken. She mustn't be anxious. And she mustn't worry about the child to come. As for you, finish your business here as fast as you can, then get back to the air base in a hurry and wind things up there, so that you can get started on the new job without delay. I don't need to tell you that we'll take good care of Tamara Vasilevna and the child. Generally speaking, don't worry about the future. And now . . ." Fyodorov looked at his watch. "And now go to see Colonel Usanov."

Aleksandr Semyonovich Usanov, the director of the hospital— a thick-chested, gray-headed man with a broad, intelligent face— received Titov in his small, modest office. Unhurriedly, he got up from behind his desk, shook the flier's hand by way of congratulation, and officially announced that Titov was now a member of the cosmonaut team.

"Congratulations," the old doctor said feelingly. "I wish you success and long flights. I'm very glad for you. We all have a high opinion of your perseverance. It does credit to you, Senior Lieutenant! Have a seat."

And he offered Titov a chair. "For us, it is very important that a man who becomes a cosmonaut *wants* to be one—that he becomes one not by chance, not without thinking about it, and not from an urge to gratify his vanity. You have stood up under some hard tests, and the medical commission believes that in the future you will justify the trust placed in you."

Titov rose, stood at attention, and replied gravely: "I thank you from the bottom of my heart. I'll do everything to justify your trust."

"Sit down. That's it. Fine. Now for all I've just said, tell me: Why do you want to go into space? You'll soon have a child. Your wife is nervous."

"That's right. My wife is very nervous. And I'm nervous, too." At this, Senior Lieutenant Titov stood at attention again—as habit had taught him to do in front of a military superior. But at an order from Usanov he immediately sat down again.

Once seated, he went on: "I'm a flier. The sky is where I feel at home. All of us fliers strive to improve our skills, to master new equipment, to be discoverers . . . And I . . ." He became confused, drew a breath, and said in a rush of words: "So long as I'm vigorous and my nerves are strong, I want to help in exploring space. When I was still a child, my father told me a lot about the stars, giving voice to his daydreams about flights through the universe. And I read Tsiolkovsky. But what I wanted most of all was to become a flier. It didn't all go smoothly for me. I had my share of difficulties. But I did become a pilot, flying supersonic fighters. At the time it seemed that all my dreams had been realized. But later I became fascinated by the new hardware—by spacecraft. And then the commission—"

"Are you convinced that you have no other motives for wanting to make space flights?" asked Usanov, looking searchingly into Titov's eyes, at his cheeks and forehead, and the wrinkles between his eyebrows. "The pursuit of fame, for instance?"

Titov lowered his gaze as though looking for something on the floor and pondered the question. Then he replied firmly: "None at all! I have only one goal, and that is to be useful to mankind in the study and exploration of space."

"And the danger? Encountering meteor showers, for instance? Or radioactivity? Or a loss of communications and the disappearance of the spacecraft into another part of the universe?" Usanov picked up a thick pencil and rapped on his desk with it. "What then?"

"I'm ready to make a flight." And Titov stood up quickly. This time the director did not tell him to sit down again. He proffered his hand and said by way of dismissal: "We'll be working together. Now wind up your affairs here and go back to your air base. Then on March 14, report to your new unit."

Fyodorov was waiting for Titov in the narrow hallway. "How did the talk turn out?" he asked with real concern.

"Everything is fine. Thank you. Thanks again."

"We'll be expecting you. Don't forget we'll be calling the muster roll of the cosmonauts on March 14. Who knows? Maybe in the distant future that day will be known as a milestone marking the boundary of a new era." Fyodorov took Titov by the arm and walked with him down the hall and out the door. "I can see the whole thing now. We'll have a space center, with trained cosmonauts, and we'll begin our space flights . . . These things will happen—they can't fail to!"

From Khodynka
to Star Town

In the countryside at some distance from Moscow, construction was begun on Zvezdnyy Gorodok (Star Town), the future cosmonaut training center.

Today, Zvezdnyy (as it is called for short) is a handsome town in the style of the 1960s, with both working areas and living quarters. But in those days it was just another of those wooded tracts so common in the region around Moscow. Here, when the wind blew, it sighed through the tops of birches, spruce, and pines. Trees predominated, except for an occasional road through the forest and, along its edge, plots tended by amateur gardeners.

Why was this site—far from the center of the capital—selected for the future base? For one thing, it offered good possibilities for construction and further development. Then, too, it was far from noisy thoroughfares, industrial plants, and the towns on the outskirts of the capital. Those who selected the site were pleased with this sunny, quiet spot where the fresh air was filled with the scent of the forest.

But the quiet was soon broken by the noise of tractors and bulldozers and the din of cement mixers. The walls of future buildings

—a hotel, a mess hall, a headquarters building, and a training school—rose up among the age-old pines. Embodied in concrete, steel, and glass, the structures of the first complex of Star Town began to take form.

Nikolai Kamanin recalls: "That first organizational stage in our work was difficult in a unique way. We had to have a clear idea of how, to what extent, and by what methods the future cosmonauts were to be trained. Each question that came up was harder than the last one. Who would train them? How? Where? And with what? On the basis of what plans, programs, training aids, and procedures?"

Kamanin mentioned one curious incident: "I was talking to the engineer who had been asked to design a trainer. In response to this assignment, he came up with dozens of questions. I said to him: 'I can only tell you in general terms what must be designed. It's up to you to provide the details, the estimates, and the proposals.'"

The engineer was plainly taken aback, but he still asked: "Where are the models?"

"Nowhere. We have to create everything ourselves—from scratch. We're the first to attempt this. The very first—do you understand?"

"It was easy to see," Kamanin continued, "that the engineer was used to a neat system of preliminary studies and plans—to laboratories, testing ranges, and everything that was already in being and operationally tested. It was hard for him to understand what it meant to work on an entirely new problem—to be, at one and the same time, an inventor, designer, and executive.

"Needless to say, the man who was to take charge of the cosmonaut team had to be a leader, a teacher, and a bold experimenter besides. There were quite a few candidates for the position. The one we picked, Evgeny Anatolevich Karpov, was a prominent specialist in the field of aviation medicine—a fine, sensitive person, and keenly observant. He had worked with fliers for many years and understood their psyches and temperaments. Karpov is a bold experimenter—a man of scope whose thought is wide-ranging. He is a tactful teacher and knows how to 'get along with people' on the job."

From the very beginning, Karpov was—as the expression has it—fired with enthusiasm for his new work and what it promised. Star Town was not yet in existence (it was still under construc-

tion), and in that year of 1959 the M. V. Frunze Central Airport
in Moscow was the cosmonauts' first home. They didn't stay there
long. But it is interesting that the history of cosmonautics is to some
extent associated with an airport which has an important place in
the history of Soviet aviation.

In 1910 one of the first Russian fliers—Boris Illiodorovich Rossinsky—built a wooden shed for his old-fashioned airplane on Khodynka Field near the Moscow–Petersburg road. Rossinsky even
spent his nights in the hangar beside his plane. Thousands of
people came to Khodynka to stare at the strange flying machine and
gaze with wonderment as a man flew into the sky.

Boris Rossinsky's hangar served to mark the beginning of Khodynka's new phase as Moscow's first airport. By 1917 hangars and
workshops had been built there, and Rossinsky himself tested the
planes built at Moscow's Duks aircraft plant. After the Soviet regime
had come into power, Boris Rossinsky, as a Red pilot, was assigned
to make flights over the airport. One of those present at the first
fly-by, on 1 May 1918, was Lenin.

Subsequently, Khodynka Field was renamed the M. V. Frunze
Central Airport. In the thirties and forties it became the central
airport not only of Moscow, but of the whole country.

With the coming of the cosmonaut team to the Central Airport,
living quarters, warehouses, and a laboratory building were assigned to them. In addition to its historical significance, the airport
offered several other advantages. Near at hand was the Zhukovsky
Air Force Academy, with its splendid laboratories and auditoriums.
Also nearby was a fine swimming pool. For that matter, the Central
Airport itself was an excellent base for carrying out flight programs.

The guard on duty at the gray metal gate with red stars on its
panels had no notion, at the time, that the young pilots passing
through the gate were the first cosmonauts. As a matter of routine,
he checked Yuri Gagarin's papers, saluted, and let him into the
Central Airport.

Gagarin had not come alone: Valya was with him. And Titov
was accompanied by Tamara. All of the cosmonauts had brought
their wives. The only one to show up alone was Andriyan Nikolayev.
He was still a bachelor.

The usual and the unusual—the novelty of the plans for them
and the routine of the barracks—were intertwined in the lives of
the cosmonauts. Morning and evening alike, they looked out at the

smooth expanse of the airfield and heard the familiar whine of jet engines. Nothing of what they saw resembled the images of space that had so stirred their imaginations. Around them were the sturdy brick buildings of the barracks, with the old control tower looming up above them; nearby the swimming pool sparkled. Such things had nothing in common with the fantastic interstellar ships and space projects they had imagined. The cosmonauts, eager for imminent flights to the moon, were somewhat disappointed.

The cosmonauts soon learned Colonel Karpov's life story. He had been born in Kiev in 1921, had been graduated in 1941 from the S. M. Kirov Academy of Military Medicine in Leningrad, and had been sent to the front immediately, as a battalion surgeon. He later became a regimental surgeon, then chief surgeon of a division. He had many flight hours to his credit, and as a flight surgeon had helped assure the success of very complex operations carried out by air force units. The cosmonauts also learned that when the war ended, Karpov was in Breslau, in East Prussia; that he had served in the Soviet armed forces stationed in the German Democratic Republic for some time, and then returned to Moscow.

Karpov became the guiding force of the cosmonaut team—unifying the young fliers and directing them toward their great goal.

In one of his first talks with the cosmonauts, he was—uncharacteristically—rather expansive.

"All of you are young fliers in blooming health," he began with a smile. "You have stood up well under hard testing at the hospital, and of course you are expecting the gates of space to open up for you immediately. But it has turned out that you had to begin your duties with the new unit under prosaic conditions. In fact it may have struck some of you as quite uninteresting. Well, there are difficulties; but they are temporary. The main thing is the future. We're going to have a space center and training installations. And you'll make flights. All this will happen."

The cosmonauts looked at one another and winked, as if to say: Now everything will be made clear.

Karpov went on: "I'll be quite frank and open with you. Nobody in the world has yet flown into space. Nobody knows with any accuracy what demands will be imposed by space on the cosmonaut. And so at this very moment, when space medicine and space biology are being born, you will be the guinea pigs—so to speak—

of these sciences. Naturally, we have studied the great body of knowledge built up by aviation medicine and biology. These sciences have achieved a great deal, and have helped to train ultrahigh-speed pilots, high-altitude pilots, and test pilots. Now the time has come to train cadres of cosmonauts. This involves a good deal that is different—even from supersonic flying. And what we expect of you is creative, active help, advice, and vigorous participation in the founding of a new profession—that of the cosmonaut."

After his talk, Karpov walked out of the barracks in the company of several cosmonauts. The intoxicating smell of spring filled the air, the melted snow gurgled in rivulets, and the sound of jet engines could be heard from the airport.

Wearily, Karpov passed his hand across his broad face. "Was it okay?" he asked Gagarin. "Spring in the world of nature, and spring in the new science." After a pause, he went on with his thought: "Construction of the space center is going full speed ahead. The site is marvelous—in the forest, among the pines, with lakes and fields nearby. Blissful. But you too will have to pitch in and work. You'll have to stand guard on the construction site and see whether the training areas and the laboratories are right for you."

"Yes, sir—we'll pitch in!" Gagarin said delightedly. "We'll set up a team to keep guard at the construction site. Titov will be the leader. He's clever with his hands, and he has an engineer's eye for checking on things."

"We'll put all of you to work: you and Titov and Nikolayev and Shonin—all of you. Not only on the construction site but in working out programs, charts, and training schedules." Karpov's eyes were sparkling. "It's very important that each of you feel that he's not just a flier but a doctor, a physicist, a radio operator, a geographer, and an astronomer—in short, a builder of the space center."

Karpov expanded this idea: "The idea of the active and conscientious participation of the cosmonauts in both study and work, runs like a thread through our whole program. The primary requirement in all this is a willingness to do anything. And there's a second requirement. When you lose confidence, when you feel you can't do it—keep working, take risks, train yourself. And when you feel strong—do it!"

Some Pages from
a Life Story

In early April 1960 the cosmonaut team shifted their base from the M. V. Frunze Central Airport to Star Town well outside of Moscow. There, construction had already been completed on the first laboratories, the sports complex, the dispensary, the mess hall, the headquarters, and the classroom building.

Karpov assembled the cosmonauts and told them without any great show of ceremony: "A base has been built for us—a center for the training of cosmonauts. This means that we can now move into the planned, ground-school phase of our work. We have very little time left before the first flight: one year, according to rough plans and estimates. In the course of that year we must do a great deal. When you meet the chief designer, Sergei Pavlovich Korolev, he will spell out this exhaustive program for you."

In those days the cosmonauts were constantly hearing such phrases as: "The Chief has ordered . . ." "S.P. insists . . ." "Korolev expects . . ." Needless to say, they were eager to see and get to know S. P. Korolev, who had directed all work on the designing of the space vehicle systems that would make possible the first manned space flight.

During the first years of space exploration, scientists were faced with tremendous difficulties that demanded of them, of the design engineers and workmen—and, later, of the cosmonauts—incredible efforts, inventiveness, and self-sacrifice. The struggle against these difficulties—not only in the Soviet Union but in the United States as well—was taking place under inimical conditions. Certain scientists, philosophers, men of affairs, and journalists were expressing the fear—either openly or in veiled language—that the tremendous expenditures required to create artificial satellites (and, later, spaceships) would be cast to the wind—or, more accurately, into space—without yielding practical results useful to contemporary mankind.

All these things must be taken into account in order fully to appreciate the vast amount of work done by Academician Korolev and the qualities he so brilliantly manifested: a magnificent will-to-victory, a clear understanding of the goal, and outstanding executive talent.

He was born on 30 December 1906 in the Ukraine—in the town of Zhitomir. At that time, the routes to the other planets had been mapped out only by K. E. Tsiolkovsky and the science fiction writers.

When Korolev was a boy of two, his family went from Zhitomir to the quiet town of Nezhin, nestled among cherry orchards near Kiev. And when the Russian flier, Sergei Utochkin, paid a visit to Nezhin, the boy's grandfather and grandmother took him out to the field on the outskirts of town where Utochkin's plane had landed. Utochkin's flight made a tremendous impression on the young Korolev, and he remembered it for the rest of his life.

His mother, Mariya Nikolayevna Koroleva, gave me this account of her son's childhood: "We were living in Zhitomir on what was then called Dmitriyevskaya Street, in a single-storyed house surrounded by birches. My husband, Pavel Yakovlevich, taught literature at the local high school. He was a man with a broad education and a keen intelligence. Before becoming a teacher, he had been graduated with a degree in languages and literature from the institute in Nezhin where the great writer, Gogol, had once been a student.

"Korolev entered the institute as a 'crown scholar': his food, clothing, and other living expenses were provided by the Government. Upon graduation, he was to enter the service of the Ministry of Education, so that the expense of his education could be recouped.

"He was assigned to Zhitomir. Within a year after the birth of Seryozha [little Sergei], my husband and I moved to Kiev. There I entered the Higher School for Women and was graduated with a degree in German and Romance languages. Later I taught Seryozha French. He learned German and English on his own."

The Korolevs' domestic life came to grief; and when Seryozha was about two, he was left in the care of his mother. When he was ten, he acquired a stepfather, Grigory Mikhailovich Balanin— a man S. P. Korolev always recalled with warmth and gratitude.

Nonetheless, the family complications had an effect on the boy; and Sergei Korolev once told me: "I was living among adults, and I had no real childhood. But I did not become introverted and asocial. High school, the Komsomol, the construction trade school, the glider club, and the polytechnical institute equipped me well for coping with life."

As a student Seryozha was fond of math, loved music, and read a lot. His stepfather was an engineer. In Odessa he first worked with the administration of the Southwestern Railroad, then became superintendent of the electric power station at the port of Odessa, moving with his family into a house next to the power station.

From near at hand, the splashing of the sea's waves could be heard. And one remote part of the harbor was used as a base for seaplanes. The little boy delighted in watching the seaplanes take off and land. The pilots and mechanics noticed the curious little fellow and let him take a look at the cockpit of a seaplane. Then came the day when Seryozha persuaded the pilots to take him up.

Way down there, under the wing, was the blue of the sea, and the white stone buildings of Odessa were surrounded by greenery. The famous flight of steps[1] seemed as though engraved. The coal dumps loomed black, and the smoke from the steamers' stacks swirled up thickly . . . The little boy's heart was stirred by this flight over Odessa, by the unusual sensation of being up in the air and by a fear which gave way to tempestuous excitement.

[1] On the waterfront. It was made famous, *inter alia*, by Sergei Eisenstein's film, *The Battleship "Potemkin."*—Translator

As a schoolboy, Seryozha Korolev was fascinated by books; he read rapidly and a lot. One day he came across an issue of the journal *Byloye* (The Past) from the year 1918, with an article about the Russian revolutionary and assassin Nikolai Kibalchich, who had designed a rocket-powered spaceship. "I am preparing this design in prison, a few days before I am to die," the young Korolev read. "I believe in the feasibility of my idea; and that belief sustains me in my frightful situation."

Sergei Pavlovich Korolev told me what a strong impression was made on him when he first came across the design worked out by Kibalchich. "Although a prisoner and under a death sentence, he was not thinking of his own death but of a rocket-powered spaceship."

Kibalchich's passionate words about serving the people, about remaining true to the great scientific ideal, and about the inventor's single-mindedness sank deep into the soul of the young schoolboy.

In the words of Korolev's mother: "Since his early childhood, Seryozha had been fascinated by flight—by the idea that man could fly. After going up in the seaplanes, he got the idea of building his own glider. In June of 1923 he joined a glider club. His stepfather, Grigory Mikhailovich, who belonged to the same club, treated Seryozha as if he were his own son, strongly encouraging his interest in gliders and helping him to understand technical points. I must admit that I was frightened by the idea of the flights. The whole thing was new, and the gliders struck me as very imperfect . . . I conceived the faint hope that Seryozha would forget about flying and become a sailor. He loved the sea, the port of Odessa had become a second home for him. He was a very good swimmer, and several times he had saved people who were drowning. But my hopes were never realized: Seryozha remained true to the skies until the end of his life."

At the advice of his stepfather, who said he had a marked talent for design engineering, the young Korolev entered a technical school for construction workers in Odessa. The school was one that was favored by many of the teen-agers: it offered a broad curriculum, and its graduates were qualified to go on to college. It had a department of architectural construction and a department of sanitation construction, and graduated bricklayers, plasterers, carpenters, roofing specialists, and plumbers. Sergei Korolev chose to

30. The high-altitude geophysical VGAS automatic station launched with the V2A rocket on 15 February 1961 for the exploration of solar corona and phenomena in the upper layers of the atmosphere during the solar eclipse.

31. The *Proton*-1 space station was put in orbit on 16 July 1965. The *Proton* satellites are the heaviest orbital automatic stations in the world. This one was designed for cosmic ray research.

32. The *Venera*-3 automatic station launched on 16 November 1965. The research equipment was housed in a special compartment, a round capsule with a diameter of 36 inches. On 1 March 1966 the station reached Venus and conveyed to its surface the Soviet Union's State Seal.

33. The *Luna*-3 automatic station was the first to photograph
the reverse side of the moon. On 7 October 1959, from a distance
of from 65,000 to 68,000 kilometers from the lunar surface,
it transmitted the pictures to earth by television.

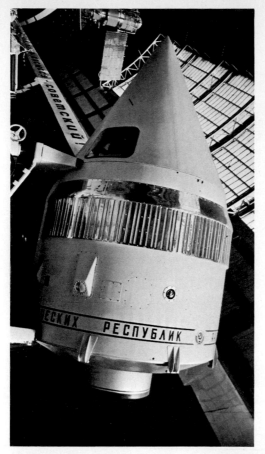

34. The last stage of the *Luna*-1's carrier rocket.

35. On 5 January and 10 January 1969, two large multistage automatic interplanetary stations were launched in the Soviet Union. They made soft descents and landings on the surface of Venus. It was the first time that automatic probes were able to take measurements of Venus' atmosphere simultaneously in two neighboring regions. The information transmitted provided scientists with unique data on temperature, pressure, and chemical makeup of the mysterious planet.

In photo: The Soviet interplanetary station *Venera*-6.

36. The final testing of the *Molniya*-1 communication satellite at the cosmodrome.

37. *In photo:* The *Intercosmos*-1 artificial earth satellite in the assembly shop.
It was put in orbit on 14 October 1969.

Scientists, engineers, and workers from the German Democratic Republic,
the Soviet Union, and Czechoslovakia united their efforts to create the satellite
Intercosmos-1 equipment. During its flight, observatories in Bulgaria, Hungary,
the German Democratic Republic, Poland, Rumania, the Soviet Union,
and Czechoslovakia carried out a common program.

38, 39. Nowadays the satellites put into space are counted by the hundreds. Most numerous are the Soviet specialized artificial earth satellites of the *Cosmos* series which are launched regularly in accordance with a program of the near-earth space studies. With their help we learn a lot of new information about the atmosphere, radiation belts, electric and magnetic fields, cosmic radiation, and short wave radiation of the sun and other celestial bodies.

In photo: Two *Cosmos* series satellites.

40. Sergei Korolev worked much on research rockets, sometimes modifying the existing ones for research purposes. He used to launch these rockets with animals on board to an altitude of 100 kilometers. After that they were returned to the earth.

In photo: Sergei Korolev with a dog just returned from flight, July 1954. (PUBLISHED FOR THE FIRST TIME IN 1971.)

41. There was an automatic trough in the second *Vostok*-type rocket launched on 19 August 1960.

In photo: Belka and Strelka being trained to eat specially prepared food from automatic troughs.

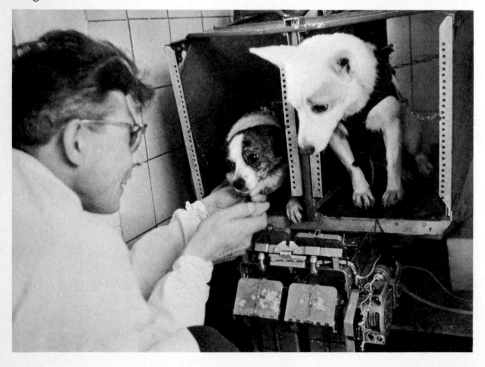

42. The head portion of the V5V geophysical rocket which landed after its flight with animals on board.

43. This dog has just returned from its trip to the upper layers of the atmosphere aboard the geophysical V21 rocket.

44. *In photo:*
Sergei Korolev, 1932.

From 1932 to 1966 Sergei Korolev headed the GIRD (Central Group for the Study of Reactive Propulsion).
(PUBLISHED FOR THE FIRST TIME IN 1971.)

45. These Soviet cosmonauts were selected in Moscow in 1960 from a large group of Air Force pilots who applied.

In photo: The first group of Soviet cosmonauts. Sergei Korolev is in the center, Yuri Gagarin at his right. Andriyan Nikolayev is at far left.
(PUBLISHED FOR THE FIRST TIME IN 1971).

46. Cosmonaut Shonin in training in 1961. Shonin joined the cosmonauts' team at the same time as Gagarin, and the two studied and trained together.

become a roofing specialist. ("That put me closer to the sky," he later said jokingly.)

Things were hard for Korolev during his student days. The nation's economy was only beginning to recover after the civil war, and everything was lacking. There was no fuel for the stoves, either at the school or at home; there were no notebooks, pencils, or even chalk for the blackboards. But the students were so eager to learn and so enthusiastic that they overcame all the hardships and difficulties. As for Seryozha, he was overflowing with energy— so much so that he used to go through the hallways walking on his hands.

Although he got some experience as an apprentice roofer on construction projects, Sergei Korolev never became a roofing specialist. He felt drawn to the sky and went in seriously for glider-flying. He designed his own glider and became the leader of the glider club. On 5 July 1924 the provincial sports commission made Korolev responsible, as a specialist, for inspecting and directing the glider clubs at several plants in Odessa.

After graduation, the young glider designer announced to his mother and stepfather that he wanted to devote his life to aviation and intended to enter the Zhukovsky Air Force Academy. But he was not accepted by the academy, since he was not yet eighteen years old. Instead, he entered the Kiev Polytechnical Institute.

Since his family could not provide him with adequate support, he had to earn money on his own. He sold newspapers on the street and worked as a stevedore. He even acted in the movies. It happened like this. In 1925 a film was being made about one of the most heroic episodes in the civil war, when Komsomol youths in the Ukraine fought a battle against some enemy bands in which many of the youngsters were killed. The film—*The Tragedy of Tripolya*—was being shot on the historic site, in Tripolya; and the student Korolev came to watch it. Being handsome, well-built, and clever, he was taken on as an extra for a crowd scene.

Along with his other jobs, Korolev worked as a roofer. Eventually he saved enough money to buy the materials and equipment he needed to design and build a glider. (Korolev spent very little on his personal needs, since he lived very simply and meagerly. He was, however, known as a bit of a dandy: his mother had seen to it that he kept his short-cropped hair neat and always wore a well-pressed suit and a fresh shirt.)

In 1926, when the school in Kiev was closed down, Korolev
went to Moscow and enrolled at the MVTU (Moscow Higher
Technical School) in the Department of Aerodynamics. He went
on building gliders. Before long he gained prominence at the All-
Union Rally of Glider Pilots.

The sixth All-Union Rally of Soviet Glider Pilots was held in the
fall of 1929 at Koktebel in the Crimea, on the edge of the sea—a
good site for a glider competition. The field was located in the
foothills of the Uzun-Syrt Mountains. Among the gliders lined
up there was one that stood out because of its elegant design—a
craft with scarlet wings called the *Koktebel*. It had been designed
and built by Sergei Korolev and Sergei Lyushin. In spite of its
considerable weight (660 pounds) and a heavy wing-loading, the
Koktebel performed beautifully.

Korolev's goal was to design the first glider capable of performing aerobatics. In this connection, he wrote: ". . . The possibility
of performing figures in a glider may have the same importance
for gliding as advanced flying does for regular aviation . . ."

Sergei Korolev got his pilot's license in 1930. In the fall of that
year he began to test-fly his new glider, the *Krasnaya Zvezda*,
in the Crimea. This glider was a high-winged monoplane with a
well-streamlined fuselage. The spacious, convenient cockpit was designed to accommodate a pilot wearing a parachute—an innovation
at a time when glider flights were made without parachutes.

But Korolev suddenly fell ill and was replaced in the test flights
by V. A. Stepanchenok—a famous glider pilot who later became a
test pilot. In the *Krasnaya Zvezda*, Stepanchenok—for the first time
in the history of free gliding—performed three loops.

In addition to gliders, Korolev was also designing light aircraft.
He submitted a design of this type as a thesis for his degree. His
thesis adviser was Andrei Nikolayevich Tupolev, the outstanding
Soviet aircraft designer. Tupolev noted the originality of his talented student and the boldness of his ideas in design work.

While working on gliders and light airplanes, Korolev was also
thinking about the "new technology," which had captured his
imagination. Once he had become familiar with the work of Konstantin Eduardovich Tsiolkovsky, the founder of cosmonautics,
Korolev became fascinated by space flight and decided to devote
the rest of his life to it.

Tsiolkovsky

Konstantin Eduardovich Tsiolkovsky was born on 17 September 1857 in the village of Izhevskoye, in Ryazanskaya Province, where his father had been a forest ranger since 1846.

"For domestic reasons" his father was discharged from his post and became a clerk in Ryazan. But "domestic reasons" actually had nothing to do with his losing his job. The real cause for the dismissal of the elder Tsiolkovsky was the fact that he—a man of rare honesty and straightforwardness—had never concealed his sharp hostility towards the tsarist regime.

Tsiolkovsky's mother, Mariya Ivanovna Yumasheva—an intelligent, hard-working, and attractive woman—stoically endured the hardships of a nomadic life. She was devoted to her family, and with incredible skill she managed to stretch her husband's meager salary so that somehow the whole family was decently fed and clothed.

From Ryazan they moved to Vyatka, a town that little Konstantin found much to his liking. He was especially fond of the river—the Vyatka, after which the town had been named. He quickly learned to swim and loved to dive. In the spring, when the ice broke up, off he would leap in boldly from one shaky ice floe to another and in this way cross the river.

Konstantin was a gay-spirited, active lad, and the family favorite. He was nicknamed Ptitsa (Little Bird) because of his liveliness.

But a calamity was lying in wait for him. One winter, after going skating, he caught a cold. Then scarlet fever set in, with fateful complications: he became deaf. For him, the outside world was immersed in silence. He no longer heard the singing of birds or the sound of the wind blowing. He could not hear the voices of his friends.

As he wrote later:

> I often behaved awkwardly among other children my age, and among people generally. Naturally, my deafness made me ridiculous. It estranged me from others and compelled me, out of boredom, to read, concentrate, and daydream. Because of my deafness, every minute of my life that I spent with other people was torture. I felt I was isolated, humiliated—an outcast. This caused me to withdraw deep within myself, to pursue great goals so as to deserve the approval of others and not be despised.

The boy was helped by his mother, whose love for him was boundless. She taught him to read and write and enrolled him at the boys' high school in Vyatka. There, for three years, Konstantin manfully coped with the classroom lessons—which for him, as a deaf boy, were very hard going. Mariya Ivanovna, who by temperament was a sociable woman, doted on her son. She inculcated in him her own vigor and love of life and her belief that he would eventually recover.

But fate had still more blows in reserve for Konstantin. When he was thirteen, his mother died. Shortly thereafter he had to drop out of high school. It was as though the road to the future had suddenly come to a dead end.

No longer able to attend school, the young Tsiolkovsky, recalling his mother's advice, began studying his brothers' textbooks. And he read the books in his father's library. At the age of fourteen, he became seriously interested in the exact sciences. From his reading in physics he got the idea of building a carriage driven by steam. (This was the first instance of Tsiolkovsky's application of the principle of reactive motion.) The study of physics prompted him to go in for inventions—to build a paper aerostat, to design lathes and windmills.

At the age of sixteen, urged on by his father, the young man decided to go to Moscow and continue his education independently, although he had not a single acquaintance there. The poorly dressed youth, confused by his first impressions of the large city, walked along the streets, reading the ROOMS TO LET signs. Finally, for a few kopecks, he rented a corner of a room from a laundress.

Every morning, before the public library had opened its doors, the young provincial would be waiting to get hold of some precious volume. Then, settling himself in a corner, he would start reading. The day would pass, night would come on, and the assistant would blow out the kerosene lamps. Only then, with a heavy sigh, would Tsiolkovsky leave the library. He was caught up in thoughts about flights beyond the limits of the earth's atmosphere.

Those thoughts gave him no rest. And during his second year in Moscow, without benefit of school or teachers, Tsiolkovsky took up higher mathematics, differential and integral calculus, and spherical trigonometry.

Scientific ideas are born in a specific social milieu and largely depend upon the world view of the scientist and/or inventor. "I am a pure materialist," wrote Tsiolkovsky with conviction. "I recognize nothing but matter . . ." Later he affirmed that the process of cognition is infinite, like the universe itself; and that this provides grounds for the greatest optimism, since it opens up fields for the victorious advance of omnipotent human reason.

"The philosophy of infinity," he wrote, "leads to discoveries and the expansion of knowledge, and the converse leads to obscurantism. The former is fruitful and progressive and the latter is nothing."

Tsiolkovsky lived in hunger and poverty and wore ragged clothes, but he was happy. He believed in the future. His acquaintanceship with science had redoubled his strength. And besides that, love had come into his life.

It was strange and transient—this first love. The landlady from whom Tsiolkovsky had rented his "corner" did the washing in the home of a wealthy man living in Moscow, where she had talked about her eccentric roomer. Her tales had reached the ears of the millionaire's daughter. The pretty, spoiled girl became interested in the unusual student and had sent him a note.

Tsiolkovsky replied immediately: he had fallen in love without even seeing the girl. They started up a correspondence, but it was soon broken off forever. The millionaire forbade his daughter to write to the suspect young man who was the "instigator" of unintelligible ideas.

Later on Tsiolkovsky married Varvara Yevgrafovna Sokolova, who did everything possible so that her husband might devote himself to his computations and his models, write articles, preside over scientific discussions, and carry out experiments. She was a devoted and loving companion who believed in Tsiolkovsky's high calling on earth.

In Old Russia there were many self-educated men of genius. But how many perished—how many were doomed to oblivion! Yet Tsiolkovsky succeeded. His bold experiments and daring fantasies attracted the attention of Russia's most progressive individuals. Such outstanding scientists as D. I. Mendeleyev, N. Ye. Zhukovsky, A. G. Stoletov, and others stretched out a hand to aid the young scientist; they encouraged him and gave him advice. But not even these men—the giants of science—could rescue Tsiolkovsky from the eternal struggle for a meager livelihood. Now burdened with a family, the deaf young man had to go on teaching school in a village near Kaluga, where he had gone after three years in Moscow. And it was only in brief periods of spare time that he could do his scientific work. Not only that, but a fire destroyed much of what he had done.

His life was heavy and hard to bear. The deafness was a torment to him. So that he could somehow hear human voices, he designed a special set of "listeners"—tin funnels that he held to his ears to hear what people were saying to him. Frequently, what he heard through the listeners was abuse, curses, and threats aimed at the "crank." Tsiolkovsky grew morose, withdrew into himself, and brooded over the thought that people didn't want to understand his sincere desire to work at science.

As he thought of future generations, of a better fate for mankind, and of human happiness, Tsiolkovsky's imagination carried him out into the universe. The realm of the stars, so amazingly well-organized, fascinated him—because of the boundlessness of space, the gigantic reserves of energy, and the astounding accuracy and harmony in the movement of the planets. As he dreamed of the future, Tsiolkovsky mentally peopled the heavens with colonies of human beings.

In the spring of 1883, taking advantage of the school vacation, Tsiolkovsky wrote his first work, *Free Space*—an investigation of the phenomena that might be observed by a human being who had gone into space. In this work, which took the form of a scientific journal kept by an explorer, the basic design of a rocket-powered interplanetary ship was first laid down. It is also noteworthy that within two months after he had started writing his monograph (on 20 February 1883) Tsiolkovsky had completed a manuscript of 149 pages, together with all the accompanying drawings. This means that as early as 1879, when he made his first rough sketches in Ryazan, he had already thought out his monograph in all details and had developed the general idea of "space travel, interplanetary communications," and the conquest of space.

Tsiolkovsky described space travel so expressively, and with such scientific accuracy, that the reader might well believe the author had actually made a space trip.

> It is frightening in this abyss [wrote Tsiolkovsky], which has no boundaries and is devoid of familiar objects. There is no earth under one's feet, nor is there even the distant sky. It is a world without reference points: there is no horizontal, no vertical, and the sensation of weight is lacking . . .

At first, the reader is frightened by the starry abyss. But he does not draw back or lose his self-possession. Instead, he follows the author on his prodigious voyage through "free space."

Tsiolkovsky's *Free Space* provided the first full description of the realm of weightlessness. Here is a passage from his account of the hitherto-unknown world:

> . . . the observed body does not, in free space, exert any force on what lies beneath it, and vice versa. Therefore, if dwellings were needed in free space, they could not—however great their size—collapse because of their instability.
>
> Entire mountains and castles of arbitrary shape and size could keep their position in free space without any support, or any connection with a support.
>
> There is neither up nor down, there. For example, there is

no such thing as down, because "down" is the direction in which
bodies move at accelerated speeds . . . There are no vertical or
horizontal lines or planes . . . There are no mountains or
chasms. No stone ever falls into a chasm, nor does any unwary
animal . . . Just as the moon hovers above the earth without
falling down to it, so a man there can hover over a chasm
which would be frightful to earthlings. He is not, of course,
suspended by ropes but hovers like a bird; or rather, like a
counterpoised aerostat, since he has no wings.

Tsiolkovsky noted that in space man needed neither floors, nor
stairways, nor chairs, nor beds: "Any place in free space could
serve as an excellent bed or an excellent chair."
He showed that this freedom from the earth's gravitational pull
would transform human life and make people happy. In a half-
jocular tone, but with a firm conviction in the truth of what he
was saying, he told of the advantages of life in space as compared
to life on earth. Later on, he succinctly formulated his philosophical
thesis: "Man will not remain on the earth forever. In his pursuit of
light and space he will at first timidly probe beyond the atmosphere, then conquer all of circumsolar space."
But how could man take his first step into space?
Tsiolkovsky's brilliant surmises as to how to build a reactive device to overcome the earth's gravitation were developed into the
first scientifically sound design for a "reactive" interplanetary ship.
The interplanetary ship would have a rocket engine. The thrust
would be obtained by means of firing spherical projectiles from
an on-board cannon.
The author of this monograph in the form of a journal also
worked out another way of developing thrust, this time by means
of a stream of gas from a tank in which the gas was kept under
pressure.
The science fiction story "On the Moon," which Tsiolkovsky
wrote in 1887, contains descriptions of a trip to the moon, a view
of the earth from the surface of the moon, aerospace phenomena,
and the state of man in free space. Today, when men have already
been on the moon, Tsiolkovsky's novella amazes one with its extraordinary preview of the future.
In the winter of 1892 Tsiolkovsky moved to Kaluga, where he
remained until his death.

Even among the provincial towns of Old Russia, Kaluga was deemed an out-of-the-way place. The town itself is pretty and inviting. It is located in a picturesque setting on the bank of the Oka, some 200 kilometers from Moscow, among groves of oak and pine.

Tsiolkovsky brought world fame to Kaluga. But for a long time, the life he and his family led there was one of semistarvation. He gave lessons and taught at the diocesan school. But expenses rose as the inventer expanded his experimental work, and the family often had only bread and vegetables for dinner.

Yet Tsiolkovsky continued his work with fierce intensity. In 1894, in his work "An Aeroplane or Ornithoid (Aviation) Flying Machine" he provided a design for a monoplane with a gasoline engine, a closed cockpit, and retractable landing gear. He also noted the possibility of using an autopilot.

Another of his experiments leaves one wondering how the poor, deaf teacher was able to scrape up the money required for it. In any case, what he did was to build—in the small house on quiet Georgiyevskaya Street occupied by the large Tsiolkovsky family— a wind tunnel, which he called a *vozdukhoduvka*. In this wind tunnel he carried out experiments on air resistance.

While continuing to develop his ideas on the aims and means of exploring space, Tsiolkovsky wrote another science fiction work, *A Dream of the Earth and the Sky,* which was published in Moscow in 1895. In this book, his ideas on the possibility of man's going into space and his description of outer space were expanded. Tsiolkovsky, in this book, first discussed an artificial earth satellite:

> The imaginary earth satellite, somewhat like the moon but arbitrarily near to our planet, would fly beyond the limits of its atmosphere; some 200 miles from the earth's surface. It would represent, with véry small mass, an example of a milieu free of gravitation.

In his book, *K. E. Tsiolkovsky: a Great Scientist and Humanist,* the Kaluga historian Daniil Andriyanovich Shcherbakov emphasizes that *A Dream of the Earth and the Sky* was held up by the tsarist censors. Their displeasure was provoked by the author's descriptions of "sky-dwellers"—people making space flights. This clashed with the dogmas of the Church and stirred up a protest on the part of official (government) science.

Tsiolkovsky's ideas on space travel made it plain that in his dreams of a life "without weight," Tsiolkovsky also had another kind of weight in mind. He was also thinking of other chains—the chains that fettered the life of the people. In another work, *A Change in the Earth's Relative Gravity*—written in 1894 but not published before the Revolution—he described the life of the inhabitants of Mercury, where gravitation is only half as strong as on earth. He remarked that on Mercury

> there are none of those disorders and conflicts among nations from which our poor earth suffers; there is not that great gulf between types of inhabitants which makes one the slave of another . . .

The year 1903 was historic—not only for Tsiolkovsky himself but for world science. In that year he published his famous article "Exploring Space with Reactive Devices." In this work, while further developing his earlier ideas on space travel, Tsiolkovsky laid down the principle for the scientific solution of the problem, introducing his well-known formula for the motion of a rocket, which has come to be known as "the Tsiolkovsky formula." He investigated the various cases of the rectilinear motion of bodies of variable mass, evaluated the effectiveness of processes of discharging particles, and determined the efficiency of rockets, pointing out the advantages offered by rocket engines at high velocities. He also provided a design of an interplanetary rocket and pointed out the advantages of using liquid fuel.

Tsiolkovsky sent his paper to *The Scientific Review*. This progressive journal had been founded in Petrograd in 1893 by Mikhail Mikhailovich Filippov, the Russian educator and encyclopedist. Its contributers included some outstanding Russian scientists. It was in Filippov's journal that Tsiolkovsky had published, in 1897, his paper titled "The Duration of Solar Radiation." This was followed by "The Achievements of Aeronautics in the Nineteenth Century," "Air Resistance and Aeronautics," and other articles. The great Mendeleyev took note of Tsiolkovsky's articles and praised them as models of bold thinking by a self-educated man.

Before sending in his latest article, Tsiolkovsky had written to Filippov:

> . . . Mikhail Mikhailovich, I have worked out several aspects of the problem of ascending into space by means of a reactive device similar to a rocket. My mathematical conclusions, based on scientific data verified many times over, show that with such devices it is possible to ascend into the expanse of the heavens, and perhaps to found a settlement beyond the limits of the earth's atmosphere . . . People will take advantage of this to resettle not only all over the face of the earth but all over the face of the universe . . .

This was written some months before the Wright brothers' airplane made its flight.

Regarding rockets as the only practicable means of making flights into space, Tsiolkovsky spelled out their advantages as follows:

> (a) A rocket is cheaper than a huge cannon and more easily built;
>
> (b) during powered ascent, the acceleration of a rocket can be varied as desired, with the result that excessively great accelerations (G-forces) can be avoided;
>
> (c) the velocity of a rocket can be changed in accordance with any law [*sic*] and in any direction; in particular, it is possible to assure a soft landing on planets which do not have dense atmospheres;
>
> (d) during ascent through the dense layers of the atmosphere the velocity of the rocket can be kept relatively low, making for comparatively slight drag and heating of the outside surface;
>
> (e) in the rarefied layers of the atmosphere, the velocity can be increased without fear of excessively high heating temperatures.

In his scientific papers, Tsiolkovsky developed the idea of a composite rocket and calculated the most advantageous distribution of weight among the rockets making up the composite—or multistage—rocket.

Tsiolkovsky was the first to calculate the most advantageous angle of ascent for a reactive device passing through an atmospheric layer of varying density. He also investigated the conditions for launching rockets from various planets and asteroids and solved the problem of the requisite reserve of fuel for a spacecraft's return to earth.

Academician A. Ye. Fersman summarized the main ideas put forth by Tsiolkovsky as follows:

(a) Tsiolkovsky emphasized the tremendous significance of science and technology in human life and the necessity for a maximum increase in knowledge for the good of mankind;

(b) the necessity for overcoming distance, not only on the earth's surface but on a cosmic scale—the overcoming of distance being possible only by means of new engineering devices (above all, rockets);

(c) the necessity for overcoming universal gravitation, as one of the ways of conquering space and distance;

(d) it is the task of mankind to conquer the entire universe; the development of new means of locomotion, the conquering of space, and the development of engineering are only the means whereby man can conquer other worlds;

(e) the struggle for universal energy: in the last years of his life, Tsiolkovsky devoted a great deal of attention to the problem of energy, striving to show the significance of mankind's struggle for the mastery of all types of energy;

(f) the struggle for life, for improving the forms of life, and for the greater adaptivity of plants and animals to their environment: to this end he began with the problem of creating life, considering the solution of that problem as one way of improving life in general;

(g) the struggle for man: the analysis and employment of his effect in the struggle for the new man and for a new organization of society . . . man's belief in life, in science and technology; his protest against the power of nature and his deep conviction that man can conquer it, mastering energy and space.

Following the Revolution, Tsiolkovsky's scientific work was supported in every way by the Soviet Government. In 1918 he was elected a member of the Socialist Academy, and in 1919 as honorary member of the Society of Friends of Natural Science. In 1921, the

Government awarded him a lifetime pension; and in 1924 the founder of cosmonautics was elected an honorary professor at the Zhukovsky Air Force Academy. Also, all of his works, many of which had been published at his own expense and some unpublished, were published.

The essential Tsiolkovsky may be found in his investigations, his bold ideas, his striving for the happiness of mankind. For him, there were no scientific propositions existing apart from his general ideas. Everything was merged into the great, unified laws of the world and man.

In the complex, continuing interplay between opposites, life merges into a beautiful picture of the universe: there are no limits to the imagination, no limits to the penetrative powers of reason, no limits to the technological power that overcomes nature.

Tsiolkovsky's ideas fascinated a large audience. Everyone wanted to go and see him—scientists and workers, engineers and peasants, students and soldiers. I, too, found myself in that stream of visitors, being at the time the aviation reporter for a young newspaper, *Komsomolskaya Pravda*. The editors had told me to ask Tsiolkovsky if he would call upon the youth of the land of the Soviets to take part in forming flying clubs and glider clubs, and train cadres of specialists for Soviet aviation—then in its infancy.

In those long-ago days, Kaluga still had the look of an old provincial town. On its outskirts, I found the steep, unused, cobblestoned street leading down to the Oka. Yellow camomiles and buttercups had pushed up luxuriantly between the cobblestones.

The wooden houses with their closed shutters stood there sleepily. Beyond the blank fences I caught a glimpse of some apple trees. At the end of the street, on the banks of the Oka, cows were grazing. Everything looked simple and ordinary.

Stopping at a two-storyed house with a veranda, I went up to the front door and rang the bell. A few minutes later I was going up a steep, narrow stairway into a room with a large window. This was Tsiolkovsky's study, complete with physical apparatuses and a desk piled high with books, manuscripts, and a printing form. Its simplicity, asceticism, and atmosphere of scientific inquiry impressed me deeply.

An old, gray-bearded, hollow-chested man in steel-rimmed glasses, who was obviously ill, was sitting in a well-worn armchair and leafing through a book with his thin, yellow fingers. Lost in thought, he was staring into a dark corner of the room. Then in that loud voice used by people who are partially or totally deaf, Tsiolkovsky began to talk to me about problems close and familiar to him.

He was pale and coughed frequently, closing his eyes each time he did so. But neither his old man's cough, nor his slow speech, nor his hunched shoulders could weaken my impression of freedom and boldness in the thought of this man who had looked, from the surface of our solidified globe, into that boundless, mysterious expanse of the universe where the planets and stars go their eternal ways.

From time to time I would break in upon the scientist's train of thought and get back to the subject of my assignment. At that time, our country was just spreading its wings: it was creating a young aviation industry and needed an army of aviation specialists. An appeal from Tsiolkovsky might well inspire our young people, spark their enthusiasm for aviation, and prompt them to enroll at flying clubs and regular flying schools.

Tsiolkovsky held his tin bell—his "listener"—to his ear, and heard me out in silence. But his eyes sparkled. Plainly, he was interested in hearing from an eyewitness about the flights and tests of new aircraft. But then, with a laugh, he began to talk about rockets moving at a velocity of 28,000 kilometers per hour; about routes from Kaluga to Mars, from Moscow to Venus. And he said that Kaluga would be an interplanetary way station.

It was as though the two of us were living on two different floors—I on the earth and Tsiolkovsky in the universe. I was too young to understand him, although it seemed to me that I had met a prophet.

Meantime, he was confidently affirming that man would not forever live on the earth—that he would conquer circumsolar space. Rocket ships would slice through the universe and carry men to near and distant planets. Artificial earth satellites would be created . . . And not just satellites! The earth would be orbited by chains of satellites—"islands in the sky" whose helioelectric power stations would provide heat and light for human beings. In hothouses established in space, flowers would give off their fragrance and vegetables would grow.

Before we took leave of each other, Tsiolkovsky suggested that when in Moscow, I should pay a visit to GIRD—Gruppa Izucheniya Reaktivnogo Dvizheniya (Group for the Study of Reactive Propulsion). As an aviation journalist, I had heard of it; but having been occupied with flying clubs, I had not given it my serious attention.

"I won't fail to go there," I promised.

Rockets

in the Cellar

The Moscow rocketeers worked in the basement of 19 Sadovo-Spasskaya Street, not far from the noisy, bustling Sulharevsky Market. When I had located the building, I went down into the basement with some misgivings. And when I met the rocketeers, I was rather disenchanted. I was used to hangars on air fields where test flights were made—to the well-lighted workshops in aircraft plants. And here I was in a cellar! This was the GIRD[1] workshop.

Later, I found out who the main organizers of the group were.

GIRD consisted of four sections, and its first section, which did research and experimental work, consisted of four teams. These four teams were headed, respectively, by Friedrich Arturovich Tsander, Mikhail Klavdiyevich Tikhonravov, Yuri Aleksandrovich Pobedonostsev, and Sergei Pavlovich Korolev.

Tsander, an outstanding design engineer and scientist, played a leading role in GIRD. He was born on 23 August 1887 in Riga.

[1] This is presumably the Moscow GIRD, founded in 1931, and headed by Korolev as director. In 1932 it was merged with the Leningrad GIRD; and later that year Korolev became director (chief) of the new over-all organization, now known simply as GIRD.—Translator

His father, Dr. Artur Konstantinovich Tsander, was from a merchant family, and his mother, nee Elena Gotshlak, was from a family of musicians. Tsander's mother died when he was two, and he was brought up by his father, who inculcated in him a love for nature, distant worlds, and books.

The writings of Tsiolkovsky made a very strong impression on young Friedrich Tsander, who wrote:

> During my last year in high school,[2] before Christmas vacation, our teacher read us part of an article written by K. E. Tsiolkovsky in 1903 under the title "Exploring Space with Reactive Devices."

In 1919 Friedrich Tsander went to work at the Motor aircraft plant in Moscow. He pioneered in several aspects of theoretical research and engineering work on rocketry and space flight. His scientific investigations and experimental and practical work made him one of the early pioneers of space flight.

In 1924, in an article titled "Flights to Other Planets," which was published in the journal *Engineering in Life,* he set forth his basic idea: the combining of a rocket with an airplane for a flight from the earth, with the subsequent burning of the plane's metallic parts as fuel in the combustion chamber of the rocket—which, in the author's opinion, would help to increase the length of the rocket's flight.

On 20 December 1930 Tsander went to work at the Moscow Institute of Aviation Machine-Building (Russian abbreviation IAM), where conditions were more propitious for his research. There he was able to build and test his first reactive engine, the OR-1, which used compressed air and gasoline.

Tsander's work with GIRD (among co-workers who both respected and liked him) marked an important phase in his life story. Apparently the stone cellar on Sadovo-Spasskaya Street was accessible only to altruistic enthusiasts and dreamers. Thus the members of GIRD who were working under S. P. Korolev formed a close-knit group and endured some severe hardships. In those trying days, food could be obtained only with ration cards, and very few of

[2] In the academic year 1904–5.—Ed.

these were issued to GIRD. After all, what was GIRD, anyway? And what kind of rockets did they have?

The ascetic-looking Tsander infected the other GIRD workers with his love for Mars—which he talked of as a living being. Whenever he came into the basement, Tsander would shout: "Forward to Mars!" And often, looking up from his calculations, he would say pensively: "Oh, Mars! Oh, Jupiter! I'll see you yet!"

He named his son Mercury and his daughter Astra.

When asked why he had chosen Mars as the goal of his dreams and calculations, he would answer, "Seemingly, Mars has an atmosphere, and it is therefore possible that life exists there."

Under Tsander's influence, GIRD's "bulletin-board newspaper" began to print appeals to take Mars by storm. This inspired the GIRD workers: the greater the goal, the greater their enthusiasm.

Tsander paid little attention to his appearance. Sometimes he seemed absent-minded, even forgetting his priceless ration card—without which one could not, in those days, get so much as a piece of bread. But concealed behind his seeming aloofness and absent-mindedness was a tremendous capacity to concentrate on the most important thing in his life: building rockets for interplanetary flights. All stages of such a flight were so clear in his mind that he often talked of them as of something already existing.

Korolev was fond of Tsander. He greatly admired his talents as a scientist, the scope of his plans, and his flair as a designer. Korolev once recalled:

> In the days when I was just getting to know rocketry, Tsander was already considered a veteran. Despite all the difficulties and hardships, he worked stubbornly at solving the theoretical and engineering problems of interplanetary flight. At that time, of course, his bold plans could not be implemented. But this did not discourage Tsander; he worked tirelessly, with rare powers of endurance.
>
> To me, Tsander was an older brother on the job—someone who had the same ideas and aspirations as I did. We had a great deal in common. Curiously enough, Tsander, who always looked far ahead into interplanetary space, was the one who inspired me to work on an immediate problem: rocket-powered flight. More precisely, I discerned the wings of that inspiration in the design of his OR-2 engine.

It should be noted that the OR-2 was the second of Tsander's experimental engines. The first, the OR-1—*opytnyy raketnyy pervyy* (experimental rocket [engines] ⅟1)—had been built before he joined GIRD.

The OR-1 had burned gasoline and gaseous oxygen. He had made tests with it, enabling him to set about designing an improved engine, the OR-2.

In science, there are no broad freeways: for every discovery, pathways must be made. The members of GIRD moved along a narrow, stony path, unafraid to climb up to the heights. If the goal of scientific thinking is to see the general in the particular and the eternal in the transitory, Korolev set a splendid example of how to dream of space flight while at the same time procuring an old work bench; of how to admire Tsander's nebulous imaginings while working on the embodiment of his OR-2 engine in metal.

Today, we can appreciate the role played by Korolev and his outstanding executive abilities, at a time when no space vehicle had yet been launched and numerous skeptics held pessimistic views on the future of rocketry.

The men who gathered in the stone cellar were fired with enthusiasm. Korolev was their leader—their source of moral support. By his side was Tsander, an outstanding scientist and a pioneer in rocket design. The four teams included talented young scientists and design engineers, each with his own ideas and projects, his own demands and views on the practical plans of GIRD. And Tsiolkovsky, in Kaluga, kept a close eye on the first steps taken by the GIRD people.

The four GIRD teams were constantly involved in creative research. They competed with one another, and at the same time they constituted a whole.

Korolev never set himself apart from the others. He knew how to live and work in a group and how to unite his fellow workers around him. He was demanding and strict toward those who made mistakes; yet he was equally attentive to everyone and concerned for the well-being of all. His intelligence and will power were chiefly devoted to directing the joint efforts of the GIRD workers toward their goal.

Korolev was fascinated by an idea that would give him no rest: he wanted to install a "rocket motor" in an aircraft. As one who had built and test-flown gliders, he felt that a glider would be best suited to this purpose.

Tsander's OR-2 engine was ready on 23 December, 1932. By that date Boris Ivanovich Cheranovsky—acting on instructions from Korolev—had built a new glider of the "flying wing" type, the BICh-11, to be used with the OR-2.

Cheranovsky, an aircraft designer who had become a friend of Tsander and worked with GIRD, was a bold thinker and determined to create entirely new designs. He had built some very unconventional aircraft with parabolic and delta wings and had designed one with folding wings. Korolev and Tsander liked the "flying wing" since, lacking a fuselage and tail assembly, it best met their requirements as rocket builders. The preliminary calculations showed that Tsander's OR-2 engine could be installed on Cheranovsky's flying wing.

The new glider was named the RP-1—*raketnyy planer pervyy* (rocket glider Ж 1). It was 10.2 feet long, had a wing span of 39.7 feet, and weighed 440 pounds without the engine. An area for the cockpit and the reactive engine was provided in the center of the delta wing, which was thicker in its middle area.

Before a flight could be attempted in the flying wing with the reactive engine, the glider itself had to be thoroughly tested. Korolev, the chief of GIRD, decided to test-fly it himself. They took the BICh-11 to Trikotazhnaya Station, near Moscow, where gliders were flown at that time. On it they installed a two-cylinder Scorpion engine with a capacity of 30 horsepower and a weight about equal to that of the OR-2.

When preparations were complete, Korolev took his seat in the BICh-11, pulled down his goggles, and started the engine. Then he revved it up and took off in the flying wing. Once in the air, Korolev was taken by surprise: when he put the BICh-11 into a banking turn, it suddenly stood on its edge and went into a steep dive. Fortunately, Korolev was an experienced test pilot and designer who did not lose his presence of mind. He brought the flying wing out of the dive and made a successful landing.

This near-catastrophe showed that the BICh-11 had to undergo another cycle of tests and that it would be a long time before the reactive engine could be installed in it.

In the basement, the work went on with increasing intensity. The rocketeers lost all count of days and nights. Many of them stayed in the basement for days on end, merely dozing from time to time over their work benches and blueprints.

Tsander was in need of rest, and his friends at GIRD sent him off to a sanatorium. On the way there he caught a case of typhus, and when he reached Kislovodsk he was in critical condition. The bulletins from the Caucasus brought bad news: Tsander was very ill, he was sinking, he was delirious . . .

Tsander's team completed the hot firing of the OR-2 engine without his supervision.

Soon, tragic news came from the Caucasus. On 28 March 1933 the entire GIRD group assembled in the basement on Sadovo-Spasskaya Street. In a shaking voice, Korolev told them: "Tsander is dead . . ."

There was a long and terrible silence. Tears came to the eyes of these brave men, who had conducted hot firings without fear. They loved, valued, and respected the outstanding scientist and designer.

The published obituary said: "This distinguished theoretician on the problem of reactive propulsion died in Kislovodsk on 28 March at 6:00 A.M." The obituary emphasized that on the basis of his theoretical and practical work, Tsander had founded his own school in the theory and design of reactive engines.

After the brief funeral held on the day of burial, Korolev went home. He slumped heavily down behind his desk, as his friends gathered around him. He was lost in reflection for a while. Then, softly but firmly, he repeated Tsander's favorite words: "Onward to Mars!"

These words struck the others like lightning. "Onward to Mars!" they repeated.

But Korolev couldn't help wondering: "What is to be done? What should I do?" Then he decided: "Yes, I'll have to notify Tsiolkovsky."

Life was putting more and more responsibility on the shoulders of Korolev.

In 1933 GIRD designed and built four types of rockets with liquid-fuel engines. They were designated 05, 07, 09, and 10. The first one ready to be launched was the 09, designed by Mikhail Tikhonravov. It was 7.9 feet long, with a diameter of 7 inches, and had a launching weight of 39.6 pounds. The 09 rocket engine used liquid oxygen and compressed gasoline—a solution of rosin in gasoline.

A clearing in a woods, far from people or dwellings, was chosen as the site for the launching of the 09. Accompanied by the engineer Nikolai Efremov, Korolev walked around the clearing, looking it over. Then he inspected the launching installation and gave orders to prepare the rocket for firing. But at this point, all kinds of defects were discovered, and the firing was cancelled.

On 11 August 1933 many members of GIRD showed up at Nakhabino on the testing range. They all gathered around the launching installation, hoping that this time everything would be all right. But defects were soon discovered in the ignition system, and Korolev suggested: "Shall we try it on the thirteenth? Of course, that's not the most desirable date. Or, to put it more accurately, it's the worst possible. But what do you expect? Somebody has to be the first to destroy the superstition . . . If we're going to dare it, let's dare it!"

The thirteenth rolled around. The rocket had already been positioned on the stand—which was very simple indeed, compared to a launch pad at one of today's cosmodromes. The tanks were topped off with oxygen; the igniter plugs and communications were checked. At Korolev's command, everyone on the testing range took shelter. This time, it seemed that all would go well. But to everyone's dismay, this launch, too, had to be scrubbed.

It was postponed until 17 August.

Everyone felt dejected. And then, as luck would have it, a dismal rain began to fall, mixed with wet snow, and the truck in which they were all riding, went into a ditch and overturned.

Fortunately, no one was hurt. Soaked to the skin, the GIRD members made their way to the nearest railroad station, finally reaching their homes late at night.

The next morning, like a true psychologist, Korolev arrived at the basement rooms carefully shaven and wearing a well-pressed suit. He was cheerful and well-disposed, as if nothing untoward had happened the day before. As he entered he smiled, looked around at his friends, and gave each of them a firm handshake. Everyone's spirits lifted.

In the creative competition at GIRD, Tikhonravov's team had surged ahead, and their 09 rocket had been on the launch pad more than once. But during this time another team—the first—

had been working hard and systematically and had built their GIRD-10 rocket on the basis of Tsander's working sketches and calculations. Each postponement of an 09 launching meant that this team might overtake, and even get ahead of, their rivals.

Preparations for the next 09 launch were begun early on the morning of 17 August; but it was not until one o'clock in the afternoon that they set out for Nakhabino. Very carefully, they laid the cigar-shaped 09 rocket down in the back of the truck. Next to it they placed the Dewar flask full of liquid oxygen. They loaded on the instruments, wire, pipes, launching magneto, Bickford fuses, and everything else required in firing a rocket.

They had scarcely got under way when a loose cobblestone gave the truck such a bad jolt that they snatched the rocket up into their laps like a child. They held it in this position during the whole trip through Moscow and along the back road to the woods of Nakhabino.

With the utmost caution, they carried the rocket from the truck to the launch pad and positioned it. Then began the solemn rites— fueling the rocket. It was so warm that there was intensive vaporization of the liquid oxygen as it flowed through the pipe, and the rocket was soon wrapped in a wispy cloud.

The fueling of the 09, and the checking of all its systems, took quite a bit of time; it was already getting on toward evening. At this point Korolev said that they couldn't launch it in the dark, so they would have to hurry.

They worked faster, and by seven o'clock everything was ready. The design engineer Zinaida Kruglova went down into the shelter and took her place at the launching magneto. She was followed by the engineer Nikolai Efremov and the lathe operator Boris Shedko, who was known as a fine photographer. Ikonnikov and Matysik climbed up a pine tree, so eager were they to see all details of the firing.

Efremov, holding a stopwatch, was watching its hand and at the same time observing a pressure gauge: at a given moment he was to open the valve feeding the oxygen into the combustion chamber and immediately signal Kruglova to crank the magneto.

But the glass on the gauge fogged over. With the agility of a cat, Efremov hopped out of the shelter, wiped off the face of the gauge, and hopped back into the shelter. Then, when the gauge showed 12 atmospheres, he signaled with his fingers: "Get ready!"

The pressure reached 13.5 atmospheres.

"Attention!"

Like a sniper, Shedko pricked up his ears and sighted through his camera.

Korolev made ready to ignite the Bickford fuse.

"Contact!" Efremov shouted and pulled the cord that opened the valve.

Korolev ignited the Bickford fuse connected to the primer of the apparatus for releasing the parachute, and Kruglova cranked the magneto for all she was worth.

A cone-shaped flame burst out of the nozzle, accompanied by a sound that they had all heard before during static tests of the engine. Then slowly, as if with reluctance, the 09 rocket began to move upward along the guide slot of the launching stand and, gathering speed, rose into the sky.

It had worked!

Shedko clicked the shutter of his camera. When the rocket was already high in the air, he leaped out of the shelter, waving his camera.

At an altitude of about 1,300 feet (in those days, heights and distances of flight were measured in feet), the 09 rocket tilted over and, having completed its ascent, began to come down in the direction of the woods. It touched the treetops, crashed down through the branches, and with a dull thud buried its nose in the earth.

Korolev, Pobedonostsev, Efremov, Kruglova, and all the others who had witnessed the launch ran to the spot where the rocket had fallen. Korolev bent over and examined the rocket. He could see that on one side, the engine's flange had burned through, causing the rocket to veer.

Crossing his smudged, dirty arms on his chest, Korolev gazed lovingly at the rocket. Then he roused himself and issued instructions for drawing up the certifying document.

Here is the way it read.

REPORT

We, the undersigned, constituting the committee of the GIRD plant for the launching of an experimental specimen of Object 09—the members of said committee being:

47. Prospective cosmonauts were given a medical check-up at the Air Force hospital near Moscow in 1960.

48. Yuri Gagarin before testing his vestibular apparatus on the rotating chair.

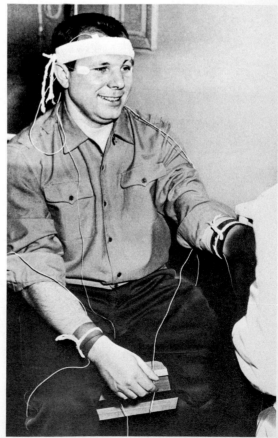

49. A centrifuge that
duplicates the acceleration
of gravity that cosmonauts are
subjected to during liftoff
and landing.

50. Assembly building of the
cosmodrome. Mounting the
return capsule and the
instrument compartment of
the *Vostok*. (PUBLISHED FOR
THE FIRST TIME IN 1971.)

51. A *Vostok* spaceship at the Baikonur Cosmodrome. The command module weighs 2.6 tons and has a diameter of 7.5 feet. It is covered with a heat shield to protect the pilot as he passes through the dense layers of the atmosphere.

52. Assembly building of the cosmodrome. Checking the *Vostok* capsule.

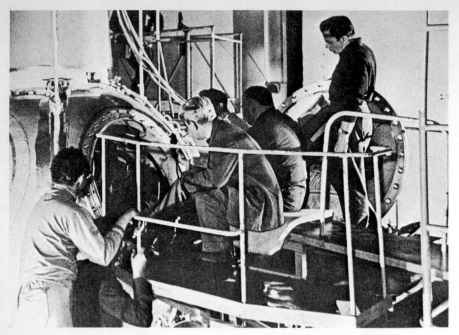

53. In the assembly building of the Baikonur Cosmodrome, Academicians Mstislav Keldysh and Sergei Korolev check the life-support system of a spacecraft before its flight.

54. The cosmonaut's seat is equipped with regular jet ejectors and a parachute.

In photo: A cosmonaut practicing on a machine that simulates catapulting to earth during preflight training.

55. Baikonur Cosmodrome, 6 April 1961. The meeting of the State Selection Commission where it was decided that Yuri Gagarin was to be the first man to travel into outer space aboard the *Vostok* spaceship on 12 April at 9 A.M.

In photo: Yuri Gagarin is thanking the members of the Selection Commission for the trust placed in him.

56. The main hall of the Co-ordinating Data-Processing Center.
Here the information received from spaceships is processed electronically.

57. Korolev, seconds before liftoff.

58. On course.

59. Yuri Gagarin in his space uniform is in the bus where
"cosmic life" begins. The bus is taking him to the launching pad
of Baikonur Cosmodrome on 12 April 1961.

60. The parachuted capsule in which Yuri Gagarin returned to the earth
from the first space flight at 10:55 Moscow time on 12 April 1961.

Senior Engineer S. P. Korolev, Chief of GIRD, Senior Engineer of Team №2, N. I. Efremov, Senior Engineer L. K. Korneyev, Chief of Team №1, and

Machinist Ye. M. Matysik, foreman of the production crew— on this day of 17 August 1933, having inspected the object and its launching apparatus, resolved that it should be launched.

The launching took place at 1700 hours on 17 August at Station No. 17 of the testing range at Nakhabino.

Approximate weight of the object: 40 lbs.

Weight of fuel (compressed gasoline): 2.2 lbs.

Weight of oxygen: 7.59 lbs.

Pressure in the oxygen tank: 13.5 atmospheres.

Duration of flight from liftoff until moment of fall: 18 seconds.

Altitude of vertical ascent (determined visually): approximately 1,300 feet.

The liftoff was slow. At its maximum height the rocket tilted to the horizontal; then, following a flat trajectory, it came down in the nearby woods. The engine was functioning throughout the flight. Upon impact with the earth, the skin was crumpled and the connecting valve was broken. The change from vertical to horizontal flight and the subsequent tumbling toward the earth were due to a gas puncture (burn-through) of a flange, producing a lateral thrust which tumbled the rocket.

At the end of the report was the following notation: "Prepared in one copy and signed at the Nakhabino Testing Range, Station No. 17, on 17 August, 1933, at 2010 hours."

When everyone else had signed the document, Korolev picked it up, read through it, and sighed. "She really flew," he said quietly and simply. "She really flew. We didn't do all that work for nothing."

Everyone was in high spirits. After so many failures, disappointments, and dramatic conflicts, things had worked out as planned! The liquid-fuel rocket had made its first flight.

All the way home, the rocketeers sang, laughed, and talked excitedly about the earlier, unsuccessful attempts to launch the 09 rocket.

After the firing of the first 09 rocket, improvements were made in its design; and the last six rockets bore the number 13. They, too, were launched at Nakhabino, reaching altitudes of 4,500 feet.

Meantime the first GIRD team, which previously had been headed by F. A. Tsander, continued intensive work on their GIRD-10 rocket. Its general characteristics were:

> Length—86.6 inches
> Diameter—5.5 inches
> Launch weight—63.8 lbs.
> Payload weight—4.4 lbs.
> Thrust—154 lbs.
> Burning time—22 sec.

The GIRD-10 was cigar-shaped, with a sharp nose cone. Attached to its rear section were four oblong tail fins which extended almost half the length of the rocket. It consisted of five compartments. In the first was a parachute, with a releasing device. The second was the oxygen tank. In the third was a two-liter cylinder of compressed air, together with the basic launching apparatus (safety valve for the compressed air, gauge, etc.). The fourth section consisted of a tank for alcohol, through which ran the pipe for the liquid oxygen. The fifth and last compartment housed the engine and piping.

Tsander's old team worked day and night, and by 25 November 1933 the GIRD-10 was on the launching stand. It had been positioned somewhat nearer the shelter, so that it could be observed through the peephole.

When fueling had been completed, those present either went off a ways into the woods or down into the shelter. Then came the command: "Contact!"

A fiery stream of gases gushed forth, and the rocket roared. The GIRD-10 smoothly lifted off the launching stand and into the sky, reaching an altitude of 263 feet, then veered off its course, owing to a loose engine fitting.

Rockets

in Retrospect

The first reliable information on the use of rockets in Russia dates from the second half of the seventeenth century. In the late seventeenth and early eighteenth centuries, "rocket workshops" were established in Moscow and St. Petersburg. Peter the Great did much to promote the development of rocketry. The rocket workshop which he founded on the banks of the Neva turned out more than a hundred specimen rockets to be used for various purposes. Onisim Mikhailov, a builder of cannon, even drew up a special report in which he gave a detailed account of rockets— "projectiles which race along and burn"—and described methods of making them.

More than three hundred years ago, Russian master craftmen had known how to make rockets. The first Russian historical and theoretical works on rockets were published on orders from Peter the Great. In 1762, Mikhailo Davydov, a major of artillery, published two works giving a detailed description of how rockets were made and how they could be used.

In the next century, Aleksandr Dmitriyevich Sasyadko (1779–1837), a talented engineer and a hero of the Napoleonic War of

1812, wrote some interesting works on military rockets. He designed a high-explosive rocket and launchers that could fire six rockets simultaneously.

Both were successfully tested near Mogilev. Rockets of the type he designed were produced at the Petersburg Polytechnical Institute and, from 1826 on, at a rocket workshop on Volkovoye Field near Petersburg.

An important contribution to Russian rocketry was made by Konstantin Ivanovich Konstantinov (1817–71). In 1859 Konstantinov became chief of a special agency for the manufacture of rockets. As head of this agency, he was able to do much to promote more extensive use of rockets in the Russian Army.

In addition to developing military rockets well suited for closely grouped, accurate fire, Konstantinov nurtured ideas about the peacetime use of rockets. He was interested in signal rockets; and he designed a two-chambered life-saving rocket for carrying lines to a sinking vessel or across a chasm in the mountains.

Konstantinov gave lectures at the Mikhailovsky Artillery Academy on the history of rocketry in Russia and described his own work in the field. In 1862 his lectures were published as a monograph in Paris (in the French language) under the title of *Military Rockets*. In 1864, a Russian edition was published in Petersburg.

There are many examples in history of the use of Russian rockets in battle. Thus when Russian troops were storming Silistria during the Russo-Turkish war of 1877–78, it became imperative to throw a bridge across the river. But the Russian engineering troops were held off by Turkish naval vessels. The enemy squadron had to be dispersed. Rocketmen on barges moved in, and with their first volley the enemy flagship blew up. At this, the rest of the squadron hurriedly withdrew to the open sea.

It was a military engineer, N. V. Gerasimov, who proposed a gyroscopic rocket. The core of his idea was that a gyroscope should be placed in the rocket, assuring stability in flight.

The subsequent history of Russian rocketry is associated with the names of such outstanding scientists and design engineers as I. V. Meshchersky, M. M. Pomortsev, A. P. Fyodorov, and others. The first to work out a design of a rocket-powered aircraft for manned flight, was N. I. Kibalchich.

Nikolai Ivanovich Kibalchich was born in 1853. In 1871 he

enrolled at the Petersburg Institute of Transportation Engineering, and later he studied at the medical academy.

Kibalchich entered the revolutionary movement, and became an activist in the populist organization, Zemlya i Volya (Land and Will), where he began manufacturing mines and bombs to be used in acts of terrorism.

On 1 March 1881, in Petersburg, Russian revolutionaries belonging to the group called Narodnaya Volya (The People's Will) assassinated Tsar Alexander II. The bomb thrown into the emperor's carriage had been made by N. I. Kibalchich. Along with the other members of the "March 1st" group, he was arrested and thrown into prison.

The twenty-seven-year-old revolutionary was not idle while awaiting his execution. All his thoughts were given over to a rocket-powered aircraft. Cooped up in a tiny cell, he worked patiently on his drawings. Death was near at hand. He only had a few days of life left. Yet Kibalchich continued to work on his drawings and computations in feverish haste.

On 3 April Kibalchich submitted a memorandum, through his defense counsel, dealing with his projected aircraft. One cannot read his words without emotion:

> . . . When explosives are ignited [Kibalchich explained in his memorandum], a large quantity of gases are formed more or less rapidly. At the moment of their formation, they possess tremendous energy. But how can one put to use, in work of any duration, the energy of the gases formed when explosives are burned? . . . This is possible only if the tremendous energy developed upon combustion of the explosives is not developed all at once but in the course of a more or less prolonged interval of time . . .
>
> If we take a pound of granular powder of the type which will explode immediately upon combustion, and form it under great pressure into a cylindrical shape, then ignite one end of that cylinder, we shall see that the combustion is not instantaneous for the entire cylinder. Rather, it spreads rather slowly from one end to the other, at a definite rate of speed. The design of military rockets is based on this property of compressed powder . . .

As to the essence of his own project, illustrated with drawings, Kibalchich wrote:

> Let us suppose that we have a cylinder of sheet iron . . . hermetically sealed on all sides with a hole in the bottom . . .
>
> Along the axis of this cylinder we place some compressed powder, likewise in cylindrical shape, and ignite it at one end. Upon combustion, the gases formed will exert pressure throughout the internal surface of the cylinder. But the pressure on the side surfaces will be counterbalanced. The pressure on the closed end of the cylinder, however, will not be counterbalanced by an opposing pressure, since at the other end the gases will have free egress through the hole in the bottom. If the cylinder is positioned with the closed end up, when the gases have generated a given degree of pressure, the cylinder will rise into the air.

None of the memoranda submitted by Kibalchich was ever acknowledged. And the day soon arrived when the following notice was posted in St. Petersburg:

> On 3 April at 9:00 o'clock the following persons, guilty of crimes against the state, will be hanged until dead: Sofya Perovskaya, a noblewoman; Nikolai Kibalchich, the son of a priest; Nikolai Rysakov, a burgher; Andrei Zhelyabov and Timofei Mikhailov, peasants.

Kibalchich was the first to mount the scaffold. He was calm in the face of his impending execution, ignoring both the hangman and the soldiers. He wore the expression of a scientist oblivious to everything except the difficult problem absorbing his attention. Kibalchich believed his idea was of the greatest importance to Russia; and until the last instant of his life he was preoccupied with thoughts of his rocket-powered aircraft. Kilbalchich's project was buried in the secret archives, unknown to anyone until 1918 when the memoranda were discovered.

After the Revolution, the study of rocketry was given considerable support by the Government. The first harbinger of this was the founding, in 1921, of a laboratory headed by the distinguished

Russian chemical engineer, Nikolai Ivanovich Tikhomirov (1860–1930).

Two years before the outbreak of World War I, Tikhomirov had submitted a description of his reactive projectile to the Naval Ministry of the tsarist government. For a long time, his bold project was passed from one bureaucrat's desk to another; it was never implemented. But after the Revolution, this scientist and inventor was able to pursue his favorite line of work. During the civil war, Tikhomirov submitted to the Council of People's Commissars a suggestion for using rockets in the battles for the young Soviet Republic. His suggestion for a "self-moving projectile" was approved. And in 1921, a special laboratory for the development of rocket projectiles was built for him in Moscow. His assistant was the pyrotechnics expert Vladimir Andreyevich Artemev (1885–1962).

By 1924 Tikhomirov and Artemev were doing most of their work in Leningrad, carrying on their research intensively. (It is worth noting that their rocket projectiles, using pressed slabs of smokeless, long-burning powder, were successfully tested on the proving grounds at Leningrad on 3 March 1928.) Their Leningrad laboratory, which was later named the Gas Dynamics Laboratory (GDL), was to play a prominent role in the future development of Russian rocketry.

In 1924 the Society for the Study of Interplanetary Communications (OIMS) was founded as an affiliate of the Interplanetary Communications Section of the Zhukovsky Air Force Academy. The intention was that it would become independent of the academy and take on the character of a civilian organization working on non-military problems of exploring space. K. E. Tsiolkovsky was elected an honorary member of the society.

The membership of the OIMS amounted to almost two hundred persons, including workers, engineers, scientists, students, and journalists. Its first meeting was held on 20 June in the auditorium of the astronomical observatory at Pulkovo. At this meeting a charter was adopted, and the new organization was officially named the Society for the Study of Interplanetary Communications. Its directors included F. A. Tsander, G. M. Kramarov, and others.

Grigory Moiseyevich Kramarov was elected president of the society. When I asked him about the make-up of the membership, he told me that among those who had volunteered for membership were 104 men and 17 women. Most of them were young. The breakdown by occupation was as follows: 53 students; 43 workers and white-collar employees; 14 science technicians; 6 journalists; and 5 scientists and inventors.

In the society's charter, I read:

> It shall be the task of the Society for the Study of Interplanetary Communications to work toward the achievement of flights beyond the atmosphere using reactive devices and other means which are scientifically sound.

Wasn't this a bit bold for the time?

No. The following article of the charter explained:

> Rather than purposing the immediate achievement of interplanetary travel, the OIMS will first strive to solve various problems associated with the use of the means mentioned in Article I. These include: investigating the upper layers of the atmosphere, high-altitude flying, the improvement of rockets, the designing of highly efficient engines, etc.

"In this connection, G. M. Kramarov told me, "it was important to bring prominent specialists into the work of the OIMS, to arrange for lectures to be given and papers to be read, and to carry on scientific research. F. A. Tsander took a very active part in the work. On 1, 4, and 5 October 1924 he participated in a debate at the Physics Institute of Moscow University and discussed the space vehicle he had invented. Professor Vladimir Petrovich Vetchinkin also gave us invaluable help."

Lectures on reactive propulsion and flights to other planets were given in many cities throughout the country: in Moscow, Leningrad, Kharkov, Gorky, Saratov, Tula, Ryazan, and elsewhere. These same subjects were continuously on the agenda of the theoretical sections of such organizations as the Moscow Society of Friends of Astronomy, and the All-Union Association of Inventors.

The year 1927 was especially fruitful. The first World Exposition of Interplanetary Vehicles and Mechanisms was held from April through June. This unusual exhibit was organized in Moscow by the AIIZ—the Association of Inventors for Inventors [sic]. The purpose of the AIIZ was to help inventors. This boisterous, aggressive organization was allotted a few rooms in a building at 69 Tverskaya Street (now Gorky Street) in Moscow, where it held its "stellar exhibit."

The steering committee sent invitations to scientists in the United States, England, Germany, and France. Answers were soon received from Hermann Oberth, Robert Goddard, Max Valier, Walter Hohmann, and other rocket specialists.

Late in 1927 a space exhibit was opened with great ceremony. The guidebook stated that the first section of the exhibit was devoted to astronomy, the second to aviation and aeronautics, the third to cosmonautics, and the fourth—the "Science-Fiction Period" —to science fiction. The visitors saw Jules Verne's famous cannon, H. G. Wells's flying machine, and a portrait of Nikolai Kibalchich, together with drawings of his invention.

The "Plans and Inventions Period," entirely devoted to Tsiolkovsky, attracted everyone's attention. The final and largest section of the exhibit was the "Invention and Design Period."

Famous theoreticians and practical workers in the field of rocketry sent in their work for the exhibit. The German inventor Max Valier sent his articles.

In his letter explaining to the organizers of the exhibit why he could not come to Moscow (he lacked the funds), Valier wrote: "I feel that you are animated by an entirely different spirit from that which prevails here. I look forward to the success of the exhibit."

A short time later, this bold investigator and experimenter was killed when his rocket engine blew up.

Among the items on exhibit in Moscow were a model rocket designed by Oberth, together with its description, and the rockets of the Frenchman Graffinier, and the Austrian Ulinski. And of course lively interest was provoked by the work of such Russian inventors and designers as F. A. Tsander, A. Ya. Fyodorov, G. A. Polevoi, and others. The exhibit was a great success.

The Roar in
the Fortress

In tracing the stages in the development of rocketry in Russia, it is important to note the great amount of practical work done by the scientist and designer Nikolai Tikhomirov. After moving his laboratory from Moscow to Leningrad, he and Artemev organized a rocket laboratory on the artillery proving ground. They were successful in developing a new smokeless powder called TPP—trotyl-pyroxylin powder—and in 1928 they successfully launched rockets burning this powder. Later in that same year, in June, Tikhomirov's rocket laboratory was renamed the Gas Dynamics Laboratory (GDL) of the Military Scientific Research Commission. The GDL was destined for an important role. At the time, the key workers at the GDL were Tikhomirov, Artemev, B. S. Petropavlovsky, G. E. Langemak, I. I. Kalugin, and V. I. Davydov.

An experimental-design organization for building electric and liquid-fuel rocket engines (ERDs and ZhRDs) was founded in Leningrad on 15 May 1929. It was headed by V. P. Glushko and came under the GDL. Subsequently, this organization played an important part in the construction of rocket engines.

In November 1931, in tandem with MosGIRD, a similar civilian group for the study of reactive propulsion—LenGIRD—was set up under OSOAVIAKHIM.[1] The LenGIRD staff included V. V. Razumov, chairman; Ya. I. Perelman, deputy chairman and chief of the Science Popularization Unit: N. A. Rynin, and M. V. Gazhala.

Thus there were two rocket organizations active in Leningrad. LenGIRD concentrated chiefly on publicity work and the designing of rockets—it made a strong contribution to popularizing ideas about space travel and the study of rocketry. The GDL group worked directly on research and designing and achieved impressive practical results. In the years 1927 to 1933 they developed takeoff rockets for light and heavy aircraft and rocket missiles of various calibers that burned smokeless powder—the latter being used especially in the armament of aircraft. Later on, at the outbreak of the Great Patriotic War, these rocket missiles served as the basis for developing the rocket launchers nicknamed "Katyushi." Those who figured most prominently in these projects at the GDL were Tikhomirov, Artemev, Petropavlovsky, Langemak, Kleimenov, and others.

It was the GDL which did the first experimental work in the USSR with a view to designing electric rocket engines (ERDs) and liquid-fuel rocket engines (ZhRDs). The initiator and director of those projects was Chief Engine Designer V. P. Glushko. Working with him were such talented engineers, technicians, and mechanics as A. L. Maly, V. I. Serov, I. I. Kalugin, Ye. N. Kuzmin, Ye. S. Petrov, N. G. Chernyshev, P. I. Minayev, B. A. Kutkin, V. P. Popov, V. A. Timofeyev, N. M. Mukhin, N. P. Pankin, and others.

Speaking of the work done by his group in those days, Academician Glushko told me: "By that time the design bureau of the Leningrad rocketeers had expanded so much that it was very cramped in the two rooms assigned to it—first in the wooded area of Leningrad and later on the artillery proving ground. So the design engineers set up shop on the third floor of the old Admiralty Building under the famous gilded spire—the admiralty needle. But the workshops and stands for testing rocket engines were located

[1] "MosGIRD" was the new name for the original GIRD organization in Moscow. "OSOAVIAKHIM" is an acronym whose formidable expansion is Society for the Promotion of Defense and Aero-Chemical Development.—Translator

behind the stone walls of the Petropavlovskaya Fortress—the old tsarist prison."

On more than one occasion the Leningraders walking past the fortress heard a deafening sound burst forth from behind the thick walls of the bastion. It was the howling and roaring of a liquid-fuel rocket engine.

Academician Glushko showed me some whitened, scorched spots on the high brick wall. "A good many years have passed, but the burn marks are still there—traces of hot firings made here by this wall."

In 1930, for the first time, nitric acid with nitrogen tetroxide, perchloric acid, tetranitromethane, and hydrogen peroxide were suggested as components of a rocket fuel. For the fuel proper, the substances proposed included beryllium, beryllium in combination with oxygen and hydrogen, powders containing dispersed beryllium, etc.

The many years of preparatory work done by the GDL played an important role in designing and developing liquid-propellant rocket engines in the USSR. It was the GDL group which developed the ceramic heat-insulated combustion chamber for zirconium dioxide, the shaped nozzle, and, in 1931, hypergolic fuel, chemical ignition, and a Cardan engine suspension system.

There were other important achievements of the GDL group in Leningrad. In 1931–32 they developed and tested piston fuel pumps activated by gas from the combustion chamber of a rocket. In 1933 they designed a turbine pump unit with centrifugal fuel pumps for engines with a thrust of 660 pounds.

Academician Glushko showed me drawings and photographs of the family of ZhRDs, beginning with the ORM and ORM-1, and running through the ORM-52. He explained that the ORM—the abbreviation for "experimental rocket (reactive) engine"—was the offspring of the Leningrad rocketeers. In 1931 they conducted about fifty hot firings of liquid-fuel rockets burning nitric tetroxide with toluene and gasoline.

In the summer of 1932 and in January 1933 the Leningraders of the GDL were visited by their colleagues from MosGIRD: Tsander, Korolev, Tikhonravov, Pobedonostsev, and their co-workers. During their visit to the GDL, this group observed the static testing of ZhRDs. The first meeting between the staffs of the GDL and GIRD, paved the way for their joint work in the future.

Late in 1933 Marshal M. N. Tukachevsky—People's Commissar for Military and Naval Affairs—proposed that the Leningrad and Moscow rocketeers be brought together in the world's first Institute for Scientific Research on Reactive Propulsion (RNII). The institute was duly founded, and a former director of the GDL, Ivan Terentevich Kleimenov (1898–1938) was appointed to head it.

Kleimenov was a vigorous, practical man who loved his work. In a short time he managed to weld the talented Moscow and Leningrad rocketeers into a single team. Until late 1933 the deputy chief of the RNII was Korolev, who had formerly headed up GIRD. Beginning in early 1934 this position was held by Georgy Erikovich Langemak (1898–1938) of the GDL. In Leningrad he had helped to design rocket missiles using smokeless, long-burning powder. During the years 1928–33, while at the GDL, he was one of the men in charge of developing the rocket missiles fired (after certain modifications) by the famous Katyusha rocket projectors used on the front lines in the Great Patriotic War.

On 7 February 1934 the chief of the RNII, Kleimenov, wrote to Tsiolkovsky in Kaluga:

> Dear Konstantin Eduardovich:
> Late in 1933, by a decree of the Government, the separate organizations and groups working on reactive propulsion were merged into an Institute for Scientific Research on Reactive Propulsion. This institute has been made responsible for designing and building airborne vehicles using the reactive principle for propulsion. Thus the dream of all investigators in this new field of human knowledge has been realized. We have a base for the colossal development, on scientific principles, of those ideas first announced by you.
> We consider that it is essential to maintain close contact with you, as the man who conceived and developed the foundations of the theory of reactive propulsion.

In his answer to Kleimenov's letter, Tsiolkovsky invited the members of the RNII to visit him at Kaluga in order to discuss the most pressing problems in the work of the institute. And within a short time he had sketched out a program for the RNII's projects.

The group brought together at the RNII consisted of talented and creative people; and they soon designed several ballistic and winged rockets, together with jet engines. Korolev, somewhat freed of the endless managerial and executive burdens he had borne at GIRD, was able to concentrate on the development of new projects. Above all, he was interested in winged rockets.

Speaking at the All-Union Conference on the Use of Reactive Airborne Vehicles in March 1935, Korolev said: "The winged rocket is of great importance for ultrahigh-altitude manned flights, and for investigating the stratosphere."

Later, Korolev stated that during 1936, 1937, and a part of 1938, several dozen hot firings of liquid-fuel rockets were carried out. The highest altitude reached by the winged rockets was 3,280 feet, and the range of their flight did not exceed 9,842 feet. These results did not satisfy Korolev, and he remarked that "given a good, powerful, and properly debugged automation system, one could achieve results very close to those planned—as regards both the range and altitude of flight."

In addition to designing winged rockets, Korolev worked enthusiastically at building a rocket-powered glider.

Early in 1934 he set about designing a two-seater contilever monoplane glider, the SK-9 (otherwise known as the RP-318). When it was ready, in 1935, he himself tested it on the ground and in the air.

Convinced of the excellent performance of his glider, Korolev arranged for it to make a long flight (1,600 kilometers) on 19 September. Towed by an R-5 biplane, its route was Moscow–Kharkov–Krivoi Rog–Koktebel. The glider pilot of the SK-9 was Romanov. With him, in the passenger's seat, was the designer, Korolev. Throughout the flight, Korolev was preoccupied with the idea of equipping his new glider with a rocket engine.

The glider designed by Korolev was 23.88 feet in length. Its wing span was 55.77 feet. The wing area was 236 square feet, and the wing-loading was 56.98 pounds per square yard. The takeoff weight was 1,254 pounds.

This glider was destined for great success. At Koktebel, where it was viewed by visitors to the Eleventh All-Union Rally of Glider Pilots, it flew for a total of seven hours and fifty-five minutes. The heavy craft, so designed that it could be flown through storm clouds in bad weather, soared freely even in a weak air current.

This glider served as the basis for building one of the world's first rocket-powered aircraft—the RP-318 rocket glider. The RP-318 was a midwing monoplane with a wide wing span. The fuel tanks were located in the fuselage behind the cockpit. The first engine to be used on it was Glushko's ORM-65, with a thrust of 330 lbs. Later, this engine was replaced by L. S. Dushkin's RDA-I-150. The glider was 25.92 feet long, with a wing span of 55.77 feet and a rated speed of 270 kilometers per hour.

As a result of years of intensive research at the RNII, it was possible on 28 February 1940 to test-fly the RP-318. There had been a cold wave that morning, and the snow on the airport was covered with a crust of ice. Notwithstanding the cold, technicians and mechanics went ahead and completed preparations for making the R-5 biplane and the RP-318 glider flight-ready.

Vladimir Pavlovich Fyodorov, the pilot who was to fly the rocket glider, checked out the engine and the rest of the RP-318's equipment and systems. Then the test pilot, Fikson, and the lead designer, Shcherbakov, got into the biplane, while Fyodorov climbed into the cockpit of the rocket glider. He tested the control stick and pedals; and when he was satisfied that everything was in order, he wiggled the ailerons to signify he was ready for takeoff.

The R-5 started to move and the long, glittering towrope was stretched taut: the rocket glider started to skid along the snow.

When he had reached the planned altitude, the pilot of the R-5 disengaged the rocket glider from his biplane. Abandoned to itself, the RP-318 seemed to hesitate as if undecided what to do next. Then a stream of flame shot out of its tail section. Its speed rapidly increased from 80 to 140 kilometers per hour, and in a matter of moments it was overtaking the biplane.

Fyodorov felt the kind of excitement he had not experienced in a long time: he was eager to dart past the piston-driven R-5 and show what the rocket plane could do. But he fought back the urge and, as a disciplined man, got busy with the duties prescribed for him in the program.

In the report he wrote after the test flight, Fyodorov said:

> The engine was switched on at an altitude of 8,200 feet. After ignition, it worked smoothly. During some five or six seconds, the speed increased sharply. The glider functioned normally, and no vibrations were noticeable. For me, as a pilot, the use of this engine in climbing produced a very pleasant sensation.

The design engineers at the RNII convincingly solved the problem of using rocket-type engines in aviation. And two ramjet engines installed as auxiliary motors on an I-15-bis fighter designed by N. N. Polikarpov had been tested in flight as early as the summer of 1939.

Back in the days of the third team of GIRD, led by the designer Yuri Aleksandrovich Pobedonostsev, work had been initiated on the designing of a ramjet engine. The third team consisted of I. A. Merkulov, G. I. Ivanov, M. S. Kisenko, A. B. Ryazansky, and others; and a ramjet engine was among the series of designs they produced. The theory of such engines had been worked out in 1926 by Academician B. S. Stechkin. Pobedonostsev did the experimental work; and in 1936 Merkulov designed a two-stage rocket including a ramjet engine. The first stage consisted of a powder-burning engine which lofted the rocket to the requisite altitude and was then jettisoned. The second stage consisted of a rocket with a ramjet engine.

The launching of the world's first two-stage rocket with a ramjet engine took place on 19 May 1939 at Planernaya Station near Moscow. Merkulov and the mechanic P. V. Karev took their places behind an armored shield, and the rocket, lifting off along the vertical guide rails of the launching stand, rose into the sky. The astronomers observing the tests at Merkulov's request ascertained that the rocket developed a velocity of 734.72 feet per second (i.e., about 800 kilometers per hour) and reached a height of 6,560 feet.

This success inspired the designer, and he decided to use his new engine on an aircraft. In that same year (1939) Merkulov drew up several designs for a ramjet aircraft engine and made ready to test them in flight.

Merkulov's PVRD (ramjet engine) was a cigar-shaped tube with a diameter of 1.57 inches, a length of 59 inches, and a weight of 26.4 pounds. These engines burned gasoline, which was preheated and, in a vaporous state, injected into the combustion chamber. Two of them were installed on an I-15-bis—a propeller-driven fighter—and tested in flight. The success exceeded all expectations. P. Ye. Pochipov, the pilot, was able to turn the jet engines on and off several times, and to regulate their thrust.

The Soviet aircraft designer A. M. Lyulka made a strong contribution to the development of pulse-jet engines. Beginning in

1934, Lyulka designed several VRDs (pulse-jet engines) using a compressor and a gas turbine (TRD). The design he elaborated in 1937 for a turbojet engine, with an axial compressor and an annular combustion chamber, preceded by some years the appearance of such designs in other countries.

As for Korolev and his RP-318 (which we were discussing earlier), the flights made by that rocket glider provided valuable data for the subsequent development of jet aviation, and the RP-318 itself served as prototype for the first rocket (jet) airplane in the USSR: the BI-1.

Equally successful were the tests of the winged rockets designed by Korolev. Between 1934 and 1938 an RNII group, under Korolev's direction, produced a series of guided winged rockets: the 212, 201, 216, and 217. The 212 was a winged, guided rocket of the surface-to-surface class using the ORM-65 liquid-fuel reactive engine designed by V. P. Glushko. The 212 was a midwing monoplane with wings of trapezoidal shape. Its takeoff weight was 462 pounds, weight of propellant (nitric acid and kerosene) 66 pounds, and weight of payload 66 pounds. Its length was 9.8 feet, and its estimated range up to 50 kilometers. It was equipped with an automatic gyropilot for stabilization and guidance in flight.

The 212 made its first flight in January 1939.

From 1935 to 1937, under the direction of Korolev, the RNII designed and successfully test-fired another winged rocket, the 216. The designer was E. S. Shchetnikov, and it was his idea that the 216 should be used at ranges of up to 15 kilometers. Others who worked on this rocket included B. V. Raushenbakh, G. D. Agarkov, M. P. Dryazgov, A. S. Kosyatov, S. S. Ravinsky, V. V. Ivanov, and S. A. Zasko. The first Soviet automatic gyro stabilization device (GPS) was specially designed for this rocket by the Automatic Guidance Section of the RNII under the direction of S. A. Pivovarov, assisted by V. P. Avdonin and V. A. Bukin. This device assured the rocket's stabilization in flight.

The institute also carried out a wide range of projects involving the designing of rockets for a variety of purposes; e.g., the 201, in the air-to-surface class; and the 217, an experimental anti-aircraft rocket in the surface-to-air class, with conventional wings; and the 217-P, with cruciform wings. In 1939–40 a group of scientists at the institute—including M. K. Tikhonravov, A. I. Polyarny, L. S. Dushkin, V. A. Shtokolev, A. B. Ionov, M. S. Kisenko, V. A. Bukin, and others—built the 604 long-range ballistic rocket, burning hybrid fuel. (Solid and liquid fuels were burned in a single combustion chamber.) The 604 was test-fired in January 1940, with good results: it achieved a range of 65,190 feet.

The 604 served as the basis for developing an improved long-range rocket and a powerful aircraft rocket.

I should note that all this was only a part of the program carried out at the RNII, where Korolev's great talents were exercised.

During the period 1933–38, a group at RNII headed up by Glushko designed a series of experimental liquid-fuel rocket engines. In 1937 they witnessed the testing of the GG-1 gas generator, one of the most important components of modern liquid-fuel rocket engines. Later on, it served as the basis for developing jet engines for various types of aircraft using turbopump feed systems. Thanks to the work of Pobedonostsev's group, a pulse-jet engine with a valve in the air scoop was designed at the RNII. More than ten years later an engine of similar design was used by the Germans on the FAU-I winged missile.

The highly diversified program of the RNII, aimed at the development of liquid-fuel rockets using nitric acid and oxygen, ballistic and winged rockets, rocket gliders, ramjet engines, and a supersonic "tube" with a reactive, air-breathing engine.

The launches of the first liquid-fuel rockets in the early thirties, and the establishment of the RNII, had delighted Tsiolkovsky. His dreams were coming true. But his joy was belated: Tsiolkovsky was ill. The hardships of his earlier years and his advanced age were beginning to tell.

Yet Tsiolkovsky went on working, in a hurry to do as much as he could, following up his philosophical views: "Man will not forever remain on the earth," he affirmed. "In his pursuit of light and space he will at first timidly probe beyond the limits of the atmosphere, then conquer all of circumsolar space." And this idea became his philosophical credo.

He wrote:

> We have looked at space from a mechanistic point of view. But it would have no meaning if it didn't yield biological life. Space is so constituted that radiant energy, the source of or-

ganic life, eternally rages there, flowing from one place to another. This means it is wisely constituted, containing infinite, inexhaustible forces—the source of life and sensations.

As Tsiolkovsky told his friend and student, Aleksandr Leonidovich Chizhevsky: "Many people think I fuss and worry about rockets for the sake of the rocket itself. But that is a great mistake. For me, a rocket is only a means—only a method of reaching the depths of space—and not an end in itself . . . There's no doubt that it's very important to have rocket ships since they will help mankind to settle elsewhere in the universe. But what I'm working for is this resettling . . . The whole idea is to move away from the earth to settlements in space. We must meet the 'cosmic philosophy' halfway, so to speak.

"In the course of the centuries, new conditions will create a new breed of beings. Their man-made environment will be weakened, and may disappear . . . But by that time these beings will be, as it were, native sons of the ether—of pure solar rays and the infinite depths of space." Tsiolkovsky was a confirmed believer in a plurality of civilizations in the universe. He wrote:

> . . . It is ridiculous to think that the material world known to us is limited to what we know [*sic*]. There are other gases, and liquids, and solids of infinitely varied properties and densities . . . There is also an infinite number of intelligent beings not constituted as on earth—not from the same materials . . . On the planets of our system it is quite possible that life is lacking entirely, or else is primitive, feeble, monstrous, and in any case underdeveloped as compared to [life on] earth, where the temperature and material conditions are especially favorable. But each of the galaxies and spiral nebulae have billions of suns, and a group of them includes millions of billions of luminaries. Each of them has many planets, and at least one of them is a planet with favorable conditions.

Believing in the inevitability of a meeting between earthlings and beings from another planet, Tsiolkovsky worked out a system of "cosmic ethics," morality, and law which would serve as a basis for relations among rational beings when they made contact with one another in space.

Tsiolkovsky worked in great haste to complete his "Program for the Cosmos." He knew that his days were numbered. Summoning up what strength he had left, he wrote, computed, and sketched out plans for man's going into space, exploring it, and staking out his claim there for the sake of a happy life for the people of the future.

His "Program for the Cosmos" was based on his unbounded belief in the inventiveness, strength, and capacity of human reason. He did not fail to take into account the tragedies that might befall life on earth: such things as a change in the atmosphere or the extinction of the sun . . . But however frightening the possible cataclysms, Tsiolkovsky affirmed that man would always triumph; that he would find a rational way out and save his breed. He believed that man was born for happiness, for joy in creativity, and for eternal triumph over the nature that had engendered him.

Tsiolkovsky was not destined to witness the flights of spaceships. Beginning in August 1935, his health declined sharply, and he rarely left his bed. His doctors insisted on an immediate operation, and he gave his consent. The newspapers carried accounts of the great scientist's illness, and the nation awaited the outcome of the operation with real anxiety.

In September 1935 Tsiolkovsky dictated a death-bed letter of bequest to the Central Committee of the Communist Party. He wrote:

> . . . All my works on aviation, rocketry, and space travel I hereby bequeath to the Party of the Bolsheviks and the Soviet Government—the real leaders in the advancement of civilization. I am convinced they will bring these works to a successful conclusion.

On 19 September, at 10:22 P.M., Konstantin Eduardovich Tsiolkovsky died.

An obelisk surrounded by a rocket has been raised in the center of Kaluga, at his grave. The frame house in which the great scientist worked has become a museum.

War, Rockets,
and Jets

The death of Tsiolkovsky brought sadness to the scientists working at the RNII. But they remembered his words, "Forward ever!" —and went on working. They conceived and developed bold ideas for various applications of reactive engines. In addition to plans for the peacetime exploration of space, there were projects of a military nature. These included the development of a jet fighter plane and the BM-13 military rocket launcher, which was later nicknamed the "Katyusha."

In 1940, after the test flights of Korolev's rocket glider, Viktor Fyodorovich Bolkhovitinov, in collaboration with the designer Aleksandr Yakovlevich Bereznyak and the engine designer Aleksei Mikhailovich Isayev, set about designing the first Soviet jet aircraft. The basic design work was completed by March 1941.

The German invasion of the Soviet Union in June 1941 made it imperative to expedite construction of a jet fighter-interceptor. The plane was built; and at the suggestion of Bolkhovitinov it was called the BI—for the initial letters of the last names of Bereznyak and Isayev.

The BI-1 was a monoplane of composite structure with stubby

wings whose entire area was only 75 square feet. Its length was 21 feet, and its wing span was only slightly less.

The plane was built under very difficult wartime conditions in the Urals, after the evacuation of Soviet war industries to that area. When the aircraft was ready, it was ground-tested by Boris Kudrin. When Kudrin was stricken by illness, the test pilot Grigory Bakhchivandzhi was recalled from the front. (During the first months of the war, Bakhchivandzhi had shot down five enemy aircraft and flown sixty-five combat missions in a short period of time.)

The tests of the BI-1 were carried out under the supervision of Professor V. S. Pyshnov, a well-known specialist in aerodynamics. He had authorized the first test flight for 15 May 1942. Everyone had assembled at the airport that morning. But the weather turned bad, with a heavy cloud cover; patches of clear sky did not appear until mid-afternoon.

Bolkhovitinov went up to Bakhchivandzhi, embracing him and kissing him on the cheek in the Russian manner, and said: "Grigory, I wish you success in carrying out your mission. Be careful."

Bakhchivandzhi put on his parachute, climbed into the cockpit of the plane, and took his seat. Silence reigned over the airport, as though everyone were holding his breath. Myriads of eyes stared anxiously at the weird-looking airplane, which had no conventional engine or propeller. It didn't look as though it could fly.

At 5:00 P.M. a green signal rocket rose into the sky.

Previously, the aviation mechanics had heard only the command: "Stand clear of the prop!" But now, for the first time, they heard the unusual command: "Stand clear of the tail!"

Everyone at the air field realized how extraordinary this experiment was.

Whatever is new involves risks, unexpected things, and hazards. Bakhchivandzhi was well aware of this. And that same morning he had told some of his friends: "Maybe I'll meet my death in this bird. But if so, it won't be for nothing."

At length, the signal flag was waved, and the plane started to move. The engineers and mechanics ducked off to one side. With a ten-foot candle of flame streaming out behind it, the BI-1 darted along the runway, and a moment later it was airborne. A thunderclap from the sky resounded on earth.

The report of the commission evaluating the results of the first test flight has become a historical document:

> The takeoff and flight of the BI-1 aircraft with a jet engine —used for the first time as the main engine of an aircraft— demonstrated the practicability of flight on this new principle, which opens up a new trend in the development of aviation.

Bakhchivandzhi made six test flights. The seventh was scheduled for 26 March 1943—almost a year after the first. Bakhchivandzhi attained a speed which, in those days, had never been reached before. Suddenly, the plane went into a parabolic flight path. It lost its stability and went out of control. Bakhchivandzhi was killed.

When he had recovered from his illness, Kudrin went on with the test flights—in an improved version of the BI-1—the BI-7— with a liquid-fuel engine designed by A. M. Isayev and L. S. Dushkin. The new jet fighter reached a speed of 900 kilometers per hour.

However, the further development of jet aviation involved the use not of liquid-fuel reactive engines (ZhRDs) but of turbojet engines (TRDs). One pioneer in the development of turbojet engines was the designer A. M. Lyulka, who back in 1937 had begun work on his first turbojet aircraft engine.

In 1941 Hitler was preparing for a thrust toward Moscow. The Nazi command had brought up heavy concentrations of troops, equipment, and ammunition to the city of Orsha. There was an especially heavy concentration of troops and armor in the public square near the railroad station, in the area of the railroad station, and in the area of the railroad junction. The *Wehrmacht* soldiers had no idea what was in store for them in the next few hours.

On 14 July 1941, at 1535 hours, from one of the defensive positions of the Soviet Twentieth Army in the woods east of Orsha, a command rang out: "On the Nazi invaders—battery, fire!"

Like a hurricane, long tongues of flame shot out, accompanied by a strange booming sound. Clouds of black smoke appeared above the treetops. Fiery arrows darted toward the German positions. Moments later the area around the Orsha station, full of Nazi troops, was engulfed by raging flame. Bewildered, with no idea of what weapon had produced this sea of flame, the fear-crazed German soldiers fled in panic.

The simultaneous explosion of dozens of rocket missiles from Captain Fyodorov's 1st Battery of Rocket Artillery had delivered the news of a new and formidable weapon—military rockets—to the enemy.

The BM-13 launching rack had sixteen projector tubes which fired 5-inch M-13 missiles, each weighing 92.4 pounds, with a range of 27,782 feet. The battery consisted of five such racks, capable of firing eighty projectiles at one salvo.

These were the rocket launchers, mounted on trucks, that came to be called "Katyushi."

The rocket artillery played a prominent role in the military operations of the Great Patriotic War. More than five hundred artillery divisions dealt crushing blows to the enemy forces. In no other army taking part in World War II was rocket artillery so broadly developed as in the Soviet Army.

I felt it necessary to give this account of military rockets and their destructive capacity on the assumption that every unprejudiced reader would understand one simple fact. In the USSR—treacherously attacked by an enemy who threw fully armed hordes against it—science, technology, industry, culture, everything, was mobilized to throw back the enemy—to defeat him and drive him out of our country.

In those days Korolev was designing liquid-fuel rockets to step up the performance of fighter planes. The team headed up by V. P. Glushko—the Experimental Design Bureau where Korolev worked as deputy chief designer for test flights—developed a family of liquid-fuel auxiliary aircraft rockets—the RD-1, RD-1x3, RD-2, and RD-3—with completely automatic firing. Many of these rockets, mounted on military aircraft, were used on hundreds of occasions.

After the victorious conclusion of the Great Patriotic War, Soviet scientists and engineers were able to return to their own interrupted struggles and the peacetime problems of using rockets to explore the upper strata of the atmosphere and make flights into space.

But their working conditions were still trying. During the war years, the Soviet people had lost twenty million lives. Yu. V. Kondratyuk, a very gifted specialist in cosmonautics, had been killed in a battle near Moscow. The talented rocketeer M. S. Kisenko had also perished. Ya. I. Perelman, that indefatigable popularizer of cosmonautics, had died during the siege of Leningrad. And

62. The first conquerors of space—
Sergei Korolev and Yuri Gagarin,
May 1961, on the Black Sea coast,
the Caucasus.

61. Yuri Gagarin's "hundred
steps of glory" at Vnukovo
Airport, Moscow,
14 April 1961.

63. Since his childhood Gherman Titov (center) was taught by his father Stepan Pavlovich to love poetry, music, and painting.

65. On 6 August 1971, Gherman Titov and his backup, Andriyan Nikolayev, in the special bus driving them to the launching pad where the *Vostok*-2 is ready to take off.

64. At a small hospital located in a birch grove near Moscow, a group of jet pilots was called up before a special medical selections commission. Those who wanted to become cosmonauts had to undergo an exhaustive physical examination: dozens of laboratory tests, talks with doctors, and numerous other procedures. At that time Gherman Titov did not dream that he would be the second man in space.

(RIGHT
67. Gherman Titov in the Unite
States. Titov with Presiden
John F. Kennedy and U.S
astronaut John Glenn
Washington, D.C., May 196

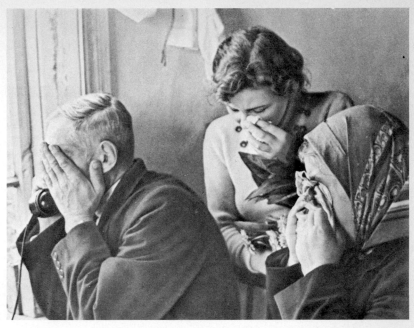

66. Tears of joy. In August 1961, news of the *Vostok*-2 launching reached Polkovnikovo, the remote Siberian village where pilot Gherman Titov's father, mother, and sister live.

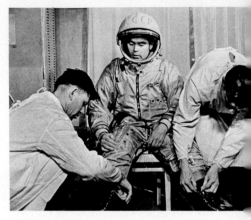

68. The rotator, a simulating device revolving within three planes.

In photo: Cosmonaut Andriyan Nikolayev before training in the rotator.

69. Andriyan Nikolayev, commander of *Vostok*-3, getting ready for his space flight on 11 August 1962. Baikonur Cosmodrome.

71. Andriyan Nikolayev minutes after touchdown.

70. Andriyan Nikolayev spent almost four days and nights aboard *Vostok*-3. His flight ended 15 August 1962.

N. A. Rynin, the theoretician and historian of rocketry, had also died.

The enemy had destroyed 70,000 towns and villages. The material losses totaled up to astronomical figures. Towns, plants, kolkhozes, scientific institutes, laboratories, and testing ranges had to be rebuilt from scratch.

On 11 March 1945, while the Battle of Berlin was in progress, the Soviet Government passed a decree for the restoration of the world-famous Pulkovo Observatory. In August of that same year I visited the heights of Pulkovo and gazed with anguish at the heaps of ruins. When the Nazi staff officers had occupied the observatory, they had issued orders for the metropolis (Leningrad) to be bombarded from the Pulkovo Hills.

Certain specialists, with a sigh of defeat, had said that it would take many years to restore the Pulkovo Observatory—the pride of Russian science, and the "window into the universe." But within an incredibly short time, thanks to the efforts of the entire nation, the buildings and astronomical towers could once again be seen from Leningrad.

The year 1946 witnessed the founding of the Crimean Astro-Physical Observatory of the USSR Academy of Sciences in Simeiz, in a picturesque part of the Crimea on the shores of the Black Sea. In that same year, likewise in the Crimea, construction was begun on a new observatory in the region of Bakhchisarai, celebrated by the great Russian poet, Alexander Pushkin. This structure included one of the world's largest tower solar telescopes. At the same time an astrophysical observatory was being built in Ashkhabad, the capital of the Turkmen SSR.

As though the cosmos itself felt it necessary to remind us of its existence, on 12 February 1947, in the Primorsky Kray—not far from the shores of the Pacific Ocean—a huge iron meteorite crashed down through the earth's atmosphere. It has come to be known as the Sikhote-Alin meteorite. Fragmented, while still in the air, into several thousand particles of different sizes, it fell like an iron meteor shower on the western spurs of the Sikhote-Alin Range, overgrown with a heavy forest. According to the estimate made by Academician Vasily Grigoryevich Fesenkov, the over-all mass of the material from the meteorite which came down through the earth's atmosphere amounted to about one hundred tons.

Beginning in 1946, rockets became a means of carrying out

geophysical and other investigations. Meteorological and geophysical rockets were launched in the Arctic from Hayes Island, from the expedition vessel *Ob,* and elsewhere.

But rockets provide information only from a territorially limited area. Explorations on a global scale require thousands of rockets. And it goes without saying that no nation in the world is in a position to carry out such an engineering operation. The needed assistance was provided by an artificial earth satellite.

Sputnik

By 1947 the Soviet regime had been in existence for thirty years. This anniversary was commemorated by the building and testing of the first long-range guided rocket under the direction of Korolev, who had been named chief designer of the Experimental Design Bureau.

In the postwar years, the international situation had proved to be complex. The "cold war" which had broken out had compelled the Soviet Union to do everything possible to strengthen its defenses.

In his capacity as chief designer, Korolev was primarily engaged in creating a solid technological basis for rocket engineering. He reported to the leadership of the Communist Party and the Soviet Government on the various aspects of the possible employment of rockets for both peaceful and defense purposes. His program was approved, and he was given support, the requisite appropriations, and broad authorization for the construction of new scientific laboratories, test stands, and testing ranges.

In retrospect, the rocket-building program of those days seems rather modest; but for its time it was remarkably extensive. The immediate aim was the building of guided intercontinental ballistic missiles. But while working up the designs for these rockets, Korolev was looking ahead, imagining the launching of a rocket which would carry a human being into space. Such dreams were considered utopian in those days. But Korolev, persistently coming back to his notions of a manned space flight, made the initial computations and sketched out the design and form of the future space vehicle.

Launchings of rockets to investigate the upper strata of the atmosphere were becoming more and more frequent, and in addition to instruments the first living things—dogs—were sent into space. Naturally, this was not done at the very outset. First it was necessary to decide what kind of creature should be sent up on these initial probes. Should it be a worm, a fly, a lizard, a mouse, a rabbit, or a dog? After considerable discussion, it was decided to send up a dog.

But what kind of dog? It turned out that screening dogs for a flight into space was not so simple. For one thing, the dog's weight could not exceed thirteen or sixteen pounds. (At the time, it was essential to make allowance for the rocket's limited capacity.) Also, it was desirable that the dog have a white coat and be a female. This last requirement had to do with the dog's "clothes"—a special anti-gravity suit with sanitation apparatus— for which females were most suitable. As for the color of the dog's coat, it was important in connection with motion picture photography and TV transmissions showing how the animal was behaving and feeling.

Zoologists and other specialists on canines went around Moscow looking for the kind of dog they needed. They made phone calls to dog owners and procured a number of mongrels—either through purchase or by other means. (Experiments had shown that for space flights there was nothing better than mongrels—watchdogs of mixed breed who were used to a hard life: they were rugged, strong, and able to withstand cold and deprivation.) Each animal was thoroughly examined, and its length, height, and weight were measured. Then it was given a nickname. The dogs accepted by the zoologists were put in a vivarium, where they were divided into three groups. In the first group were the even-tempered dogs —those whose movements were moderate. In the second were the restless ones, whose motor reactions were intense. In the third were the sluggish ones.

The even-tempered dogs were used on long flights. This group included Laika (Barker), Strelka (Little Arrow), Belka (Squirrel), Lisichka (Little Fox), Zhemchuzhnaya (Pearly), Chernushka (Blackie), Zvezdochka (Little Star), and others.

The dogs' temperatures, pulse, and respiration rates were checked regularly. Electrocardiograms and X-rays were taken. The animals became accustomed to the confining capsules, to special trays, to the sanitation apparatus, and to the simulated noise and vibrations. They were conditioned in decompression chambers, on vibration stands and centrifuges. And they were taken up to high altitudes in aircraft.

Professor A. V. Pokrovsky told me: "At first nine dogs were used in the trial shots. Of these nine, Albina (Whitey), Kozyavka (Gnat), Malyshka (Little One), and Tsyganka (Gypsy) made more than one flight. The dogs' behavior, the state of their physiological functions, and their temperature showed no change while in flight. Only at liftoff were there slight deviations in the pulse rate and the nature and rate of respiration. After returning to earth, their conditioned food reflexes were fully retained: the dogs felt completely normal."

It was decided that a new experiment should be made: sending dogs up in an "open"—unpressurized—capsule. Special space suits, including a detachable helmet without an oxygen mask, were designed. For the landing, an ejection chassis was provided. It was equipped with an oxygen supply system, a parachute system, and instruments for recording the dogs' physiological functions in flight. Also installed in the unpressurized capsule was a motion picture camera with a bright-up lamp and two mirrors. (Owing to the darkness in the capsule, the filming was done with the aid of mirrors—by the reflection method.)

This time—in addition to such veterans of rocket-powered flight as Albina, Malyshka, Kozyavka, and Tsyganka—eight more dogs were trained for the experimental flight and landing by parachute.

Albina and Tsyganka had been selected for the first shot. Early in the morning, three hours before liftoff time, they were brought to the launch pad.

When the signal was given, the rocket rose into the sky. At the planned altitude, the right-hand chassis containing Albina was jettisoned from the nose section of the rocket. Three seconds after ejection of the chassis, the parachute system began to function.

It took more than an hour for Albina, in her spacesuit, to parachute down to earth from a height of 85 kilometers. Her descent was followed by that of Tsyganka.

The fact that the animals' condition remained normal during the ascent of the rocket convinced the scientists that, in time, a human being could endure similar stresses. Furthermore, it was proposed that the manned flight should not be vertical but orbital —beyond the limits of the earth's atmosphere.

But there was still a long way to go before a manned flight. It was necessary to design a rocket system capable of putting a spacecraft into orbit. But what kind of spacecraft should it be? What shape should it have? And what thrust would the booster rocket have to have?

The International Geophysical Year (IGY) provided great impetus for the development of cosmonautics. By agreement among scientists in fifty countries, it was decided that global investigations of the atmosphere, the hydrosphere, the Antarctic, and the Arctic —in short, the entire planet—should begin at 0000 hours on 1 July 1957.

Never before had the scientists of all countries and nations so joined forces in the investigation of nature as during the preparations for, and the implementation of, the IGY. The Soviet Union undertook to launch a series of meteorological rockets from the territory of the European part of the USSR, from Hayes Island, from the archipelago of Franz Josef Land in the Arctic, and from the diesel-electric ship *Ob* during its cruise in Antarctic waters.

The scientists who attended the International Astronautical Congress[1] held at Copenhagen in August 1955, having discussed the achievements of rocketry in exploring the upper strata of the atmosphere and vicinal space, agreed that in 1957–58, during the IGY, it would be useful to launch an artificial earth satellite. The delegates from the Soviet Union consented to the inclusion of a Soviet space laboratory in the broad program of the IGY. Similar consent was given by the United States delegates. Intensive preparations for the building and launching of an artificial satellite were begun on both sides of the Atlantic.

At this point I must take the liberty of quoting myself. Prior to the launching of the first Sputnik, *The Spark*—a Soviet magazine

---

[1] The Sixth Congress of the International Astronautical Federation.—Translator

for general readers—published an article of mine in which, for the first time, I discussed the great impending event. I wrote:

> The artificial earth satellite is a small metallic sphere containing a variety of apparatuses. It may become a satellite, provided it is lofted through the upper strata of the atmosphere. A rocket will be used for that purpose.
>
> It will take about an hour and a half for the Sputnik to make a complete revolution around our planet. In the course of 24 hours, it will make 16 revolutions. Using an ordinary field glass, it will be possible to see this bright little spark as it darts from one horizon to the other.

Today, my article on the Sputnik may seem naïve. But at the time it was regarded as a sensation. It was reprinted by many newspapers and broadcast over radio and television. The world was awaiting a miracle of science and engineering; this flight into space became the most discussed topic of the century.

A TASS item dated 22 August 1957 brought home the imminence of this important event. It stated:

> In accordance with the plan for scientific research projects, successful tests of an ICBM have been carried out in the Soviet Union . . . The rocket flew at a very high altitude—one never before reached . . .
>
> The results show that it is possible to send rockets to any part of the earth . . .

This staggering news quickly spread around the world. Proponents of the "cold war" evaluated the USSR's development of a powerful intercontinental rocket from a strictly military viewpoint. The Soviet Union, however, was also striving to use the new, powerful rocket for peaceful purposes. The high level of rocket engineering had made it possible to realize an age-old dream: to put an artificial earth satellite into orbit.

On the rough drawings it was denoted by two letters, PS, meaning "rudimentary satellite." The design engineering was directed by Korolev.

Although the little, aluminum-plated sphere was called the PS, the people assembling it called it the SP, i.e., Sergei Pavlovich.

When he found out about this, Korolev said sternly: "'S.P.' means me, Sergei Pavlovich. But our first rudimentary Sputnik is called 'P.S.' I must ask you not to confuse the two."

Early in September 1957 a group of researchers, designers, and engineers from the plant went out to the cosmodrome at Baikonur. The huge assembly structure already loomed high, as did the service towers of the launch complex. The Sputnik had been brought from the plant to the cosmodrome, and after being checked out, it was transported on a light dolly to the assembly area. Viewed against the background of the big rocket, it seemed tiny.

Clutched in the grappling hook of a crane, the silvery sphere was hoisted up to the nose section of the rocket. Its four collapsible-whip antennas, like long mustaches, were pressed against the nose cone.

Now the time had come to test the Sputnik's radio transmitter. Engineer Aleksei Ivanov, who took part in the launch of the Sputnik, told me:

"Silence reigned in the big room. The members of the State Commission, Korolev, the chief designers of the engines, the guidance systems, and other basic systems were standing silent beside the rocket.

"The command was given, and in that huge room we could hear the clear, distinct signals: *Beep, beep, beep.* Later, the whole world heard them. But when they came through the loudspeaker of the testing system, those signals were really exciting."

The transmitter was turned on, the last plug-and-sockets were connected, and the safety clamp was removed from the contact. Now it would be cut in only after the Sputnik had separated from the rocket, in orbit.

The rocket had been loaded onto a specially designed flatcar. The polished nozzles of its engines glittered. Shuddering at each joint of the rails, it slowly moved through the huge doors of the building—which had opened noiselessly—into the starry darkness of the southern night.

By the morning of 3 October the rocket had been positioned on the launch pad, and the final tests of all its systems and instruments had begun. The sun blazed up over the flat steppe, bringing warmth, then heat. In order to avoid overheating of the Sputnik, it was covered with a white fabric. Then, when it became apparent that this was not helping things, it was cooled with compressed air from a hose.

Korolev went up to the top deck of the service tower, where he briefed the specialists and reported to Moscow on the preparations for the launch. Outwardly, he was calm and reserved; but he was even more demanding than usual.

A portrait of Tsiolkovsky hung on a wall in the small, unpretentious house where Korolev lived and worked. Before flying to Baikonur—on the day when the nation was celebrating the hundredth anniversary of Tsiolkovsky's birth—Korolev made a major speech at a great rally in the Pillared Hall of the Palace of Unions in Moscow:

"In our time," he said, "rocket engineering is one of the foremost fields of modern science and technology. Soviet rockets are making flights above the earth's surface at very great altitudes, hitherto unattained."

Then, without raising his voice, he added: "In the very near future, the first experimental launchings of artificial earth satellites will take place in the USSR and the USA for scientific purposes."

At the time, very few people realized that Korolev was talking mostly about the imminent launch of a Sputnik.

On the hundredth anniversary of Tsiolkovsky's birth the newspaper *Pravda* published a long article by Korolev titled "The Founder of Rocketry." By way of conclusion, Korolev wrote:

> Soviet scientists are working on problems of deep penetration into cosmic space. We are witnessing the realization of Tsiolkovsky's remarkable predictions of rocket flights and the possibility of flying into interplanetary space—predictions made more than sixty years ago.
>
> His ideas and research will attract more and more attention as rocketry develops. Tsiolkovsky was a man who lived far ahead of his time—as any great and genuine scientist must live.

After making his speech in the Pillared Hall, Korolev went back to work at the Design Bureau, in the workshop, and in the "Sputnik room." Then came the day when he flew off to Baikonur to direct preparatory work for the launch of the Sputnik.

Finally the bugler made his appearance at the launch pad, illuminated by floodlights. The clear tones of the bugle were heard above the noise of the machines on the pad. Blinding flames swirled about, and a deep, rolling thunder was heard. The silvery rocket was instantly enveloped in clouds of vapor. Its glittering, shapely body seemed to quiver and slowly rose up from the launch pad. At that same moment, a brilliant splash of light shot up into the sky. A raging flame burst forth from the launch pad, and its candle dispelled the darkness of a night on the steppe. So fierce was the glare that the silhouettes of the work towers, the machines, and the people were clearly outlined.

The rocket, as though feeling at home in its own element, rose smoothly and ever more rapidly. Gradually, the contours of its form began to blur. And when, after smoothly programming into its trajectory, it receded from view with greater velocity, the launch control team could see only a little star among the constellations above the steppe.

"She's off! Our baby is off!" Everybody in the vicinity of the launch pad was overcome with joy. People embraced, kissed, waved their arms excitedly, and sang. Somebody began to dance, while all the others kept on shouting: "She's off! Our baby is off!"

After this spontaneous outburst of enthusiasm, everyone rushed to the radio receivers. Sputnik's first signals, from the time of its separation from the carrier rocket to when it passed beyond the radio horizon, had already been recorded on tape. With bated breath, everyone listened to the satellite's voice. Some ninety-five minutes later, having circled the earth, it once again passed over Baikonur, its cradle, sending out a loud, clear signal: *"Beep, beep, beep . . ."*

A meeting was held at the launch complex. It happened spontaneously. After everything they had experienced, people wanted to pour out their feelings and congratulate one another. Korolev, flushed with excitement, mounted an improvised speakers' platform. S.P. was usually self-contained, strict, and even stern. But now his eyes were sparkling and he was radiant with joy. Restraining his excitement, he said:

"Today we have witnessed the realization of a dream nurtured by some of the finest men who ever lived, including our outstanding scientist Konstantin Eduardovich Tsiolkovsky. Tsiolkovsky brilliantly foretold that mankind would not forever remain on the earth. The Sputnik is the first confirmation of his prophecy.

The conquering of space has begun. We can be proud that it was begun by our country."

Korolev concluded his speech with some words of gratitude to all who had taken part in building the Sputnik and the booster rocket and in carrying out the historic launching: "A hearty Russian thanks to all!"

At the same time, the following TASS bulletin was being communicated to the whole world via teletype, radio, telegraph, and telephone: "On 4 October, 1957, the first artificial satellite was successfully launched in the USSR."

The bulletin went on to mention plans for the future:

> The Soviet Union proposes to launch several more artificial earth satellites in the course of the International Geophysical Year. These later Sputniks will be larger, and a broad range of scientific experiments will be carried out on them . . .

Finally, the TASS bulletin stated: "Artificial earth satellites will pave the way to interplanetary travel . . ."

The Sputnik startled the world. Thousands of telegrams and letters came in from everywhere, addressed simply: "Sputnik, Moscow." The French scientist Frederic Joliot-Curie exclaimed: "This is a great, outstanding victory for man, which marks a turning point in the history of civilization!" The New York *Times* said: "It is now clear that 4 October 1957 will go down in the annals of history as the day of one of the greatest achievements of man . . ." The *Christian Science Monitor* noted: "Long live the era of interplanetary flights!" And it added: "Broad new horizons have opened up before mankind, thanks to the possibilities of the Soviet 'moon.'" And the French newspaper *Combat* said: "The launching of an artificial earth satellite by the Soviets is undoubtedly the chief event of our age."

Dr. Joseph Kaplan, chairman of the United States National Committee for the IGY, stated: "I am astounded by what they have managed to do in the short period of time they had at their disposal. It seems to me that this is a remarkable achievement. They did it—and they did it first."

A photograph of the Sputnik appeared in newspapers and magazines, and on the screen. Not only specialists but millions of laymen knew that the Sputnik was a silvery sphere with a diameter of 22 inches and a weight of 190.5 pounds. Its surface had been carefully processed to assure the correct coefficient of heat radiation and absorption of the sun's rays. In order to maintain an even temperature within the sphere, it was filled with nitrogen, circulated by a small fan. This produced heat exchange between the Sputnik's equipment and its outer shell, which was subjected by turn to the sun's rays on the light side and to the cold of space on the dark side. The Sputnik had two radio transmitters operating on frequencies of 20.005 and 40.002 megacycles, respectively, i.e., on wave lengths of about 15 and 7.5. The capacity of the transmitters assured reception of their radio signals by a great many "ham" radio operators. These signals took the form of telegraphic impulses with a duration of about 0.3 second, interrupted by pauses of equal duration.

The Sputnik flew around the earth in an elliptical orbit, rising to an apogee of up to 947 kilometers and descending to a perigee of up to 228 kilometers. Its period of revolution around the earth was 1 hour 35 minutes.

On 9 October, as the first Sputnik continued to orbit, *Pravda* wrote:

> . . . In order to make the transition to manned space flights it is necessary to study the effect of space-flight conditions on living organisms. To begin with, animals will be used for such studies. As was done with the high-altitude rockets, the Soviet Union will launch a Sputnik carrying animals as passengers. Detailed observations will be made of their behavior and their physiological processes.

The first Sputnik continued its existence as a body in space for ninety-two days. It completed 1,400 revolutions around the earth, covering about 60 million kilometers in that time, i.e., about the distance from the earth to Mars.

Laika

On 3 November 1957 the following announcement was made by TASS:

> In accordance with the IGY program for the scientific investigation of the upper strata of the atmosphere, and the study of physical processes and life conditions in cosmic space, a second artificial earth satellite was launched in the Soviet Union on 3 November.

Sputnik-2 differed from *Sputnik*-1. It was not a sphere but a cone that contained all the scientific and measuring instruments, together with a pressurized cabin serving as an abode for the world's first live space traveler—a dog nicknamed "Laika" (Barker).

Sputnik-2 was very heavy: 1,118.26 pounds. It carried instruments for investigating cosmic rays and solar radiation in the short-wave, ultraviolet, and X-ray bands of the spectrum; instruments for analyzing temperature and pressure; and measuring instruments for transmitting to earth the data from the scientific observations.

It had two transmitters operating on the same wave lengths as those of *Sputnik*-1. Laika's cabin was of particular importance.

Before the dog was placed in the cabin, she was carefully groomed. Her coat was sponged with a weak alcohol solution and combed with a fine-toothed comb. Those areas where the electrodes were to be attached were painted with iodine and powdered with a streptocide. (During these preparations Laika displayed her usual even-tempered behavior.) Then a special harness was put on her, and she was placed in the pressurized compartment.

When open, the compartment resembled an elongated, ellipsoidal nest with high walls covered with soft material. On the bottom, along the sides, and at the top—everywhere—were intricate instruments providing life support for the four-legged explorer.

The rocket carrying *Sputnik*-2 was launched in the daytime. Laika suffered no ill effects during the vehicle's ascent and injection into orbit. While weightless, she took food from an automatic dispenser, barked, and moved about.

Sputnik-2 followed an elliptical orbit with an apogee of up to 1,671 kilometers above the earth's surface—almost twice as high as that of *Sputnik*-1. Its perigee was 225 kilometers. It completed 2,370 revolutions around the earth and covered about 100 million kilometers. It continued in existence for 163 days.

In 1957 Korolev wrote:

> As a result of the observations made during the flight of both Sputniks, and the recording of massive data from the measurements, we have obtained unique information of great value. . .
>
> . . . All of the basic assumptions utilized in the designing of the Soviet Sputniks were brilliantly confirmed. Both Sputniks attained the planned terminal velocity and went into orbit with very great precision.
>
> The data gathered on cosmic rays during the flight of *Sputnik*-2 are of great value . . . The study of biological phenomena made during the space flight of a living organism—something done for the first time in *Sputnik*-2—is of tremendous interest . . .
>
> The time will come [Korolev wrote prophetically] when a spacecraft carrying human beings will leave the earth and set out on a voyage to distant planets—to remote worlds.

Today this may seem only an enticing fantasy, but such in fact is not the case. The launching of the first two Soviet Sputniks has already thrown a sturdy bridge from the earth into space, and the way to the stars is open.

The sturdy bridge from earth into space had been built. But man did not immediately set out across that bridge.

Laboratories
in Space

On 15 May 1958, an automatic scientific laboratory, gigantic for its day, began to function in space. It was installed on board *Sputnik*-3—the world's first geophysical satellite. Everyone was greatly impressed by its weight of 2,919.4 pounds, 2,129.6 of which consisted of scientific apparatus, radiometric instruments, and sources of electric power.

Sputnik-3 carried a computer installation which assured the functioning of the scientific and measuring instruments.

The Sputnik itself was in the form of an almost perfect cone 11.7 feet long, with a maximum diameter of 5.67 feet. Its system of heat regulation was successfully tested in flight, as were its solar batteries.

The automatic scientific laboratory made 10,037 revolutions around the earth, and in the 691 days of its existence covered more than 448 million kilometers.

Sputnik-3 carried out its scientific mission in an elliptical orbit with an apogee of 1,880 kilometers and a perigee of 226 kilometers. Prominent among its scientifically important achievements was the discovery of the earth's outer radiation belt.

The launching, on 2 January 1959, of *Luna*-1 (*Mechta*)—the first space vehicle sent in the direction of the moon—must be regarded as one of the most important events in the history of cosmonautics. The rocket's last stage achieved the "second cosmic velocity" (about 11.2 kilometers per second)—something that never had been done before—and put the probe into a trajectory headed for the moon. This marked the opening of the era of flights to other celestial bodies.

Luna-1's payload, including the scientific equipment, radio apparatus, and telemetry system, weighed 794.9 pounds.

On 3 January, at 0357 Moscow time, when *Luna*-1 was 113,000 kilometers distant from the earth, a faint golden-orange cloud of sodium gas appeared in the sky above the Indian Ocean. This was a tracer left by the *Luna*-1 probe so that observers on earth could follow its movement visually. Soviet astronomers took photographs of this, the world's first artificial nebula.

On 4 January at 0600 hours, the probe flew past the moon at a distance of from 5,000 to 6,000 kilometers from its surface and became the first artificial satellite of the sun. It is still in flight between the orbits of the earth and Mars, making one revolution around the sun every 450 days.

The scientific data transmitted by *Luna*-1 included very valuable information on the earth's radiation belt(s) and on cosmic space. It was established that there is no strong magnetic field near the moon. And, for the first time, those strong flows of ionized plasma called the "solar wind," were recorded in interplanetary space.

The next historic event was the launching, on 12 September 1959, of a second space probe whose last stage had a dry weight of 3,324 pounds. In the last stage was an automatic interplanetary station (AMS) whose over-all weight, including scientific instruments and radiotechnical apparatus, amounted to 858.4 pounds. *Luna*-2 was a spherical cannister containing instruments and equipped with pennants bearing the national emblem of the Soviet Union.

Luna-2 followed its planned trajectory accurately. At the scheduled time it gave off a sodium cloud visible through telescopes, which was photographed by astronomers.

At 0002 hours and 24 seconds, *Luna*-2 impacted on the lunar surface near the Sea of Serenity and the craters Aristillus, Archimedes, and Autolycus.

For the first time in the history of mankind, a material object had been moved from one celestial body to another—whereby the basic possibility of space travel was confirmed. The investigation of cosmic space in the vicinity of the moon established that the moon had no significant magnetic field or radiation belts.

The way to the moon was open.

The second anniversary of the launching of the world's first artificial earth satellite was celebrated by the launching of a third space probe with a last stage whose dry weight was 3,416.6 pounds. This last stage carried an AMS, *Luna-3*, which weighed 612.7 pounds.

It was launched on 4 October 1959. At 1730 hours on 5 October, it passed within 70,000 kilometers of the moon's surface and continued along its planned trajectory around the moon. At 0630 hours on 7 October, after reaching a point from some 65,000 to 68,000 kilometers distant from the lunar surface, the probe began to photograph the dark side of the moon.

The photographing of this formerly mysterious dark side of the moon went on for forty minutes. The photographs were taken with both a short-focus and a long-focus lens on special 35-mm film. The cameras photographed almost half of the moon's surface. The film was automatically developed on *Luna-3*, and the on-board photo-television scanners transmitted the photographs to earth when *Luna-3* was some 40,000 kilometers distant from it. Mankind's first successful experiment in photographing another celestial body and transmitting the images back to earth, enabled Soviet scientists to put together the first globe of the moon. And taking advantage of the discoverers' rights in such matters, they named the new seas, bays, and craters. Henceforth all globes of the moon will show the *Mare Ingenii* (Mechta Sea), *Mare Moscoviensis* (Sea of Moscow), and Tsiolkovsky Crater. Subsequently, a very large bay (thalassoid) was named after S. P. Korolev.

The main road for man's penetration of space was paved by the creation of manned orbital stations. To this end it was necessary that a human being spend time in space and ascertain whether he could live and work in that mysterious, unknown ocean of space.

The first spacecraft of the *Vostok* type was launched in the USSR on 15 May 1960. Not including the last stage of the carrier rocket, it weighed 9,988 pounds. The spacecraft had a pressurized cabin with an over-all weight of 5,500 pounds and carried a load equivalent to the weight of a cosmonaut. The spaceship went into an orbit with a perigee of 312 kilometers and an apogee of 368 kilometers. The purpose in launching this first satellite spacecraft was to refine and test all systems assuring a safe flight for a human being and his return to earth.

The second spacecraft, which was launched on 19 August 1960, carried a whole zoo: two dogs, Strelka (Little Arrow) and Belka (Squirrel), forty mice, two rats, and fifteen flasks full of Drosophilae, plus such plant life as spiderwort and Chlorella. In short, it was a regular Noah's ark. Exclusive of the carrier rocket's last stage, the spacecraft weighed 10,120 pounds.

It was put into an almost circular orbit with an apogee of 339 kilometers and a perigree of 306 kilometers. On 20 August, when in its eighteenth orbit, after having covered more than 700,000 kilometers and completed its mission, it received the command to return to earth. It landed with great accuracy, touching down at a point only 10 kilometers from the planned site.

For the first time in history, living organisms had completed a space flight and returned to earth safe and sound.

This was a tremendous success, and it might have seemed that the time had come to send a man into space. But Korolev was in no hurry. Together with a large group of scientists, he went on—stubbornly and systematically—launching spacecraft. The third one was launched on 1 December 1960. Its passengers included the dogs Pchelka (Bee) and Mushka (Little Fly), mice, insects, and plant life.

On 2 December 1960, owing to a faulty trajectory, this spaceship was destroyed upon re-entering the dense layers of the atmosphere.

The second heavy earth satellite was launched on 12 February 1961. That same day witnessed the launch of a space rocket guided from earth. This rocket put the AMS probe *Venus-1*—weighing 1,415.7 pounds—into a trajectory headed for Venus. In the latter part of May 1961, the probe passed the vicinity of Venus and went into orbit as an artificial satellite of the sun.

The exploration of space was proceeding in many different ways, but the main emphasis was on preparing for a manned flight.

The launching of the fourth spacecraft, weighing 10,340 pounds, took place on 9 March 1961. It carried the dog Chernushka (Blackie), guinea pigs, mice, and other living organisms. The capsule also carried a "wooden man"—a dummy. The fourth spacecraft came back to earth after completing one orbit.

The State Commission decided to launch one more spacecraft—the fifth. The launch was scheduled for 25 March 1961. Its weight, minus the last stage of the carrier rocket, was 10,329 pounds. The capsule was occupied by the dog Zvezdochka (Little Star) and a dummy.

Among those present at the landing site of the fifth spacecraft were Yuri Gagarin, Gherman Titov, and their fellow cosmonauts.

After this digression into the past, let us return to our interrupted account of the flight made by Yuri Gagarin and the preparations for his backup, Gherman Titov.

There was now a new task: completion of a day-long manned flight. The State Commission named Gherman Stepanovich Titov as commander of the spacecraft *Vostok*-2.

Seventeen Days and Nights in Twenty-four Hours

After flying to Baikonur, Titov went to the cosmonauts' cottage, which was already familiar to him. Back in April he had been quartered there with Gagarin, when he was the latter's backup. With Titov this time was his own backup, Andriyan Nikolayev.

Once inside, Titov indicated with a glance that Nikolayev should take Gagarin's former bed. He himself sat on the edge of the one he had slept in before.

"I'm used to this one," he explained to Nikolayev. "Make yourself at home on that one. It will bring good luck. Yuri slept there."

Titov went over to a window and flung it open. The sun-baked steppe was covered with a thick growth of various grasses giving off a rather acrid scent. Far off on the horizon, a mirage shimmered.

"Now it's my turn," Titov said with a sigh.

Everything that had happened in April seemed like a curious rehearsal for his own flight. Titov would always remember the preparations for Gagarin's flight and the last night before they were driven to the launch pad. Now he himself had to travel this same road. He had a backup with him; but Titov was sure that his stand-in would go no farther than the launch pad.

After Gagarin's flight, Titov was often asked by the doctors and journalists how he had felt as a backup, and what he was thinking—on that twelfth day of April—after taking his leave of Gagarin on the launch pad.

In a full-length documentary film about Gherman Titov's life and his flight—a film made under my direction with the title *Once Again Toward the Stars*—I included a taped conversation between Titov and a psychiatrist. This conversation took place in the hospital where, in preparation for his flight, Titov was winding up his training.

"How are you feeling?" the doctor asked.

Titov shrugged. "I feel fine. Really fine. Even top-notch."

The doctor twirled a finely sharpened pencil between his fingers, wrote something on a file card, and looked probingly at Titov. The latter awaited his next question with lively interest.

"During the final phase," the doctor said, "you had to undergo some critical tests and training sessions. Didn't they have an adverse effect on the way you felt?"

Titov raised his eyebrows. "The way I felt?" he asked in astonishment. "During the final phase there were no special training sessions . . . But then, come to think of it, the training did involve some parachute jumps."

The doctor's curiosity quickened. "How did it go with the parachute jumps?"

Titov shrugged in a vague gesture. "No injuries—so it was okay."

"How did you feel about Gagarin's flight? How did you feel at the launch pad?"

"What should I say? H'm . . ." Titov spread out his hands, then crossed them on his chest, and immediately let them fall into his lap. "H'm . . . Both Gagarin and I prepared for the flight. Both of us had been driven to the launch pad, where we took leave of our buddies. Then Yuri climbed into the spacecraft. As for me, well, I waited until the preparations were completed. When everything was ready, Yuri reported that he felt fine. All the work was done, and I left. H'm. I went with the others to the communications center, and from there we watched the liftoff."

"What did you feel at that moment?" asked the doctor.

Titov replied: "A flier who is staying on the ground when one of his buddies makes a flight will necessarily pay close attention to how he takes off and flies, observing all aspects of the flight, and how they were performed. In this way he learns something useful to himself. These were pretty much the same feelings I had when Yuri lifted off and went into orbit. For that matter, I felt a bit strange. 'What is this?' I asked myself. 'A moment ago Yuri was here next to me, and suddenly he is in orbit.'"

As Titov spoke, he gesticulated in a lively way, smiling and demonstrating how much he had been astonished by the unexpected occurrence.

That had happened back in April. Now it was August. What was Nikolayev thinking at this moment? How was he feeling as a backup?

Nikolayev was totally unperturbed. His face did not show the slightest anxiety. His dark eyes did not betray his feelings. Coolly, he observed the doctors, scientists, and cameramen who kept coming into the cosmonauts' cottage to see Titov or himself.

Titov—slender and rather short—was wearing a checked shirt and looked especially young when he and Nikolayev showed up at the launch pad. One of the technicians of the launch crew was astonished when he got a look at Titov's curly head and his checked shirt and heard his jocular talk. Turning to Karpov, the director of the cosmonaut team, he asked: "Is *this* lad going to make a flight?"

In those days, Titov might well have seemed too jocular and too young, because of his quick gait, his rumpled hair, his gaily sparkling eyes, his restlessness, and his mischievous wit. But that same technician who at first had been so critical of Titov later remarked (after he had got a good look at Titov and listened to his questions): "This is a real spacecraft commander."

As Karpov told me: "Many people, upon first meeting Titov, had the impression that this fun-loving fellow was by no means fitted to make a flight: he talked very lightly about flights, engineering, and scientific problems. But when they got to know Titov better, they realized that his outwardly flippant attitude—his bravado and inexhaustible cheerfulness—merely concealed an iron will, a keen mind, inquisitiveness, and the great talent of a serious, thinking man."

The arrival of the cosmonauts at the launch complex marked the beginning of some intensive workdays. Korolev was caught up in work and worries. Nonetheless, at an opportune moment he met with the reporters who had been beleaguering him and talked to them about the significant aspects of the new space flight.

Unhurriedly, weighing every word and looking closely at the reporters, Korolev said: "Titov is faced with a difficult flight. If Gagarin's flight was the first test, then tomorrow's flight may be considered a test in depth. Titov is to make a full day's flight. He will be the first to experience a twenty-four-hour life cycle, encountering little-known phenomena. What is involved here is not merely G-loads during ascent and re-entry: we already have a good notion of this. But he will be face-to-face with prolonged weightlessness. A thorough study of the effects of weightlessness on living organisms is impossible under terrestrial conditions. But Gagarin's flight has given us hope. Our medical people are particularly concerned about prolonged weightlessness. And I'm on the alert myself. If necessary, the spacecraft will immediately be brought back to earth."

Needless to say, the reporters asked Korolev: "Does Titov know all about this?"

"Yes," replied Korolev. "We have informed the cosmonauts of the complexities—and even the risks—of the impending flights. Their agreement bears witness not only to an understanding of the problems they must solve but to their courage—and their resolve to make their own contribution to science. For this, we scientists value and respect them."

After lunch, having wound up their business in the cosmonauts' cottage, Titov and Nikolayev once again took the bus to the launch complex. They rode up in the elevator to the top deck of the tower, from where they had a panoramic view of the steppe.

Right on their heels came Korolev. He looked on, smiling, as Titov and Nikolayev checked out the spacecraft in every detail.

"Do you feel at home?"

"We've already inspected and touched everything," Titov answered cheerfully.

"Don't be in a hurry, boys," Korolev said in a warm voice.

The cosmonauts fell silent. With a smile, Korolev told them: "You're going to fly in this spacecraft. Give it a good look-over. Check everything out carefully. I myself used to be a test pilot. I used to spend hours sitting in the cockpit of a new airplane. People are finicky about taking measurements for nothing more than a new suit of clothes. But this is a spacecraft."

72. The photo taken with the help of the motion picture camera on board *Vostok*-4. Weightlessness. Cosmonaut Pavel Popovich.

73. Pilots Andriyan Nikolayev of *Vostok*-3 and Pavel Popovich of *Vostok*-4 arrive at Vnukovo Airport in Moscow after their joint flight, August 1962.

74. Valentina Tereshkova spent many days in complete isolation, training for her space flight.

75. Valentina Tereshkova, the first woman cosmonaut, went into space on 16 June 1963 as pilot of the spaceship *Vostok*-6.

76. Baikonur Cosmodrome, 16 June 1963. Nikolayev seeing off Tereshkova.

(ABOVE)
77. Baikonur Cosmodrome,
16 June 1963. Pilot-Cosmonaut
Valentina Tereshkova on her
way to the *Vostok*-6 spaceship.

(RIGHT)
78. The launching pad at
Baikonur Cosmodrome,
16 June 1963. Valentina
Tereshkova at the *Vostok*-6
just before starting on her
space flight.

79. The TV image of Valentina
Tereshkova, pilot of *Vostok*-6,
taken by the Soviet communications
stations from the spaceship's
television broadcast and transmitted
by the Soviet central TV stations,
16 June 1963.

80. On 15 August 1962, *Vostok*-3 was retrieved as planned after participating in the world's first joint flight.

In photo: The inhabitants of the touchdown region are hurrying to welcome the man from the cosmos, Andriyan Nikolayev.

81. Re-entry capsule of *Vostok*-6 spaceship right after landing in the predetermined area. In the capsule was Valentina Tereshkova, the world's first woman cosmonaut. She went into space on 16 June 1963.

82. Cosmonauts Andriyan Nikolayev, Valentina Tereshkova, and Pavel Popovich visit Leonid Brezhnev, now General Secretary of the Central Committee of the Communist Party, at the Kremlin in 1963.

The chief designer shifted his glance from the cosmonauts to the space vehicle and, without taking his eyes off it, asked: "Do you like it?"

"Very much!" Titov exclaimed.

"Well, then, as the saying goes, God speed you! Tomorrow is the launch."

That evening after dinner, Korolev visited the cosmonauts' cottage and asked Titov and Nikolayev to take a walk with him. The three of them set off along a path through the steppe. The sun had already gone down. They walked along closely bunched together, with Korolev in the middle, Titov on the left, and Nikolayev on the right. As they moved along, in step, Titov listened carefully to the Chief's advice.

"During your flight," said Korolev, "you are to make a thorough test of the manual control of the spacecraft and the possibility of landing it at any given point."

It was already late. Korolev glanced at his watch—which was enough of a hint for the cosmonauts to take their leave of him. He shook hands with both young men, wished them a good night's sleep, and went off to the launch pad.

Titov's account of his last night before the launch is as follows:

We went back to the cosmonauts' cottage, where the doctors made their routine examination. My pulse was quiet, my respiration even, and my blood pressure normal. Then they put electrodes on us, to record our physiological functions. This whole procedure was already familiar to me. I had become accustomed to it when I was acting as backup for Yuri Gagarin before his flight. I checked on my emotional state, and it was just as calm as it had been on that earlier occasion.

Nikolayev and I went to bed in the same room. It was stuffy. We had to open the windows and set up fans near our beds. Andriyan turned over on his left side and went off to sleep immediately. After listening to the metallic sounds coming from the cosmodrome and the steady hum of the fans, I too fell asleep.

During the night it got cold, and I woke up and turned off the fan. Andriyan was still sleeping quietly in the same position—on his left side, with both hands under his chin. I noticed that there was a bouquet of roses on the table. I didn't know who had sent them, but it was good to realize that our friends had not forgotten us.

In the morning I was awakened by Karpov. I felt the touch of his cool hands and came awake immediately. At the same time, Andriyan was awakened by Dr. Andrei Viktorovich. It occurred to me that both doctors had stayed awake all night, to see that we were not disturbed.

Next came the usual things: medical examination, setting-up exercises, and breakfast. Finally I went into the cosmonauts' dressing room to put on the orange-colored spacesuit. V. A. Plaksin, the sports commissioner, handed me the certificate, filled in the documents, and then left for the launch complex to record the launch of the spacecraft *Vostok-2*.

It was a beautiful morning. The sun rose higher and higher; birds were singing in the clear sky; and exhilarating music was coming from somewhere. All this harmonized with my high spirits. Andriyan and I left the cosmonauts' cottage and took our seats in the bus, where our friends from the cosmonaut team were waiting for us. The route to the launch pad was already familiar to me. We sang and joked. I was thinking: Right now Yuri is in Cuba or the United States. He'll be glad when he hears of the launch. And he may even be there for the touchdown.

Then Titov looked at his friend and backup. Andriyan, in his orange spacesuit and glittering white space helmet, was sitting calmly in the second seat. Like all the others in the bus, he was singing and joking, as though his usual mood of imperturbable concentration had given way to another. Titov was caught up by the atmosphere of cheerful confidence and gaiety, friendly sympathy, and joy which reigned in the bus. He made free with his jokes until the concrete slabs of the launch pad came into view.

The bus stopped. Titov walked to the door, waved good-by to the driver, and stepped down to the concrete slab.

He was soon riding the elevator up to the top of the space vehicle. From the elevator he could see the steppe and the long, deep shadows of the rocket and work tower stretching over the ground. Waiting for Titov on the top deck were assistants in dark jackets with red armbands.

He paused at the edge of the platform looking around at the

steppe and, in the distance, the buildings of the Baikonur housing development. Then, aided by the assistants, he climbed into the capsule of the spacecraft *Vostok-2*.

When he was settled in the comfortable contour couch he felt remarkably calm. Everything in the cabin was familiar to him from his training sessions in the simulator. He was well acquainted with all the tumbler switches, push-buttons, and instruments, and was pleased with the blue globe on the instrument panel and the Vzor optical device.

Vostok-2 lifted off at 9:00 A.M. on 6 August 1961. Hardly had the words "Liftoff! We have a liftoff!" been uttered, when Titov's rather mischievous shout of delight could be heard in the ether: "She's off and running!"

When Korolev heard the shout, he smiled and held up one thumb in an old flier's gesture.

Titov bore up well under the roar of the engines, the vibration, and the increasing G-loads as the spacecraft was injected into orbit. In the first few seconds after liftoff he was already at work—checking his instruments, maintaining two-way radio communication with Ground Control, and watching the receding earth through his viewport. The horizon expanded, and the sky and sun loomed larger.

Titov could feel the effect each time a stage of the rocket was jettisoned. He waited for the mysterious condition of weightlessness to set in. This happened after separation of the rocket's last stage. Titov had the impression that he had turned a half-somersault and was flying upside down. But this sensation soon vanished, and he got back to work.

An important task had been set for him: to find out how a human being would bear up under the factors of a daylong space flight and how he would feel after prolonged weightlessness, while under G-loads, and during re-entry. In the course of one day the spacecraft was to make seventeen revolutions around the earth, and there was a special work schedule for each orbit.

Seventeen times in the course of one day the cosmonaut saw the sun rise and night fall. For a while, his spaceship would be flying in the earth's shadow, and inky-black darkness would set in. Then it would emerge from the darkness, and Titov would behold the beauty of the sun rising over the earth.

Here are some excerpts from the taped conversations between

Titov, whose code name was Eagle (*Orel*), and Ground Control, with the code name of Dawn-1 (*Zarya*-1).

> *Ground Control:* Eagle, this is Dawn-1. Control is observing your flight. We all send you greetings.
>
> *Titov:* Thanks. Thanks for your good wishes. Bye-bye, dear friends. See you soon. See you soon!
>
> *Ground Control:* Eagle, this is Dawn-1. Tell me how you are feeling. Over.
>
> *Titov:* Dawn-1. Dawn-1. This is Eagle. I feel splendid. Just splendid . . . Everything is going fine. Everything shipshape.
>
> *Ground Control:* How are you holding up under zero G conditions? Do the straps seem to be pushing against you on either the right or the left? Over.
>
> *Titov:* Dawn-1, this is Eagle. The straps aren't pushing against me yet. Straps not pushing yet. How do you read me? Over.
>
> *Ground Control:* Eagle, this is Dawn-1. Request you give your attention to your general impression of the flight. How does the earth look? What do you see through the viewports?
>
> *Titov:* Dawn-1, this is Eagle. Roger. Roger. All right. The earth is very beautiful, particularly when I'm looking back at it through the Vzor . . . The earth is [an] unusual [sight] when it is in shadow and looks like a glittering sickle . . . Right now a large area is covered by clouds . . . almost everything is clouded over . . ."
>
> *Titov* (somewhat later):
>
> Dawn-1. Dawn-1. How do you read me? Right now I'm looking at a mountainous region . . . Mountains and more mountains . . . They're snow-capped. The view is simply splendid! The peaks are in the clouds . . .
>
> *Ground Control:* Eagle. Eagle. This is Dawn-1. You are authorized to use manual control . . . Report on how manual control works.

At the time, slicing through the darkness of night, *Vostok*-2 was entering the earth's shadow. Titov already felt at home in space, but he became anxious when he heard Korolev's voice. Would the spacecraft obey the man in it? Were all those projects for the future really viable? Would the spaceships prove completely obedient to the will of the cosmonauts?

Unhesitatingly, he grasped the control handle. The spacecraft immediately followed his command. Overjoyed, he reported to Ground Control: "Dawn-1, this is Eagle. The craft responds well to manual control. It responds well. I think the velocities are adequate for the first time. The angular velocities. Everything is going along fine—just fine."

Korolev listened very closely to Titov's report. He made some notes on a pad and smiled. One of the major objectives of the flight had been achieved.

While in his third orbit, Titov ate lunch, as prescribed by his schedule. Gagarin's flight had lasted 108 minutes, and during that time it was of course important to resolve the big question: Could a human being live and work while on a space flight? But this time, with the flight lasting a full day, it became possible to resolve other questions as well. For instance, how could a man take food in space? However convenient the tubes may be, might it not be necessary to alter the diet that had been worked out? Could the eating schedule that had been established in the course of many years—breakfast, lunch, and dinner—be maintained during a space flight that lasted a full day?

The people who had worked out the "space menu" and studied the problems of human vital activity during a space flight were observing Titov on a television screen. They watched him as he began to eat his lunch. There were no plates, spoons, forks, or napkins in the capsule. Titov simply stretched out his hand toward the food containers and grasped a tube. On earth it had weighed about .33 pound, but in space it weighed nothing. Titov squeezed the tube of puree, and its contents began to come out in the form of a ribbon, like toothpaste, which he took into his mouth. Doctors, biologists, physiologists, psychologists—all watched the television screen with intense interest as this first "space lunch" was consumed. They noted with satisfaction that Titov ate the puree normally, with no difficulty. He did likewise with some meat and liver pâtés, then began to drink black currant juice from another tube.

A few drops of the black juice escaped from the tube and, looking like berries, hovered in the air before the cosmonaut's face. Curious, he watched them. Scarcely quivering, they began to float through the air in the cabin. Using the top of the tube, Titov caught some of the drops and swallowed them with pleasure.

In addition to the nourishment from the tubes, Titov took solid food. He ate a few small chunks of bread and some peas with vitamins added. Also, of course, he drank water from a special apparatus.

The specialists working on problems of providing nourishment for cosmonauts were not the only ones to be delighted by how well things turned out. Korolev was so pleased with Titov's report that one might have thought the latter had made a great discovery.

Gherman Titov did another piece of work that was of great importance for cinematographers, writers, and reporters. At the scheduled time, using a Konvas camera, he took several shots of the horizon when entering the earth's shadow and when emerging from it into the sunlight. Then he photographed the starry heavens.

A movie camera possesses one astounding property: whoever looks through the viewfinder sees, in a tiny frame, a whole world compressed and reduced to the size of a postage stamp. At the same time the choice of the framework—the fact that the world around one is compressed when seen through the viewfinder— prompts one to select only that which is especially impressive. To Titov, the moon did not look the same as when viewed from the earth. It was already on the wane; but it shone brightly, and he had the impression that the spacecraft was standing still while the moon drifted rapidly past the viewport.

Titov was greatly impressed by the earth itself. It was light blue, greenish, and gray by turns. Continents and islands stood out clearly on its surface. And he was struck by the magnificence of the hydrosphere.

To get somewhat ahead of the story: after the flight, the color film was developed, and everyone eagerly awaited the viewing. Titov had brought us the first film of the earth that had ever been made from space. For the first time, people were able to see their own planet from a great distance.

Vostok-2 made one orbit after another around the earth. Later, Titov said: "Before the spacecraft emerged from the earth's shadow, it was interesting to watch the movement of twilight along the terrestrial surface. Part of the earth was bright, and the other part was totally dark. Between the two was a rapidly shifting, grayish zone of twilight, with pinkish clouds overhead. All this was unusual, beautiful, and impressive.

"Space [he added] is waiting for its own artists, poets, and of course scientists who will be able to see everything with their own eyes, interpret it, and explain it."

The flight proceeded normally. Now, according to his schedule, it was time for Titov to sleep. Having by then completed six revolutions around the earth, he got ready to take his rest. The doctors were waiting to see how a man would sleep in space.

Even today, scientists and cosmonauts are concerned about weightlessness. Back then, at the dawn of the space era, it was a source of anxiety—a blank area on the map of science.

During the 108 minutes of his single orbit, Yuri Gagarin had borne up well under weightlessness. It had even been pleasant for him. But in this prolonged flight it took its toll . . . The state of weightlessness had a peculiar effect on the so-called otoliths—the tiny "stones" in the liquid-filled, sealed antrum of the internal ear in humans. Under ordinary conditions, when there is a change in the position of the head, the otoliths are displaced and excite various bundles of sensitive nerve endings within the antrum of the inner ear. These nerve endings then send the appropriate signal to the nerves and the brain. But in flight conditions, under zero gravity, the otoliths could not send the correct signals to the brain and, consequently, orient the cosmonaut in space.

Titov took the appropriate steps. He assumed his initial, relaxed position and tried to avoid abrupt movements of his head. Supposedly, sleep would not only dispel the fatigue that had come over Titov but also free him of the unpleasant sensations caused by the disturbance of his vestibular apparatus.

Yuri Gagarin's flight had somewhat reassured the doctors, who were apprehensive that zero gravity would have a harmful effect on the human organism. But Gherman Titov's daylong flight prompted the scientists to make a very thorough study of the cosmonaut's condition during prolonged weightlessness. In Titov's case, the advent of zero gravity produced the illusion of an inverted position: the instrument panel bobbed up above him, and he seemed to be flying upside down.

This feeling continued for about one minute. Titov became aware of unpleasant sensations—slight vertigo and nausea—which were aggravated when he moved his head abruptly or observed rapidly moving objects. They made for some discomfort, but did not impair his working capacity.

At 1815 hours *Vostok*-2 passed over Moscow, and Titov reported:

"Now I'm going to lie down and sleep. You can think what you like, but I'm going to sleep."

Having awakened the whole world with his flight, Gherman Titov went to sleep. He slept soundly. In fact, he overslept thirty-five minutes. He was not awakened, but was allowed to rest so as to get rid of those unpleasant sensations.

This calculation proved to be correct. Titov awoke fresh, cheerful, and vigorous. The unpleasant sensations had vanished.

"I didn't dream at all," Titov reported. "I had a good sleep, like a child . . ." Then he did his setting-up exercises. They consisted in trying to raise up his body, held down to the contour couch by restraining straps. This conditioned the muscles by means of abdominal pressure. Other exercises limbered up his joints and put his muscles into working condition.

Finally, the spacecraft went into its seventeenth orbit, and Titov heard the voice of Korolev: "Are you ready for re-entry?"

"Ready!" the cosmonaut replied immediately.

When he heard Titov's unhesitating reply, Korolev smiled. "Well, all good things must come to an end," he said jocularly. "It's important for the doctors to find out whether Gherman's unpleasant sensations were a result of his own idiosyncrasies, or whether they hold true for everybody."

Later, in response to my request for a comment on Titov's condition after his daylong flight, Professor Vladimir Yazdovsky stated:

Basically, there were no pathological deviations in any physiological functions of the organism while in flight. Gherman Titov's pulse rate ranged from 80 to 100 per minute, which is not beyond the limits of the initial preflight level. His respiration rate was 18–22 per minute. While Gherman was asleep, his pulse rate dropped to 54–56 per minute, which was in line with the background data obtained in the course of prolonged tests made shortly before the flight. The form and intervals of the tracings on Gherman Titov's electrocardiogram did not undergo any substantial changes. Despite the great complexity of the flight and the in-flight tasks, Titov's working capacity remained at an adequately high level throughout the flight. He successfully piloted the spacecraft, kept the log, maintained good communications with the ground, and gave jocular answers to many questions and remarks from Ground Control. As for those few unpleasant sensations experienced by Gherman Stepanovich Titov, they will compel us to make substantial changes in the general training program and figure out how best to condition the vestibular apparatus. In any case, it is now clear that Soviet and world science will obtain—as a result of Gherman Titov's prolonged flight—a great quantity of important scientific data facilitating man's further penetration into cosmic space.

The flight was about to end. On the ground and on shipboard, preparations were being made for the touchdown.

As *Vostok-2* went into its seventeenth orbit, a computer sequencing unit, which would assure the spacecraft's re-entry and landing at the planned site, was switched on in accordance with the flight program. This time the selected touchdown point was near the Volga—not far from the place where Yuri Gagarin had landed.

Vostok-2 was oriented, the retrorockets were fired, and the spacecraft went into a re-entry trajectory. Titov did not close the shutters on the viewports. And as *Vostok-2* entered the dense layers of the atmosphere, he found it interesting to observe the flames in the air flowing past the spacecraft. The changes in its speed and altitude were accompanied by marked changes in the blaze: from a delicate pink it thickened into scarlet, then purple, and finally crimson. Titov looked at the thermometer. The temperature in the capsule was normal: 72 degrees Fahrenheit. Then he looked through the viewport at the brilliant hues of the flames raging outside.

Now he was no longer weightless: the G-loads were coming into play. They increased, pushing him back against his contour couch, as if a mysterious force were flattening him. But before long that force grew weaker: the G-loads were gone.

Then the earth loomed below him.

Titov had a choice between landing in the capsule of the spacecraft without leaving his contour couch and being ejected together with the contour seat, then cutting loose from it and parachuting to earth. After the retrorockets had been fired and *Vostok-2* had been put into a re-entry trajectory, Titov evaluated his situation and decided to try the second means of descent—by parachute.

On 7 August 1961, at 10:18, Gherman Titov landed, safe and sound, near the village of Krasny Kut in the Saratovskaya Oblast.

According to the calculations of the sports commissioners, the spacecraft *Vostok-2*, with Titov aboard, had flown 703,143 kilometers in 25 hours 11 minutes. In making more than seventeen revolutions around the earth, Titov had set a world record for duration and range of flight in general, and a world record for duration and range of flight in the class of orbital flights.

The first of the cosmonauts to greet Titov in the field was his friend and backup, Andriyan Nikolayev. He had flown to Krasny Kut and was waiting there for Cosmonaut Number Two.

The two friends embraced and slapped each other on the back. It seemed that it had been years, rather than one day, since they had seen each other.

"Well, how was it up there?" asked Nikolayev.

"Very interesting!" Titov exclaimed. "Later I'll tell you everything in detail. But right now there's one thing more important than all the rest. We must work hard at conditioning the vestibular system of the inner ear. Zero gravity is a serious business. This must be the basic goal for all of us in our work in the future."

That same day the two friends reached the cosmonauts' "R-and-R Center" in the picturesque Zhiguli Hills overlooking the Volga. Yuri Gagarin came there, too, after a long flight from America—thus keeping his parting promise to greet Titov upon his return from space. He and Titov embraced. Then, fighting their way through the crowd of doctors, reporters, and cameramen around them, they set off for a walk along the bank of the Volga, taking Andriyan Nikolayev along with them.

Then came the hero's welcome at the Vnukovo Airport in Moscow; the triumphal procession, in an open limousine garlanded with flowers, along Leninsky Prospect; the rally in Red Square; and the official reception in the Kremlin Palace.

After the ceremonies, Titov and his fellow cosmonauts visited a plant where new spacecraft were under construction. These welcome guests were greeted by engineers, workers, designers, and scientists—headed up by Korolev. In his speech at this rally, Titov said: "I know what a vast amount of work was done by the scientists to make this flight possible—how great were your labors, dear comrades! Allow me to present a gift to you: the log of *Vostok-2*, which I kept during the flight."

Titov stepped down from the speakers' platform and, flushed

with emotion, handed Korolev the logbook, bound in white. The chief designer gave the cosmonaut a firm handshake, embraced him, and accepted the logbook. In his speech he said it was a precious gift for the whole plant.

Korolev had invited the cosmonauts to his home after the rally where he talked of the future, of space flight, and of construction of orbital stations—noting that they were now very feasible.

Titov asked: "And what about the next flight, Sergei Pavlovich?"

Soon afterward, I told Nikolai Kamanin: "The film about Titov's flight has been completed. What should we look forward to now?"

Kamanin replied: "To use the language of writers and reporters, the space era has only just begun. [Right now] we are taking a breather and studying results. Later on—most likely within a year—there will be a major flight. We'll have the time to make thorough preparations for it. It will be the world's first team flight. Who will go up? Well, Titov's backup, Andrian Nikolayev, is a likely candidate. And who else? Pavel Popovich is well suited for the job. Naturally, in the course of a year many things can change. But in any case, these are our tentative notions. We are getting started on a training program for the assembly, in space, of orbital stations and laboratories."

What would the program for future flights consist of? What was its chief goal? These questions excited my curiosity, and once again I went to Korolev for the answers.

The Chief Dreams,
Calculates,
and Creates

The traffic light winked its green eye. I made a sharp left turn, and the two metal panels of the gate opened before me with dignified slowness. I drove ahead into the "mousetrap"—a barren, asphalt-covered area protected by blank walls.

Getting out of my car, I went to S. P. Korolev's office in the Design Bureau. It was a modest, plain room, with two colors predominating. The walls were bright green, and the furniture—a work table, an armchair, and some straight-backed chairs—were upholstered in a cream-colored fabric. A sheet of plexiglass covered the top of the work table. On the wall was a portrait of Lenin; and on top of the file cabinet stood a silvery model of *Sputnik*-1. There was also a small safe, bookshelves, and a round table in one corner. On top of the work table were a notebook, a piece of dark metal, a black fountain pen, and a gold watch that Korolev had removed from his wrist.

Behind the work table stood Korolev. He shook my hand. But instead of asking me to sit down, he gestured toward his other visitors—a group of design engineers and planners—as if to say: "What a mess! "

Korolev's aspect was anything but official. He was wearing a knitted shirt, open at the neck, and dark blue pants. Everything about him indicated that he paid little attention to external appearances.

It was also evident that he was tired and heavily burdened. He had just come back from the testing range, and was preparing to fly off to some plant or other the next morning.

As he gestured toward the people gathered in his office, he told me: "You must forgive me. These co-workers have come on pressing business, so I'll be held up a bit . . . But what about you? What can I keep you busy with, so you won't be wasting your time?"

After a moment's thought, he showed me into a small office next to his. "I'll be through with the others very soon, and then we can talk about everything in detail. All right? Meantime, come over here . . ."

He took me to a table piled high with books, journals, and albums with photographs of the moon. "Take a look. There's some new stuff here."

"But this is a real treasure trove!" I exclaimed.

"Well then, look it over. Make yourself at home. And please don't stand on ceremony."

At the Design Bureau, this little room was called the "sanctum sanctorum." This was where Korolev worked in solitude: where he prepared for new experiments, where he did his thinking. It was also where he went to be alone when things had gone badly.

On the wall hung a portrait of Tsiolkovsky, together with a blown-up photograph of the far side of the moon. No doubt Korolev spent hours looking at that photograph, while formulas, drawings, and designs took shape in his mind.

After a lapse of time which I had scarcely noticed, Korolev came back. He was smiling, and his eyes sparkled. Obviously, he was pleased with the conference that had just taken place.

"They've left! Let's sit down. We have things to talk about."

Back in Korolev's office, I took a seat opposite him. Immediately, he looked at his watch. With him, keeping check on the time seemed to be automatic.

Before taking up the subject of films about space, I handed him several books of mine, all warmly inscribed to him.

"Thank you," he said. "I always like to have books given to me. I collect them and treasure them. Thanks again."

The day before I had shown Korolev the rough cut of a film. (I was consulting him on all stages of its production—from the original treatment to the final cut.) Now he demanded that the director eliminate some of the frames in which he figured.

"There should be more emphasis on the cosmonauts, the scientists, the workers, and the technicians," he said. "After all, our work is carried on by a very large collective. But you've concentrated on the chief designer . . . Why, I'd be embarrassed in front of the people I'm working with on this entirely new job of ours. Do you know what I mean?"

When we were through talking about space, films, and Tsiolkovsky, Korolev took up the subject of linguistics. "Earth-dwellers," he said, "have given themselves the name of 'man.' But they have provided themselves with 'subcategories' of that concept: a European, an American, a Muscovite, a Leningrader . . ."

Korolev rose heavily from his chair, frowned as though in pain, and gazed out the window. Then he sat down again and continued: "In any case, and under any circumstances, all these species and subspecies mean one and the same thing: a human being. And Yuri Gagarin's flight changed everything. People began to regard the earth as a part of the universe. And now they realize that our planet is not the only place where humans can live."

He picked up a piece of chalk and, on a small slate, drew a circle representing the earth. Then he dotted the whole slate with little white chalk marks.

As he went on dotting the slate, he asked: "Today we've begun to think seriously about other civilizations and the possibility of encountering them—isn't that so? This is not a dream or a utopia but a reality of our time. But while thinking of Martians and Venusians, we have naturally wanted to keep for ourselves—and only for ourselves—our distinctive name of earthlings. We have gradually become accustomed to it."

On the slate, he drew some white lines from the dots to the earth. Then, after some reflection, he put down the piece of chalk and turned back to his desk.

He sighed, and exclaimed: "Yes, we are earthlings. But the time will come when we are Martians and Venusians and moonmen, just as—today—we are Russians, Americans, Muscovites, and Europeans."

As though he had just remembered something, Korolev looked

at his watch, then rubbed his little finger along his eyebrow in a gesture of vexation.

"There isn't time enough for anything! But wait a minute! In my files I have a clipping from *Pravda*. It's that article you wrote under the title 'They Moonlanded.' That was a very accurate phrase —'moonlanded.'[1] Then it was a probe that landed on the moon. But the time will come when human beings will do the same. I keep daydreaming about that.

"Fine. They've 'moonlanded.' But what about Mars? What about Venus? What will you say then? Well, that's your job. We launch the space vehicles, and you writers find the right verb."

I asked Korolev to say something about the next flight and its unique features.

"As a matter of fact," he replied, "I've just written an article for the first issue of a journal called *Aviation and Cosmonautics*." He handed me a typescript. "Take a look at it while I talk with my co-workers." Then, glancing at the "monk's cell" next to his office, he asked: "Would it be more convenient for you to read it in that room?"

I took the typescript into the little adjoining room, where everything was quiet and cozy. Meantime, a conference was beginning in Korolev's office.

His article began as follows:

> The moon, Mars, Venus . . . The constellations of near and distant galaxies. Today we speak of flights into outer space, not in the language of a fantasist, but as a completely feasible task within the grasp of mankind—as a future development of Soviet science and engineering.
>
> Starting from the first manned flights into space, we must move on to the mastery and conquest of cosmic space. The successful flights of the spacecraft *Vostok*-1 and *Vostok*-2 provide convincing evidence that these problems can be successfully solved.

Without quoting S. P. Korolev's brilliant article in full, I should like to excerpt those passages in which he voices his ideas as

---

[1] The reference is to an invented Russian verb analagous to the French *alunir*.— Translator

to the future. In this connection it should be borne in mind that the time of writing was late 1961—shortly after the flights of Gagarin and Titov.

Korolev went on to say:

> The further conquest of space will make it possible, for example, to create systems of satellites making daily [synchronous] revolutions around our planet at an altitude of some 40,000 km, and to assure universal communications and the relaying of radio and television transmissions. Such an arrangement might prove more useful, economically, than the construction of radio relay systems over the whole surface of the earth.
>
> The great accuracy of movement of these satellites will provide a reliable basis for solving navigational problems for transoceanic ships and aircraft.
>
> The next problem is that of weather satellites. The future will witness the elaboration of special methods for acting on climatic conditions, a system of weather forecasting, etc.
>
> With a view to solving this or that problem associated with the conquest of space, it would not be useful in all cases to put one's own satellite into orbit. What is needed, obviously, is a well-thought-out system of orbital space assemblies in the form of satellites, stations, and other vehicles, eternally (or for a very long time) existing in their orbits around the earth and performing their assigned functions reliably and on schedule.
>
> Obviously, the designers and engineers, the builders of satellite spacecraft, still have much work to do in this field. Given the conditions of weightlessness, the assembling of such structures in space will involve some unique problems. Vast possibilities will open up in the field of design and the utilization of new materials, of solar energy, of creating (at first partially, then more fully) a biological cycle of substances for prolonged life support in cosmic space . . .

My reading was interrupted by Korolev, returning from what had obviously been a stimulating conference. "Did you find anything useful in that?" he asked matter-of-factly.

"It reads like science fiction. I can see, now, that the third flight will have to do with problems of creating orbital stations in which people can live and work."

The Chief Designer sat down behind his desk.

"In general, that's true," he said. "But it's still a long way to the kind of orbital stations Tsiolkovsky dreamed of. First of all, we have to see whether two spacecraft can be put into orbit together and make a team flight. Whether they can fly wing-to-wing, as aircraft do. There is a great deal to be done . . . There will be different kinds of flights—group flights, with big crews . . . Then we must find out whether a human being can live and work outside the spacecraft, in open space. For this purpose we'll have to design a new spaceship, different from the *Vostok*, with an air lock [transfer tunnel] for egress. And then? Then there'll be other craft. I keep thinking about the problem of docking. Without docking, and without maneuvering in orbit, it will be impossible to assemble an orbital station . . . Yes, we have lots to do . . . many problems to solve before an orbital station is created. We're the pathfinders, and things are never easy for a pathfinder . . ."

Korolev took me through the conference room and into his secretary's office, where another group of designers, engineers, and scientists were waiting for him. Then he indicated me with a glance. "The thing is, we were discussing a film."

"But you're not late, Sergei Pavlovich," his secretary told him. "In fact, you're one minute early . . ."

I walked out of the "mousetrap" and got into my car. The green eye of the traffic light winked, and I joined the stream of traffic.

The Space Brothers

The snow had been cleared from the asphalt of the main street of Star Town. Along each side of it, painted a gleaming silver, were frames of light metal tubing in which big portraits of future cosmonauts were to be placed. As yet, however, there were no portraits; and through the empty frames one could see dark spruce trees, green pines, the white trunks of birches—and, on a post, a road sign. On its yellow disk were the words NO HONKING! SILENCE! And painted against the yellow background, by way of a symbol, was a black bugle.

Every day, a bus carrying the cosmonauts went along this street past the empty frames. They would sing a song they themselves had made up—"Landysh" (Lily of the Valley) and jokingly try to guess whose portrait would take its place beside those of Yuri Gagarin and Gherman Titov.

I went into a small building painted yellow—the headquarters building—and then into the office of Evgeny Anatolevich Karpov.

"After Gherman Titov's flight," Karpov told me, "some very thorough scientific work was done by way of processing the huge quantity of telemetric data gathered, during that flight, on the functioning of the cosmonaut's organism and on his life-support systems. We also analyzed and evaluated all of Titov's own sensations while he was in orbit."

"And what happened?" I asked.

"Nothing to really be frightened about. During the first minute of weightlessness, Gherman had the sensation that he was flying in an inverted position, as though 'hanging there with his head down' —in his own words. But after a minute, or perhaps ninety seconds, this sensation vanished."

"Is that all?" I asked. "Then why so much anxiety, and so many changes in the training program?"

Karpov ran his hand through his curly hair. "We don't have the right," he said very seriously, "to ignore these phenomena. It is our duty to study each new phenomenon very carefully, and to draw conclusions from it."

He reflected for a moment then added: "As a result of our studying this phenomenon, two serious problems were solved. Methods of conditioning and training future cosmonauts have been corrected, and we have refined the methods for evaluating the stability of the vestibular apparatus. Also, light has been thrown on the conditions that will obtain during a more prolonged state of weightlessness in a manned space flight. As you know, the next flight is to be a team flight—a long one, demanding great efforts from the cosmonauts. Frankly, we're taking quite a risk. The thing is, we don't yet have adequate scientific data on how well a person can bear up under prolonged weightlessness. But since zero gravity can't be successfully reproduced on earth, the risk is unavoidable."

"Could you tell me who, in your opinion, are the most likely candidates for the flight?"

"I'd say the choice will fall upon Andriyan Nikolayev and Pavel Popovich."

"Why choose two men who are so unalike? One of them—and I mean Popovich—is a happy-go-lucky daredevil always bubbling over with good spirits. But Nikolayev is a model of reserve and icy composure."

Evgeny Anatolevich frowned slightly. "There's nothing accidental about that. In a prolonged flight it is important to test persons of differing personalities, to see how each withstands weightlessness, how each feels and whether they perform their tasks differently."

In the film *The Space Brothers,* dealing with the lives and flights of Andriyan Nikolayev and Pavel Popovich, I included a sequence shot by a camera concealed in the isolation chamber. On the fifteenth day of Andriyan Nikolayev's confinement—in total solitude and oppressive silence—the doctor in charge decided to run some tests.

"Get ready to shoot," he told us. "Now that Nikolayev is accustomed to silence and solitude—and of course fatigued by that solitude—we're going to test him. Look and listen."

Nikolayev, wearing a blue sweatsuit wound about with leads from the sensors taped to his body, his head swathed in a rubber bandage holding electrodes against his forehead, was sitting at a table and concentrating on writing in his logbook. In front of him was a green-shaded reading lamp, some pencils, a few books, and the instruments from which he read the orders given him by the doctors conducting the experiment.

The doctor in charge made a signal with his hand, and the lights in the isolation chamber went out. First a rustle could be heard like that made by the slithering of a snake—or perhaps more like the scratching sound of a mouse gnawing on something. Then came a muffled, frightening explosion, followed by moans and wails at which even I—a man standing in a well-lighted laboratory and realizing that this was only an experiment—felt my flesh creep. At that same moment the doctors switched on deafening howlers that could infuriate anyone. Lights flashed through the chamber: scarlet, light blue, white and green. The blinding flashes of light, combined with the howling and hissing, was enough to drive any other man out of his mind. And Nikolayev?

During the showing of *The Space Brothers,* viewers could see on the screen everything I have described above; and they could hear the cacophony. At the same time they could watch the behavior of Nikolayev as filmed by the hidden camera. What he did was to set his logbook to one side, cross his arms on his chest, and wait imperturbably for the lights to come on again and the frenzy of noise to subside.

"He's not a human being—he's all iron!" the doctor in charge exclaimed.

"He could listen to that for a year!" another doctor agreed. "It's all the same to him!"

In the isolation chamber, the regular lights came on and the noise died down. Nikolayev, who had been sitting pensively with his arms crossed on his chest, calmly picked up the logbook and, as if nothing had happened, resumed making his entries.

With Popovich, we shot a similar sequence. He had been sitting in the isolation chamber for about two weeks and had got used to the silence and solitude. Unlike Nikolayev, he sang from morning till night, whistled his favorite Ukrainian tunes, and even danced. He was a restless type with a lively, dynamic personality. One sometimes had the impression that nothing could make Pavel Popovich sit still for so much as an hour or two.

He was subjected to the same thing as Nikolayev. The isolation chamber was darkened; then came the sounds of hissing, grunting, and whistling. Eerie lights flashed, and alarm bells were rung. During those moments—when the blinding lights flashed through the chamber, illuminating in turn the cosmonaut's face, the instruments, the chair, the walls—we could see Popovich's wide-open blue eyes. He was laughing, waving his arms in pleasure, and even jumping about. "Wow, they're pouring it on!" he shouted. "They're really pouring it on!" The regular lights came on in the chamber. Popovich, in gay spirits and happily excited, reached for the logbook and his fountain pen. Then, whistling a tune, he began to write down what had happened to him in the isolation chamber.

He went on writing, whistling and singing a Ukrainian folk song about the Dnieper and the free life. He sang with feeling—as he used to do on the stage at the metallurgical technical school in Magnitka, when he was in flying school, and when he was with his air force unit.

While the cosmonauts were training for their flights in *Vostok*-3 and *Vostok*-4, a new phase began in the exploration of space by means of pilotless automatic vehicles. The first satellite in the *Kosmos* series was launched on 16 March 1962. Like a number of others subsequently put into orbit around the earth, *Kosmos* made it possible to study the structure of the ionosphere, its temporary shifts in latitude and longitude, and in particular, the electronic concentration every one or two kilometers. Some of the *Kosmos* satellites were long-lived geophysical stations designed to investigate high-speed charged particles and meteor showers in the upper layers of the atmosphere.

Kosmos-4 was launched on 26 April 1962, equipped with a

special counter to measure the intensity of radiation caused when its outer skin was bombarded by electrons.

Kosmos-7, whose mission was to investigate the radiation caused by the explosion of an American nuclear device, was launched on 28 June 1962. This was necessary in order to check on radiation safety for the impending team flight of *Vostok*-3 and *Vostok*-4.

The twelfth of April 1962—the anniversary of the first manned space flight—was declared a national holiday—Cosmonautics Day. In Star Town, cosmonauts, engineers, all went about congratulating one another. Yuri Gagarin, the real culprit (hero) of the festivities got the lion's share of the congratulations. A holiday issue of the bulletin-board newspaper was put out—one on which the editor-in-chief, Alesksei Leonov, worked especially hard. And the cosmonauts reminisced about the first flight. That evening they went to Moscow for a great rally.

After the holiday came more training, course work, flights, and a detailed study of the spacecraft . . . Then it was time for the preflight examinations.

Long tables covered with green felt were set up in the big room, and sketches of spacecraft, charts, maps, and calculations decorated the walls. A spacesuit was displayed as a special exhibit. As in a classroom, there was a blackboard, complete with chalk and erasers.

When the examining board had assembled, its chairman, Lieutenant General N. P. Kamanin, asked the cosmonauts to come in. Andriyan Nikolayev, Pavel Popovich, Valery Bykovsky, and Vladimir Komarov walked in with soldierly precision, stood at attention before the examining board, and reported they were ready to be examined.

My heart pounded as I listened to the reports of Andriyan Nikolayev and Pavel Popovich. To stand up and speak before a council of famous scientists was an awesome thing. But fears proved groundless. The cosmonauts performed extremely well. Their answers were excellent, and they were given high marks.

In addition to written questions, they had to answer direct oral questions from the scientists. Thus Korolev asked Nikolayev about the manual control of the spacecraft. Cupping his chin in his hand, Korolev listened closely, nodding his head in approval from time to time. He also questioned Popovich; and when the latter answered, smiled at him. Apparently the chief designer was recalling something very amusing having to do with Popovich's jokes and facetious remarks.

"Very good," Korolev said. "Very good!"

Then Kaminin read the decision of the examining board, recommending that Andriyan Nikolayev and Pavel Popovich make the flight in *Vostok*-3 and *Vostok*-4.

Their backups also received a high rating.

Next came the preflight meeting of the cosmonauts. When it was over, Andriyan Nikolayev went home to his spacious bachelor apartment. Soon it was crowded with friends and acquaintances. They had brought fruits and wine and were laying the table, apparently unaware that Andriyan was standing alone by the window.

He wanted to gather his thoughts, having grown accustomed to a certain degree of introversion and self-analysis. And now he was wondering whether he realized the imminence of that moment when he would leave his bachelor apartment—where his friends were now pouring out goblets of wine—and set out on that important voyage for which he had trained so long and unrelentingly.

"Andrei! Come to the table!" his friends shouted. He left the window, sat down at the table, and raised his glass.

In the same apartment building where Nikolayev lived, Pavel Popovich was also making ready for his departure. His pretty, energetic wife, Marina Lavrentevna Vasilyeva-Popovich—herself a famous racing pilot—and his daughter Natasha were helping with the preparations. Natasha kept climbing into her father's arms, playing with him, and making him carry her on his shoulders. Then she would help her mother pack daddy's suitcase, putting in shirts, handkerchiefs, and ties.

"Well, daughter, everything seems to be in good shape, doesn't it?" her father asked.

Natasha, the acknowledged poet of the household, immediately made up a verse:

> Papa's going far away,
> We've packed his things nicely,
> Come back soon, Papa dear,
> For me and for my friends.

Popovich picked Natasha up in his arms, rocked her, and kissed her. His eyes expressed so much love—such a strong feeling—that I felt a pang in my heart.

Marina cast a stern glance at her daughter. "Natasha, off to bed with you!"

But Popovich didn't want to part from Natasha. He rumpled her hair and sent her off to bed. Then he uncorked a bottle of Cahors wine and set some plums and apples on the table. Everyone who had come to this going-away party raised his glass: "Bon voyage!"

Popovich had received permission to spend the night at home. But Nikolayev left his apartment at 11:00 P.M. and went to the so-called dispensary—more accurately, the cosmonauts' hospital.

At the hospital, before "lights out," everyone had assembled for a planning session—the last planning session to prepare for the flight from Star Town.

Nikolayev reported: "All supplies are on hand: thermos bottles, fruits, and fuel."

On every other occasion before the flight to the launch complex at Baikonur, the cosmonauts had invariably elected Andriyan Niko-layev as their "quartermaster," since he was a thoughtful, punctual, and scrupulous provider of foodstuffs and drinking water. And even this time, when Nikolayev himself was to make a flight, his friends—mindful of the tradition—insisted that he, Cosmonaut Number Three, play his usual role as quartermaster.

After the planning session, Andriyan took leave of his friends and went to the room where Yuri Gagarin and Gherman Titov had spent the night before flying off from Star Town to the cosmodrome. He undressed, opened the window, drew up the shade just a bit, and crawled under the blanket. Then he turned off the light on the night table and went to sleep.

The next day he and Popovich were at the cosmodrome.

On 6 August Gherman Titov had suggested a celebration of the anniversary of the second manned space flight, and invited S.P. The other cosmonauts liked the idea and set about making the preparations. They knew that Korolev liked flowers. But where could they find any on the sun-scorched steppe?

Pavel Popovich suggested that they ask some cottagers who had

83. Driving the carrier-rocket
with the spaceship *Voskhod*
to the launching pad of
Baikonur Cosmodrome.

84. A cabin of the *Voskhod*
series multiseater spaceship.
In the center, the instrument
panel with a globe, below a
porthole with *Vsor* optical
device.

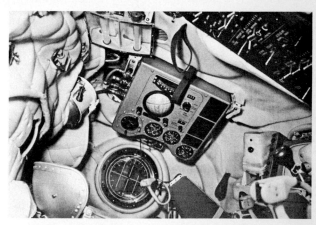

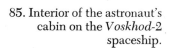

85. Interior of the astronaut's
cabin on the *Voskhod*-2
spaceship.

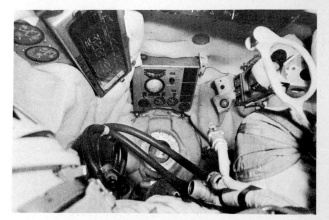

86. Nearing the launching pad of Baikonur Cosmodrome, 12 October 1964. The team of the first multiseater *Voskhod* spaceship: Vladimir Komarov, Boris Yegorov, and Konstantin Feoktistov.

87. The launching pad of the Baikonur Cosmodrome, 12 October 1964. Yuri Gagarin, pilot-cosmonaut of the USSR, is wishing Feoktistov good luck on the flight. (PUBLISHED FOR THE FIRST TIME IN 1971.)

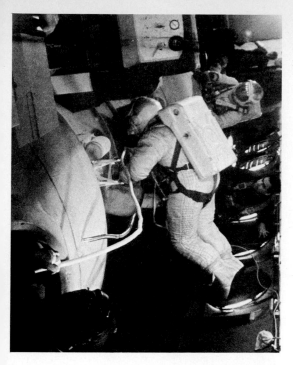

88. Practicing the transfer between spaceships in a condition of weightlessness in a flying laboratory.

89. Aleksei Leonov is training for his walk in space by practicing orientation and balance co-ordination in a simulated weightless environment.

90. The *Voskhod*-2 spaceship in orbit. The historic flight, during which man for the first time stepped into the cosmos, began on 18 March 1965 at 11:34 Moscow time.

In photo: Cosmonaut Aleksei Leonov is entering the lock chamber.

91. Aleksei Leonov saying good-by to his wife before leaving for the cosmodrome. Moscow, March 1965.

92. Cosmonauts Aleksei Leonov, Pavel Belyayev, and other cosmonauts going to a training session in the spaceship's cabin accompanied by doctors and testers.

93. On 18 March 1965 cosmonaut Aleksei Leonov, in his spacesuit, comes up to be lifted to the spaceship.

94. Pavel Belyayev, commander of *Voskhod*-2, and Aleksei Leonov, second pilot, inside the space capsule before takeoff. Baikonur Cosmodrome, 18 March 1965.

(RIGHT)

97. On 19 March 1965, spacecraft
commander Pavel Belyayev, aboard
the *Voskhod*-2, received clearance
to return to earth. At this point,
Belyayev discovered that the
automatic orientation system
connected with his braking system
had failed. He had to switch on
the manual attitude control system.
This first experiment in landing by
manual control was a success, and
at 12:02 Moscow time, 19 March
1965, the *Voskhod*-2 made a soft
landing in a forest 180 kilometers
northwest of Perm.
(PUBLISHED FOR THE FIRST TIME
IN 1971).

95, 96. Twelve historic minutes.
On 18 March 1965 Soviet cosmonaut
Aleksei Leonov walked in space.
The earth is spread more than
400 kilometers below. Only twelve
minutes, but they proved the
possibility of working in outer space.
These stills show some moments of
Aleksei Leonov's walk in space.

98. The historic "walk-in-space" flight is ended. The *Voskhod*-2 has landed 180 kilometers northwest of the city of Perm.

In photo: The recovery team has come to the place where the *Voskhod*-2 has landed. In the center, Aleksei Leonov.

99. At the cosmodrome. The *Soyuz* spaceships are delivered here for thorough systems testing.

100. The Komarovs at tea.

flower gardens. They gladly made a gift of their precious flowers to the cosmonauts.

A festive spirit reigned in the cozy room. Andriyan Nikolayev laid the table, decorated it, and asked his friends to sit down. But they all decided to wait for the Chief. Would he come? Or wouldn't he? After all, he was very busy. He had to launch one space vehicle after another. It was a pioneering job and very complicated.

But then the door opened quietly, and in came Korolev—tired, with bloodshot eyes. The cosmonauts gave him a warm welcome and asked him to the table.

"Thanks, friends," he said. "This get-together was a wonderful idea. An anniversary like this one shouldn't be forgotten . . . Yes, a year has gone by already . . . and we're about to make another flight. It will be considerably more complicated. It should give us the answers to many questions and show us if our calculations were correct."

Korolev told the cosmonauts how anxious he felt before and during every launch. Even at this late date, he told them, he had to check everything many times over, until he was sure of success. He looked affectionately at Nikolayev and Popovich, and everyone understood that in coming to this friendly gathering he wanted once again to give them faith in their success—to sustain their good spirits and cheerful mood.

On the night of 10 August, Andriyan Nikolayev and his backup, Valery Bykovsky, occupied the same room in which Yuri Gagarin and Gherman Titov had slept before Gagarin was launched. In commemoration of this event, portraits of the two cosmonauts had been hung on the walls above the beds.

Nikolayev chose the bed on which Gherman Titov had slept before the launch. He lay down and went off to sleep immediately. He was unaware that, twice during the night, Korolev visited the cosmonauts' cottage and asked the doctors how the two men were sleeping, then went back to the launch pad.

Nikolayev awoke promptly at the scheduled time. He did his setting-up exercises, ate breakfast, put on his spacesuit, and hurried off to the greenish-blue bus.

Popovich rode in the bus with him. When they caught sight of the rocket glittering in the sunlight, Popovich announced with a completely serious expression on his face: "*Vostok*-3 is ready, sir."[1]

On 11 August 1962, at 11:30 A.M., the last command rang out: "Liftoff!"

"Full speed ahead!" Nikolayev said approvingly. And he reported over his voice radio: "Everything normal."

Vostok-3 was accurately injected into its orbit with a perigee of 183 kilometers and an apogee of 251 kilometers above the earth's surface.

Later, some reporters asked Korolev what character traits he most prized in Andriyan Nikolayev. Sergei Pavlovich answered: "Equanimity and reliability."

In their preparatory work for this longer space flight, the design engineers—under the direction of Korolev—had seen to it that things were very convenient for the cosmonaut. Thus *Vostok*-3 was provided with an improved communications system, the latest-model television cameras, and special automatic equipment assuring two-way communications between the two spacecraft while in flight. Also, the contour couch had been made more convenient, enabling the cosmonaut to take the stress of G-forces more easily.

The pilots of the first two spacecraft had remained strapped to the couch throughout the flight. At that time, the flight directors had not yet decided to free the cosmonaut from the restraining straps and let him move about at will within the cabin. They were apprehensive of a great many unforeseen developments that might take place. For instance, what would happen to the cosmonaut if, after floating about in the cabin, he tried to get back to the contour couch but couldn't? No one could help him . . . This would create an emergency situation fraught with serious consequences.

Nikolayev, however, had instructions to make the experiment—a risky one at the time—of leaving the contour couch. He had long been training for this experiment. On several occasions, he had made flights in a "zero-gravity swimming pool" aboard an aircraft, leaving the contour couch in the "pool" and coming back to it. But it is one thing to make the experiment under the conditions of the earth's atmosphere—in an aircraft, with friends and instructors standing by. To do it in cosmic space is something else.

[1] "*Vostok-Tri podan.*" The phrase suggests a butler announcing that breakfast is served, a porter announcing that one's carriage has been brought up, etc.—Translator

Over the voice radio, Korolev asked Nikolayev: "How are you feeling?"

"Everything is in order. I feel fine. I'm ready to carry out my tasks," Nikolayev replied.

He had been advised to use great care when making the experiment of leaving the contour couch: that he should move cautiously and slowly, freeing himself first from the left strap, then from the right—but in no case making abrupt movements. Then, when he felt that the straps were no longer holding him down on the couch, he should try slowly to get up.

Cosmonaut Number Three followed this advice. Unhurriedly, he removed the shoulder straps. Now nothing was holding him down. He made a few movements and immediately rose up to the top of the cabin. It turned out that a person in a state of weightlessness could move freely about in the cabin without encountering any difficulties. All Nikolayev had to do was touch one side of the cabin, and his body would immediately move in the opposite direction. And when he touched the top, he would instantly go down to the contour couch. This first "free swim" lasted about one hour.

Later, Nikolayev reported: "It was an amazingly pleasant state of both body and soul, not to be compared to anything else. You don't weigh anything, you aren't supported by anything, and yet you can do everything. Your mind is clear, your thoughts precise. All your movements are co-ordinated. Both vision and hearing are perfect. You see everything and hear everything transmitted from the ground. There was no trouble with my vestibular apparatus, either before or in that condition [weightlessness], and no vegetative dysfunctions."

Back in his contour couch, Nikolayev fastened on the restraining straps and then recorded his sensations in the log. This done, he reported to Ground Control—in a delighted tone of voice—the successful completion of the experiment.

In view of what had happened on the second flight, Professor Yazdovsky had warned Nikolayev that in his sixth or seventh orbit he might experience symptoms like those of seasickness. The scientists were waiting attentively to see what would happen to Nikolayev on his sixth and seventh orbits. But nothing happened. Cosmonaut Number Three was in good spirits and felt fine. The changes made in the cosmonauts' training program, with a view to long flights, had borne good fruit.

There was one more new feature noted by millions of people. For the first time, a television broadcast was made from a spaceship. As Andriyan Nikolayev orbited in *Vostok*-3, he was visible on the light-blue screens of millions of television sets.

Nikolayev smiled at his audience and tried to show them what weightlessness was like by letting his logbook or a pencil float about. Or again, he would undo his straps and float about himself, cheerfully waving his hand.

The chief purpose of the flight was to have two spacecraft function simultaneously in orbit. The first team flight was to provide the answers to many questions. For instance: Could two cosmonauts fly "wing-to-wing" as if in aircraft, and talk to each other and to Ground Control? Wasn't it dangerous for the craft to come close together?

With a view to carrying out this program, another spacecraft, *Vostok*-4, was launched on 12 August 1962, at 11:02 A.M., and injected into orbit. It was piloted by Pavel Romanovich Popovich. Now two spacecraft were in orbit at the same time. No such experiment had ever before been made.

At the moment when *Vostok*-4 was launched, *Vostok*-3 had already completed eighteen revolutions around the earth and covered more than 740,000 kilometers. The initial orbital period for *Vostok*-4 was 88.5 minutes. Its perigee was 180 kilometers, and its apogee 254 kilometers. The two spaceships were within close range of each other.

In commenting on this new space event, Korolev noted that the difference in orbital inclination between the two spacecraft was only a few minutes of arc, and the difference in their distances from the earth's surface was only a few kilometers; that is, less than one two-thousandth of the orbital radius. At the moment of *Vostok*-4's injection into orbit, the two craft were at a distance of 6.5 kilometers from each other. This meant that, for the first time, two spacecraft had successfully been brought close together— something of great importance in implementing the program for assembling orbit stations and laboratories in the future.

The participants in this first team flight, Andriyan Nikolayev and Pavel Popovich, reported to Ground Control that everything was going well; that they felt fine; and that the on-board instruments and systems were functioning perfectly. Also, reliable two-way communication had been established between *Vostok*-3 and *Vostok*-4.

Then came a new development. Nikolayev, who was manually controlling his craft, looked out of a viewport and actually saw *Vostok*-4, piloted by Popovich. Yuri Gagarin, who was acting as "CapCom," warmly congratulated his friends on their success.

The flight continued. The following excerpt from the tape of their conversations, gives a good idea of the cosmonauts' conditions.

> *Nikolayev* (*on board* Vostok-3): Everything is going along well. I read you loud and clear. I feel excellent.
> *Popovich* (*on board* Vostok-4): I can see the earth through the clouds. On the right, through the viewport, I see a very dark sky. My mood is splendid. Everything is going normally.
> *Gagarin* (*at Ground Control*): Everything is very good, friends. I congratulate you. See you soon, back on earth.

Several times during the flight, both cosmonauts unfastened their restraining straps and left their contour seats. They maintained communications with each other, Nikolayev using the code name "Falcon" (*Sokol*), and Popovich, "Golden Eagle" (*Berkut*). Falcon passed on his own experience to his friend; the two of them traded impressions and even sang duets.

The images of the cosmonauts transmitted by the television cameras were repeatedly relayed by Central Television, USSR, and *Intervideniye:* "cosmovision" became an integral part of television programs.

And there was one more novelty worthy of note. On this team flight, Pavel Popovich acted as the world's first TV commentator from space:

> Attention! Attention! I'm speaking to you from the Soviet spacecraft *Vostok*-4. The spaceship is passing over the Pacific Ocean. In the cabin the lights are on, but outside it is night. Through the first viewport I can see the earth beneath a heavy cloud cover. In the Vzor I can now see the moon. What a beauty! She looks more bulky than from down on earth: you have the feeling of seeing a ball surrounded by

emptiness . . . The earth—or rather, the clouds—have a grayish cast.

The spacecraft is flying at an incredible speed, so the view keeps changing. Now I can see a starry sky through the right viewport. It is inky black. The big, bright stars are visible as from on earth, but they don't twinkle. The little ones look like bright pin points.

Oh, wait just a minute! I have to eat my second breakfast, according to my routine. I'm going to have a sausage, sandwiches, and cherry juice.

Now that's something! I'm skipping the rest of my breakfast, because the spacecraft is coming out of the shadow. What a view! A person on earth will never see anything like it! This is the cosmic dawn! Just look! The earth's horizon is a vivid wine color; then, without any smooth transition, a dark blue band appears. Next comes a bright blue band, shading off into the dark sky. Now this band keeps widening, growing, spreading out, and the sun appears. The horizon turns orange and a more delicate, lighter blue. Beautiful!

By the morning of 15 August the flight program had been completed. This time the planned touchdown point was not on the banks of the Volga but in Kazakhstan, at latitude 48° north, where the steppe spread out over hundreds of kilometers.

At 9:24 A.M. the retrorockets of *Vostok*-3 were fired, and six minutes later the same thing happened on board *Vostok*-4. One after the other, both spacecraft began to descend. When they had passed through the zone of high temperatures and heavy G-loads, the cosmonauts were separated from their spaceships in their ejection seats, and their bright-orange parachutes opened above them.

Andriyan Nikolayev touched down at 9:52 on 15 August 1962, near the city of Karkaralinsk in the Karagandinskaya Oblast. The duration of Nikolayev's flight, from the moment of liftoff to his ejection from *Vostok*-3, was 94 hours, 9 minutes, and 59 seconds. In the course of that time he had covered 2,639,600 kilometers, making more than sixty-four revolutions around the earth.

Pavel Popovich touched down at 9:59 near the village of Atasu in the Karagandinskaya Oblast. In the course of 70 hours, 43 minutes, and 48 seconds his spacecraft had flown 1,981,050 kilometers and orbited the earth forty-eight times.

After completion of the team flight and the welcoming ceremonies for the cosmonauts in Moscow, I asked Yuri Gagarin to give me his impressions of the experiment and tell me something of his own plans. I located him in a classroom at Star Town, where he was attending a class in celestial mechanics. The session had just come to an end, and Gagarin was picking up his books. In his full-dress Air Force uniform, with the gold medals glittering on his breast, he had a somewhat festive appearance. (The fact was that in another hour or so he had to go to Moscow to address a workers' rally.)

"The flight was very interesting, and very important," Gagarin told me. Then, looking pensive, he went over to a big globe and began to turn it slowly. Painted continents and oceans passed before his eyes. Not long ago he had viewed them from space.

Giving me a serious look, he repeated: "It was a very interesting flight—very important . . . I was responsible for maintaining communications with the cosmonauts during the countdown and the active portions of the flight[2] . . . And so I talked with Nikolayev and Popovich several times during those four days. Falcon and Golden Eagle were in good spirits—vigorous and cheerful. They felt fine. A space flight, you know, is not like taking a stroll. There's a lot of work to do—every hour and every minute. The cosmonauts were ready for any emergency. We still know too little about that new milieu that Tsiolkovsky talked about as the future habitat of mankind.

"What can I tell you about the results? Now it is evident that man can live and work in space for a long period of time. This is a real and important discovery. It is to be expected that in the future, men will make even longer flights of greater duration."

Gagarin turned the big globe, watching with evident pleasure as the continents passed under his gaze. Then he brought it to a stop with his finger, and continued:

"It's important to note the perfect functioning of the mechanisms. The engineers built an excellent spacecraft, and excellent rocket, and splendid engines. But in my opinion, aerospace engineering will go even farther. We will have better spacecraft and better engines. We cosmonauts are grateful to our scientists, designers,

[2] In Russian, the phrase "active portion of the flight" generally refers to powered ascent. But when used in the plural, it may also refer to subsequent burns.—Translator

and workers for their great labors, their discoveries, and their inventions. The team flight yielded much new information for science and engineering. It encouraged all of us and opened up fine prospects for the future."

Gagarin smiled boyishly, showing an even row of sparklingly white teeth, and spun the globe vigorously.

"What more can I tell you? Let me change the subject. I want to thank all of you film people for those movies. Now you can get ready for a new job.

"You film people are sly! Are you doing a film on Valentina Tereshkova? If so, you're doing the right thing. I'm sure she will make a flight. And it will be a remarkable one!

"At first glance," Gagarin said thoughtfully, "it might look like a duplication—the same thing that Andrei and Pavel did. But that's not true. For the first time, a woman—Valentina—will make a space flight. But Valery Bykovsky will lift off before she does, in the first spacecraft. He will remain in space longer than anyone. Bykovsky is perfectly trained. He was Nikolayev's backup."

Gagarin began to spin the globe again and went on: "I keep thinking about the technical progress in the conquest of space, and it seems to me that this is a very complex process. One flight will follow another: they'll be like steps on a ladder up to the sky. Flights will become routine, everyday matters. That's essential. And when some great discovery is made, it will be a result of the efforts made by everyone who has climbed that ladder to the sky. And in time, even the great discoveries will become steps of the ladder, too. That's how it's always been."

"Seagull" and "Hawk"

Women had begun to show up at Star Town: pilots, parachutists, engineers, and designers. Outstanding among them was Valentina Tereshkova—a slender girl with short hair who wore simple, light dresses and had formerly worked in a textile plant. She had come from Yaroslavl, on the banks of the Volga, where she had worked at the Krasny Perekop Textile Combine.

I remember that evening after dinner when the female cosmonaut candidates first met the regular cosmonaut detachment. At first things were a bit awkward. But this feeling was soon dispelled by Yuri Gagarin, the leader of the regular cosmonaut team, who warmly welcomed the "female reinforcements."

And Pavel Popovich, extending his arms in a handsome gesture, told them: "It's like this, girls. You'll have a hard time, but we'll help you. We've had our own share of difficulties. But we're sure all will go well with you. The main thing is to keep up your spirits, keep your mind on the goal, and never lose heart when things go wrong. And if things get really tough, we'll sing. With singing comes joy."

Sometime before the girls' arrival at Star Town, Yuri Gagarin had called a meeting of the cosmonauts and told them: "Some lady cosmonauts are on their way to join us. Let's be considerate and helpful toward them. There must be no teasing or anything else offensive to them. We already have more than enough pranksters and wits as it is . . ."

In the laboratories, preparations were made for receiving the women. The training methods to be used with them were considered from all angles, and equipment was made ready for their training sessions.

Exercising his rights as leader of the cosmonaut detachment, Yuri Gagarin acted as a guide for the group of women, showing them through the newly organized museum of Star Town. Needless to say, we hurried there with our movie cameras. One sequence we shot for the film called *The Road to the Stars* showed Gagarin familiarizing the women (including Tereshkova) with models of Soviet rockets, satellites, and spacecraft.

Back in her home town of Yaroslavl, Valentina operated a loom in a textile plant and demonstrated a thorough understanding of its workings. She was equally familiar with the layout of the plant and the entire combine. And she had come to feel at home at the local flying school and loved to make parachute jumps. But at Star Town, a whole new world opened up for her.

"The exploration of space," Gagarin told Valentina as though speaking in a lecture hall, "involves two methods: the use of probes and the use of manned spacecraft." Then he showed her models, photographs, and drawings illustrating a series of Soviet space probes—those which had flown to the moon and photographed its previously unknown far side and those sent to Mars and Venus.

In explaining the purpose of manned flights, Gagarin brought in Tsiolkovsky's notion of creating orbiting "celestial islands"—gigantic manned satellites. He was fascinated by Tsiolkovsky's ideas about man's moving into space and populating the boundless stellar ocean.

Valentina soon made herself at home in Star Town and got to know everyone. Then her training sessions began. At various times she could be seen on the madly whirling centrifuge, in the thermochamber, on the "striped rotator," in the decompression chamber, on the "Rhine wheel," and in the quiet of the isolation chamber. The former loom operator withstood all these tests.

Valentina was an unusually resolute and purposeful girl. When we were getting some takes of her in the quiet and solitude of the isolation chamber, I was much impressed by certain apparently trifling details. As she awoke on what I seem to remember as the twelfth morning, she opened her bright eyes wide and smiled— although she could not see anyone. What a wonderful, innocent smile that was! Then, in an abrupt movement, she threw off her plaid shawl, stretched, and checked the position of the sensors on her body. This done, she opened a drawer of the table in front of her and took out a mirror.

As I watched her through the porthole I was thinking: Not long ago various psychologists here and there in the world were maintaining that the isolation chamber was absolutely contraindicated for a woman; that a woman could not bear up under such oppressive solitude and nerve-wracking silence . . . And here was Valentina, disproving this theory beyond any doubts. One was convinced that she would dispel the doubts of the skeptics and prove that a woman could do anything.

Before Valentina took her turn on the centrifuge, the doctors, biologists, physiologists, and psychologists had held several discussions among themselves. The big question was: Should they finally agree to putting a woman through the test on the "devil's merry-go-round"? Could the female organism withstand the great G-forces?

Then came the day of her "flight" on the centrifuge in the big, round room. I watched her as she came in, wearing her orange spacesuit. With her were some laboratory technicians, who helped her into the cabin. On the control panel, switches were flipped. The centrifuge came to life, and the little cabin was spun around furiously. I watched Tereshkova's face on the light-blue television screen: she seemed calm and was even smiling. Then, abruptly, she froze: the first (already noticeable) deformation of her face had occurred . . .

A ride on the centrifuge is rough—and sometimes even very painful—for a man. But for a woman? One might think it would be a hundred times worse for her.

Finally, the centrifuge came to a stop. The technicians hurried over to her—accompanied by Andriyan Nikolayev, who had been standing by the control panel.

She leaned back in the seat for a few moments, resting, then recovered herself. And when she stepped out into the glare of the klieg light, she was cheerful and in high spirits. Turning to Andriyan, she said jokingly: "So you thought only you men could

stand up to that "devil's merry-go-round"? Women can do anything!"

His friends on the cosmonaut team had begun to notice that
Andrei (they insisted on calling Andriyan Nikolayev "Andrei")
was trying to help Valentina in every possible way. The two of
them were often seen together in the gymnasium, in the library, in
the mess hall, and in the corridors of the classroom building.

Pavel Popovich explained: "They're both from the Volga country.
Andrei is from the Chuvash region, and Valentina is from Yaroslavl.
And all people from along the Volga are what you might call
neighbors—fellow countrymen. Then, too, of course, they're both
single—and that counts for something."

The other cosmonauts were full of admiration for Valentina's
perseverance and great strength of will as she completed all phases
of her training. They knew that, as a little girl, she had lost her
father, who was killed at the front. Her mother, Elena Fyodorovna,
who had long been a loom operator in Yaroslavl, had inculcated
in her children a willingness to work hard.

Valentina spent both her childhood and her youth in Yaroslavl,
an ancient Russian city (it is a thousand years old). These were
years of hardship. After graduation from school, she worked for a
few months at a tire plant. Then, at her mother's suggestion, she
took a new job at the Krasny Perekop Textile Combine. When she
got her first pay check, she hurried off to buy her mother a gift. She
did not get her flowers or perfume (the family's lot was hard in
those days) but, rather, a big, warm shawl. Her mother wept from
sheer happiness . . .

The young loom operator became a sportswoman: She developed
an interest in parachute jumping. She would get up at dawn and,
before going to work, hurry out to the flying club to practice.
She had her share of setbacks. Once, for instance, she came down in
the Volga and almost drowned. But she went on parachuting.
And it was at the Yaroslavl Flying Club that she conceived her
dream of making a space flight.

Andriyan Nikolayev became Valentina's tutor. He helped her in
her lessons, and set up a regular examination in the cabin of the
Vostok simulator. No sooner had Valentina taken her place in the
pilot's seat than Nikolayev's dark eyes were peering in through the

hatch. For our film, we got some takes of this examination, and recorded their conversation.

> *Nikolayev:* Now you're seated in the cabin of the spacecraft. What do you do next?
> *Tereshkova:* After taking my place in the cabin, I must check the functioning of the equipment . . .
> *Nikolayev:* Correct. That's good.
> *Tereshkova:* I begin by checking the equipment on the port side: the pilot's control panel, the instrument panel, the functioning of the shutters and the Vzor light filter . . .

As she answered her examiner's questions, Valentina pointed to the instruments, systems, and apparatuses involved.

> *Nikolayev:* In flight, how are you going to use the handle for manual control of orientation?

He stuck his strong, tanned hand through the hatch and grasped the handle. She reached out her own small, girlish hand; and quite unexpectedly, their fingers touched. Andriyan promptly withdrew his hand, and Valentina confidently proceeded with the manual orientation.

> *Tereshkova:* Using the manual control stick, you can orient the spacecraft along three axes: pitch, roll, and yaw.
> *Nikolayev:* Right. Everything's fine.

The next day I came across Valentina at the edge of the woods near one end of the athletic field. She was gathering wild strawberries and seemed pensive.

I, too, began looking for berries, asking Valentina in an offhand manner: "Do you feel you're ready to make the flight?"

"Speaking frankly?"

"Speaking frankly."

"In Yaroslavl I learned to make parachute jumps, but I never flew an airplane. And without that, I couldn't make a flight up there." She looked up at the sky. "And so now I'm 'bearing down hard'—as they say—on flying. Valery is helping me, and so is

Andrei. And I'm learning celestial mechanics. I'm working fast. I'm trying. In general, things seem to be going all right . . ."

We sat down on a hillock. Valentina proffered some of the strawberries in the palm of her slight, narrow hand. "Very tasty," she said.

I thanked her, tossed down a few berries, and then asked her about her girl friends—the other prospective cosmonauts.

"They're very good!" she exclaimed with real enthusiasm. "One of them is a really first-rate flier. For that matter, they're all good pilots. Some of them are college graduates, and other even have advanced degrees. I'm learning a lot from them. They're far ahead of me, but I'm not discouraged."

Later on, when I met up with Yuri Gagarin, I asked him for his opinion of Valentina Tereshkova.

"She was born for space."

"Has flying been difficult for her?"

"Valentina has amazing abilities. She is doing very well in flight training, celestial mechanics, and many other things. And she's modest. She's not afraid to say: 'This is something I don't know about. Help me.' And we help her. She may be thin and weak-looking at first glance, but she has great strength, energy, and will power. She's a real Russian woman."

Our talk shifted to the general subject of women's making space flights.

"Medicine and biology have established the fact," Gagarin said, "that the female organism possesses very great potential. It must be developed. Life offers many examples of rare staying powers and working capacity in women. During the war they performed miracles. And they will make a very good showing in space—I'm convinced of that. Before you know it, they'll set up a celestial matriarchy." Gagarin laughed. "As for Valentina, I've often watched her in training sessions and in the classroom. She's great! I'm convinced she'll come out on top in the examinations, and be the first woman to make a flight. For that matter, all the girls are first-rate. And they're all very well trained."

Although the summer was taken up with course work and strenuous training sessions, the cosmonauts had been concerned because Korolev had been hospitalized during the late summer. In September Gagarin brought very good news: Sergei Pavlovich Korolev had recovered and would soon be discharged from the hospital. Valentina was overjoyed. She remembered her meeting with him, his concerned attitude toward the new additions to the cosmonaut team, and the good wishes he had expressed to her personally.

Korolev was discharged from the hospital on 15 September 1962. He was in good spirits; and even mirthful.

"I was bored there—but now we can really get to work!" he said, looking around at his friends and acquaintances. "I thought out a lot of problems: things that have to be changed and revised . . . But how are the girls getting along in their training?"

The doctors had prescribed rest for Korolev, and he and his wife, Nina, went off to Sochi. Once there, however, he did not let a day pass without making telephone calls or sending off written instructions and orders. "Well, the cosmodrome has really got going!" his assistants exclaimed in delight.

In Sochi, Korolev conferred with Kamanin and Yazdovsky. Once again they had to decide which of the candidates would pilot the spacecraft on the next flight.

Throughout that winter, intensive preparations continued. In May, at a meeting of the State Commission, Valery Bykovsky was named commander of *Vostok*-5, and Valentina Tereshkova commander of *Vostok*-6.

The radio code names for Nikolayev and Popovich, it may be recalled, were "Falcon" and "Golden Eagle." For this flight, bird names were again employed. Bykovsky's code name was "Hawk" (*Yastreb*), and Tereshkova's was "Seagull" (*Chaika*).

"*Chaika!*" Tereshkova repeated pensively. "*Chaika!* . . . That's good. Thank you. I like it!" She was recalling the white-winged gulls soaring above the Volga in her part of the country, and the Chekhovian seagull on the dark curtain of the Moscow Art Theater.

Announcement of the approved radio code names is always a signal that a launch is imminent. Valentina made ready to leave for Baikonur. She ironed a dress, had her hair done at a beauty parlor, and when everything seemed to be ready, she sat down by a window and gave herself over to her thoughts. She would have liked very much to go to Yaroslavl: to see her mother and tell her about everything; to see her friends, her brother Volodya, and the instructors at the flying school. But there wasn't enough time left for the trip, so she called her mother on the telephone.

Later, Tereshkova told me: "Of all people on earth, Mama is the closest and dearest to me. She put all her strength and health into raising my older sister, my brother, and me. Ever since I came of age, I have tried to repay her for this with a daughter's tenderness and concern."

Valentina Tereshkova and Valery Bykovsky flew off to the cosmodrome. There, on 14 June 1963, Gherman Titov and his assistants helped to suit up Valentina's "space brother," Valery Bykovsky. Back when Titov had been making ready for his liftoff, Bykovsky had helped *him* put on his spacesuit.

"Try it out for freedom of movement," Titov advised him.

Bykovsky stood up to find out whether he was comfortable in the spacesuit he would be wearing for several days. He bent over in various directions. Everything was fine. He was ready.

At the time, neither Bykovsky nor Titov was aware that dramatic events had occurred at the launch pad. Owing to an error in the calculations for the liftoff, there had been a deviation from the technical documentation in carrying out one of the procedures. Korolev, badly worried, had ridden up in the elevator to the top of the space vehicle, and gone over to the egress hatch.

One of the technicians later recalled: "We had been informed via the intercom that—to put it mildly—Sergei Pavlovich was very displeased with us. We were expecting a 'bawling-out.' But when Sergei Pavlovich came up to where we were, he was outwardly calm. He asked us what had happened, and whether the mistake could be rectified. When he'd heard what we had to say, he gave us some advice and told us not to be in a hurry: that there was still time, and everything must be done just right. He stayed with us until the error had been corrected."

By the time Bykovsky had arrived at the launch pad, Korolev had come down in the elevator to the concrete slab. When he greeted the cosmonaut near the microphones, he behaved as if nothing had happened.

Vostok-5, piloted by Valery Fyodorovich Bykovsky, was put into orbit at 3:00 P.M. on 14 June 1963.

The first day's flight program called for physiological tests (in particular, tests of the vestibular apparatus), monitoring of the state of the cosmonaut's organism, maintaining comunications via short-wave and ultrashort-wave channels, observation of the earth's surface, and the sun and moon. During one orbit Bykovsky took over the controls to check the manual system of orientation. As he passed over North America, he sent greetings via radio to the people of the United States.

During his eighteenth orbit, Cosmonaut Number Five removed his restraining straps and floated freely about in the capsule. On their television screens, viewers could see Bykovsky floating about in the cabin and demonstrating the marvels of weightlessness as he set adrift a fountain pen, his logbook, a flask of water, and a movie camera.

Bykovsky was up there all alone, waiting for Valentina to be launched. When he received a congratulatory radiogram from her, he thanked her for her good wishes and said he was lonely and waiting for "Seagull" to go into orbit.

Valentina didn't delay for long. The next morning she showed up at the cosmonauts' "dressing room" and got into her orange spacesuit. Then, like the woman she was, she looked at herself in the little mirror on her sleeve. It was as though she was wondering: How does my spacesuit look on me? And is this white space helmet right for me?

Accompanied by her backup, she got into the bus and set off. The two women sang songs, laughed, and ate the candy gallantly offered to them by the male cosmonauts. Then, through the windows of the bus, they caught sight of the rocket, gleaming in the sunlight.

"I had seen it several times before," Valentina said later. "But that morning I looked upon it as a wondrous creation of human hands, with a strange fluttering sensation."

The bus came to a stop on the concrete slab, where Andriyan Nikolayev was waiting for her. Carefully taking her by the arm, he helped her out of the bus. Then, squeezing her slender hand in his own, he gently urged her ahead—encouraging her and tacitly wishing her good luck.

When Korolev greeted "Seagull" he jokingly remarked that everyone on the launch pad, including himself, envied her for her flight.

"Cheer up, dear Sergei Pavlovich!" Tereshkova replied, joking in her turn. "We'll still make a flight together. When I come back from space, we'll think about where to go next: to the moon, or to Mars . . ."

"Seagull" rode up in the elevator to the top deck of the spacecraft. She gazed out over the steppe and down at the people gathered below, then quickly got into the capsule. Through her earphones she heard the resonant, cheerful, and confident voice of Yuri Gagarin, the technical director of the flight: "Seagull! Seagull! This is Dawn. How are you feeling? Do you like the music we're playing for you?"

"Dawn, this is Seagull. I feel fine. I'm in good spirits. The music is wonderful. Thanks."

There in the capsule, she could feel the wind and catch the scent of the steppe and the wild flowers. But then the hatch was closed, and a new life began for Valentina Tereshkova.

She aligned the orientation globe, checked the Vzor optical system, and opened up on her voice radio.

As he watched "Seagull" on his television screen, Korolev was thinking, "After many years, people will still remember this morning."

Vostok-6 lifted off at 12:30 on 16 June 1963. For the first time in history, a spacecraft was being piloted by a woman cosmonaut— Valentina Vladimirovna Tereshkova. The flight of *Vostok*-6 around the earth followed an orbit with a minimum perigee of 183 kilometers, and a maximum apogee of 233 kilometers.

Once injected into orbit, "Seagull" established radio communication with "Hawk." The two cosmonauts greeted each other joyously. They exchanged information on their flights, on the functioning of the spacecrafts' apparatuses and systems.

The chief designer saw Tereshkova's image in his television screen and told her with feeling: "I see you. I can tell from your smile that all is well with you."

That same day, some reporters asked Academician Korolev: "What new contribution to cosmonautics has been made by the close approach between *Vostok*-5 and *Vostok*-6, as compared to the team flight of Andriyan Nikolayev and Pavel Popovich?"

Korolev's answers were as follows:

Korolev: This new penetration into space was dictated by the necessity of accumulating experience for more prolonged orbital flights, for the subsequent development of manned, earth-orbiting stations, and for future flights to the nearest planets.

Thus the purpose of both the first and the second team flight was to accumulate experience. We are faced with the problem of debugging all equipment under in-flight conditions—

of perfecting all of the many on-board devices and systems assuring the life-support of the crew. Such matters as gaining experience in piloting spacecraft and orienting them in space are of great importance.

Finally, there is one very important problem of a biological and physiological nature. We must find out how a human being behaves in a weightless condition—especially when he is in that state for a long period of time.

After a pause, Korolev offered a few general conclusions.

To put it simply, without rhetoric (of which we have given you more than enough). The first manned flights in circum-terrestrial space may be evaluated as follows: Gagarin's flight was the first serious probe. Titov's flight was a probe in depth. The flight of Nikolayev and Popovich was one more step ahead. And the flight of Bykovsky and Tereshkova is still another step ahead—both in the sense of duration, and as regards the scientific and engineering problems posed for them.

Query: In addition to those already mentioned, what other scientific goals have been set for the current flight?

Korolev: A series of astronomical observations of the constellations. Our plans call for continuous photographing of the sun. We decided to photograph the transitional spectra during sunrise and sunset. The value of these photographs lies in the fact that they will be taken without the interference caused by the atmosphere. Also, very great importance attaches to the actual measurement of the radiation background—of ionizing radiation—at those altitudes reached by *Vostok*-5 and *Vostok*-6. The observations of the earth—both visually and by means of optical instruments—are likewise very important.

Query: Is it not true that the three- and four-day flights of the cosmonauts have shown that the fears of the skeptics were groundless—that weightlessness is not as dangerous as they held it to be?

Korolev: I'm a great optimist, and I believe that very long, interplanetary, manned flights will take place in the near future. Nonetheless, we are still far from knowing everything about weightlessness and its effects on the human organism. Optimism alone is probably not very meaningful in this respect.

This problem is being studied by large collectives headed up by ranking scientists in the fields of biology and medicine. We're waiting for a decisive answer from them.

Query: The orbits of *Vostok*-5 and *Vostok*-6 are very close to each other. What is the significance of this proximity?

Korolev: The problem of two spacecrafts' effecting a rendezvous and joining up (or, as we say, "docking") is a big one, and a very important matter. It has been placed on the agenda for space navigation. Its solution will give us a lot to work with. We shall be able to build huge orbiting stations which can be used for research purposes and at the same time serve as "terminals" for spacecraft.

While this discussion was going one, the two spacecraft were continuing to orbit the earth, and their commanders were talking to each other.

"Hawk," said Tereshkova, "just so you won't get bored, I'll try to sing you the cosmonauts' favorite song."

"Thanks, Seagull, I'll be listening."

The clear, resonant voice of "Seagull" rang out in space. She sang just as she had back home on the Volga, at the textile mill, at flying school, and in Star Town.

"That was very good, Valentina. I enjoyed it a lot. Thanks."

The program called for "Seagull" to make a flight lasting only one day. But she had been authorized to prolong it if she felt all right.

"I feel good," she reported to Ground Control. "I feel fine . . ." And so Valentina Tereshkova was allowed to extend her flight time to three days and touch down at the same time as Valery Bykovsky.

As she passed over the Volga—almost directly over Yaroslavl— she said to Ground Control: "Tell my mother she shouldn't worry."

The dual flight of "Seagull" and "Hawk" continued for about three days. On the evening of 18 June the chief designer asked Bykovsky over the radio: "How are you feeling?"

"This is Hawk. Everything is in order. I feel splendid."

"You'll be landing tomorrow, as per schedule."

"I can keep going. There's power to spare, and enough oxygen and water. I'm prepared to continue the flight."

Korolev switched over to "Seagull": "How are you feeling?"

"I feel fine . . . . Everything is in order on the spacecraft."

"We're glad you're in good spirits, and we wish you a successful completion of your flight."

"Seagull" was the first to return to earth. *Vostok*-6 re-entered from its planned forty-ninth orbit, touching down at 11:20 A.M. at the preselected point 620 kilometers northeast of the city of Karaganda, in Kazakhstan. *Vostok*-6 had been in flight for 71 hours, making more than 48 revolutions around the earth, and had covered about two million kilometers.

The cameramen filmed Tereshkova drinking fresh milk from a bottle as she stood beside her spacecraft in the steppe. People from the neighboring kolkhozes surrounded the metallic sphere and peered in through the hatch. They asked Valentina about her flight and offered her cheese, *lepeshki* (flat cakes), *kumiss* (fermented mare's milk), and bread. From every direction, herdsmen on horseback came galloping up to see the spaceship. The helicopters of the search party hovered above the touchdown point.

"What's that bruise on your nose?" a woman doctor asked Valentina.

"Oh, that's nothing at all!" Valentina ran a finger across the bruise. "I just bumped it a little."

"And how is Valery?"

"He's on his way in to land."

Re-entering from its planned eighty-second orbit, *Vostok*-5 touched down at 2:06 P.M. 540 kilometers northwest of Karaganda. Both spacecraft had landed at the same parallel of latitude—55° north. *Vostok*-5 had been in flight for more than 119 hours, had made more than 81 orbits around the earth, and covered a distance of more than 3,300,000 kilometers.

I asked Nikolai Petrovich Kamanin to give me a "summing up"—to comment on the results of the joint flight of the two spacecraft.

He told me: "In the course of the second team flight, the cosmonauts flew their spaceships manually, personally monitored the operation of on-board systems, carried out a series of scientific investigations, and made observations of the earth's surface and its cloud cover, of the sun, the moon, and stars. At regular intervals throughout the flight they conducted physiological, vestibular, and psychological tests, and did special exercises, while in a condition of weightlessness.

"Reliable two-way communication," continued Kamanin, "was

maintained between *Vostok*-5 and *Vostok*-6. While in flight, the cosmonauts talked easily with each other and with Ground Control. The telemetric data from the medical monitoring system, and the direct television observation of the cosmonauts' physical state of health (maintained continuously during the flight) showed that both Valery Bykovsky and Valentina Tereshkova bore up well during injection into orbit, throughout the several days' flight, and during re-entry. And it should be noted that the extensive program of scientific investigations in space was fully carried out. Valentina Tereshkova showed that a woman can live and work in space."

The flights of *Vostok*-5 and *Vostok*-6 marked the end of the Soviet program for manned flights on spacecraft of the *Vostok* type. The basic aims of this program included making the first manned space flight, and flights of several days' duration, by way of preparing for building earth-orbiting stations and, in the future, making interplanetary flights. All six of the launchings in 1961–63 were based on the results and experience gained from preceding flights. Soviet cosmonauts flew a total of 383 hours in the *Vostok* spacecraft.

The "Stellar Crew"

In October 1964 the spacecraft Voskhod[1] (rise, as in "sunrise"), along with its carrier rocket, was moved along the railroad track to the launch pad.

Soviet cosmonautics had entered a new phase.

The new spacecraft was more capacious than its predecessor, Vostok. It could accommodate a team of three cosmonauts. Moreover, Voskhod was so designed that the crew could make the flight in "shirtsleeve" conditions: without spacesuits, or space helmets, or space gloves.

Also, Voskhod had a reserve retrorocket engine, new on-board equipment, a second orientation system using ionic sensors, and improved television and telemetric equipment. The over-all weight of the three-seat spacecraft was 5.32 tons.

Voskhod was designed so as to consist of a pressurized cabin and an instrument compartment. There were duplicate retrorocket engines and a duplicate landing system. The craft could be con-

[1] Voskhod, in its archaic sense—which is what I suspect its namers intended—means the same thing as Vostok, i.e., east.—Translator

trolled both automatically and manually. It could also be landed either automatically or manually—making a soft landing, with the crew inside, at a velocity of virtually zero.

The building of *Voskhod* and of a new, powerful booster made it possible to implement a new space program. The latter was based on the very logic of the development of cosmonautics: long flights cannot be made by one person alone. In order to carry out extensive and complex scientific investigations, the crew must include cosmonauts with training in different specialties.

While the *Vostok* flights were still in progress, the Design Bureau had worked out the design of a new spacecraft. The engineers who worked with S. P. Korolev still recall one particular day when he invited them into the space museum, led them over to Gagarin's *Vostok,* and said: "We have to think up better ways of designing a spacecraft that will accommodate several people. Some rough plans have been prepared, but I don't like them . . ."

Their lively discussion gave rise to the idea of designing a three-seat spacecraft capable of making a soft landing.

When the prototype of *Voskhod* was ready, Korolev called N. P. Kamanin on the telephone: "Get the cosmonauts together, and come on over."

When the cosmonauts arrived they looked over the prototype. Then, at the chief designer's invitation, they got into the contour seat.

"Is there room for three?" Korolev asked.

"Easily," Kamanin answered.

"Well, all right. It's feasible in terms of room. Ditto for the weight. We'll design it for three."

At Korolev's instructions, a series of *Voskhod*-type spacecraft were launched, until he was convinced that the soft-landing system worked impeccably. Then, on 12 October 1964, at 10:30 A.M., for the first time in the world, a three-seat, manned spacecraft, *Voskhod,* was put into orbit around the earth. Its crew consisted of the commander, pilot-cosmonaut Vladimir Komarov, a colonel in the engineering corps; scientist-cosmonaut Konstantin Feoktistov, Candidate in Technical Sciences[2]; and physician-cosmonaut Boris Yegorov.

The cosmonauts wore no spacesuits in flight. They lifted off in

[2] Roughly the equivalent of the American Ph.D.—Translator

101. Brought to the Baikonur Cosmodrome on a special platform truck, a *Soyuz* carrier rocket is mounted in the launch tower by powerful hydraulic devices.

102. After the rocket is mounted in the service structure and the service masts are raised, the transportation platform is taken away from the launch pad. Special remote-control devices begin checking all the rocket's systems. (PUBLISHED FOR THE FIRST TIME IN 1971.)

103. The *Soyuz*-1, launched on 23 April 1967, introduced a new series of spaceships. The pilot was Colonel Vladimir Komarov. After carrying out the test program, Komarov took the craft out of orbit and was returning through the earth's atmosphere. As a result of defects in the parachute system, the craft descended at excessive speed and crashed, killing the cosmonut. Komarov died a hero, trying to conquer the unknown.

In photo: The plaque on the Kremlin wall where Komarov's ashes are immured.

104. Yuri Gagarin's study at his home in Star Town.

(RIGHT)
106. Colonel Pavel Belyayev, commander-pilot of the *Voskhod*-2 spaceship, was born into a family of a medical assistant, in the Vologda Region. When he visited his native town, the children would surround him as he told them about his flights into space.

105. On 27 March 1968, the people of Moscow pay their respects to Yuri Gagarin, the world's first cosmonaut, who was killed in a plane crash. Valentina Gagarina is in the center.

(RIGHT)
109. The first team of Soviet cosmonauts vacationing on the Black Sea coast in May 1961. (PUBLISHED FOR THE FIRST TIME IN 1971.)

(ABOVE, RIGHT)
107. A real nature lover,
Valery Bykovsky likes to go to
the forest on Sundays.

(RIGHT)
108. Sergei Korolev
(1906–66), for years the
chief Soviet rocket designer
and director of numerous
space research and design
projects, relaxes with a group
of cosmonauts in May 1961.
He is second from the left,
in the rear. (PUBLISHED FOR
THE FIRST TIME IN 1971.)

110. Colonel Gherman Stepanovich Titov.

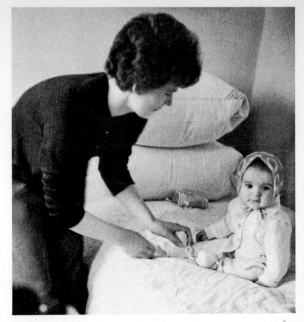

111. Lenochka and her mother Valentina Tereshkova Nikolayeva, wife of cosmonaut Andriyan Nikolayev.

113. The *Soyuz* carrier rocket is mounted in the launch tower, an intricately engineered structure that holds the rocket in a vertical position for the liftoff, fuels it, and prepares it in other ways for the flight.

114. The cosmonaut's general training includes classroom study of many theoretical subjects.

In photo: Georgy Beregovoi at class on photography and cinematography in September 1968.

(LEFT)
112. After his space flight, Aleksei Leonov paints cosmic views.

116. *Soyuz*-4 on the launching pad at
Baikonur Cosmodrome, 14 January 1969.

115. The spaceship of the *Soyuz* series
is a complex research laboratory suitable
for conducting a variety of experiments
in outer space. It can carry up to
six cosmonauts very comfortably.

In photo: Cosmonaut Beregovoi during
training-landing in various climatic
conditions.

117. A *Soyuz* carrier rocket on the
launching pad of the Baikonur
Cosmodrome. (PUBLISHED FOR THE
FIRST TIME IN 1971.)

118. Photo of the earth taken by cosmonaut Georgy Beregovoi from the spaceship *Soyuz*-3.

119. Assembling and testing the multiseated *Soyuz* orbital station.

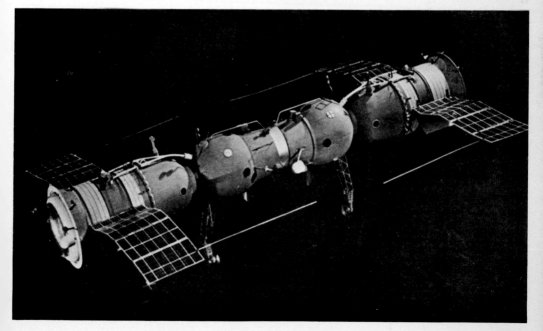

120. Rendezvous and docking of *Soyuz*-4 and *Soyuz*-5 on 16 January 1969. Model of docking.

121. *Soyuz*-4 spacecraft maneuvering before docking with *Soyuz*-5.

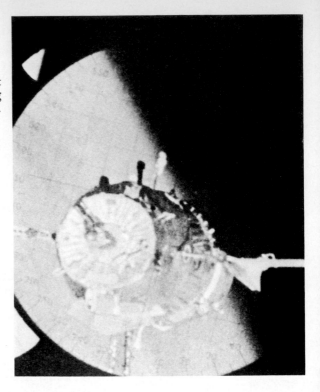

122. *Soyuz*-5 spacecraft before the docking with *Soyuz*-4.

the same clothes they were wearing when they stepped out of the bus at the cosmodrome: light-blue sweatshirts, dark-blue trousers, and white caps. (The cabin was so well protected against depressurization that it was felt that there was no longer any need for spacesuits.)

Not so long ago, people had felt great anxiety when Andriyan Nikolayev loosed his restraining straps and left his contour seat . . . And only yesterday it had been difficult to imagine that cosmonauts could make flights without clumsy, heavy spacesuits, without space helmets, space gloves, and pressurized boots . . . And now came this new achievement.

"Ruby! Ruby! How are you feeling?" the chief designer asked over the voice radio, using the commander's code name, *Rubin*.

The whole crew—Komarov, Feoktistov, and Yegorov—answered almost in unison: "Fine!"

Later in the flight, Komarov radioed a request to Korolev: "We've seen lots of interesting things. But we'd like to make more and closer observations. The whole crew requests that the flight be prolonged for another day."

The scientist replied to Komarov with a line from Shakespeare: "'There are more things in heaven and earth, Horatio—'" Then he ended the conversation abruptly, almost sharply: "Of course there's a lot that's interesting. But we're going to carry out our program!"

A short time later, Korolev—his eyes sparkling with pleasure at the successful launch of the new spacecraft—was answering questions from the reporters, who were especially interested in the new landing system.

"The re-entry and landing of any spacecraft," he told them, "is a difficult matter—hardly less difficult than putting a craft into orbit. Re-entry involves solving the reverse problem: how to get rid of the velocity imparted to the spacecraft by the rocket. First of all it must be remembered that the craft is entering the dense layers of the atmosphere at a tremendous speed. Great thermal and dynamic loads come into play. Obviously, a great deal depends upon how the spaceship re-enters these dense layers. Correct re-entry assures the integrity of the craft. We know that the earth is well covered by its gaseous envelope. The majority of the meteorites entering the atmosphere burn up. But the spacecraft must not burn up. This depends, of course, upon how the craft is designed;

but not only upon that. How it re-enters—the engineering of re-entry, so to speak—is also important.

"Our spaceship will re-enter on a specific trajectory that we can select. And it will make a 'soft' landing. When it touches down, its velocity will be either zero or very slight. For this purpose, *Voskhod* has been provided with a special system."

"And what if it touches down in the water?" asked the reporters.

"That's a good question," Korolev replied. "In that case the touchdown velocity will also be either equal to zero, or very slight. And the spacecraft is unsinkable. In the course of refining the soft-landing system we brought the spaceship down in a very strong wind, and at sea when the waves were high . . ."

But there was still a long way before touchdown; and the crew of *Voskhod* was living and working in conformity to their schedule. In their flying laboratory the cosmonauts made astronomical and geophysical observations, and carried out scientific experiments which could not have been made in a single-seat spacecraft. Dr. Boris Yegorov made some special tests having to do with the state of the vestibular apparatus in a state of zero G. And as a physician, he was able—under actual, in-flight conditions—to determine the cosmonauts' condition and evaluate the hygienic conditions in the cabin.

The psychologists were particularly interested in the problem of compatibility, that is, how three men of differing temperament and psychological traits would get along in one cabin. This would be one of the major problems in long flights to other planets: an unsociable person with odd character traits could poison things for the whole crew. On this particular flight, which lasted 24 hours 17 minutes 3 seconds, everyone on this first space crew felt fine. All three felt friendly toward one another, were in good spirits, and their esprit de corps was good.

Voskhod-1 came in for a landing on 13 October, having completed its flight program. In 24 hours 17 minutes and 3 seconds it had covered 669,784.027 kilometers.

As on the *Vostok* flights, the spacecraft's parachutes opened at an altitude of 7 kilometers. When it came close to the ground, the soft-landing system automatically went into operation. Streams of gases, expelled from nozzles in the direction of the ground, reduced the touchdown velocity to virtually zero. The cosmonauts did not feel the impact.

They touched down at 10:47 A.M., 312 kilometers northeast of the city of Kustanai. The spacecraft settled down onto the steppe like an airplane, and the three cosmonauts in their sports clothes stepped out. Soon they were surrounded by members of the search party and workers from a nearby sovkhoz (state farm).

The flight of the three-seat spaceship marked the beginning of the new *Voskhod* program.

The next important stage on the way to conquering space was the flight of *Voskhod*-2. By this time, Soviet scientists had systematically solved the critical problems of determining whether man could live and work in space. Now they took up a new problem: Could a human being live and work outside the spacecraft?

Steps in Space

Korolev used to tell the cosmonauts: "A person making space flights really must perform extravehicular activity—EVA—just as, for example, when you're sailing on the ocean and fall overboard, you have to be able to swim. And in order to perform EVA, it is essential to carry out certain procedures. I'm thinking of the kind that might be required when two spacecraft meet; when special observations are being made in space; or finally, of those occasions when something on the spacecraft has to be repaired. For instance," he said emphatically, "we have given serious thought to the fact that during EVA, the cosmonaut should be able to do any repair work that may be required—including welding. This is not a fantasy: it is a necessity. Man must learn how to live and work in open space."

With a view to solving this complex problem, *Voskhod-2* was equipped with a special lock chamber, or air lock. Its crew consisted of Pavel Belyayev and Aleksei Leonov. Both had been on the cosmonaut team for a long time.

In terms of temperament, Pavel Belyayev was the polar opposite of Aleksei Leonov. Leonov, like Pavel Popovich, was known as a cheerful, witty, and happy-go-lucky fellow. Belyayev, on the other hand, was reserved, taciturn, self-controlled, and very well organized. He had been made responsible for coolly directing a most critical operation. And Aleksei Leonov—although he was volatile, poetic, and always ready to take a risk—clearly understood all the difficulties he had to overcome.

One opinion current at that time held that a man who took a "space walk" would be faced with an insurmountable "psychological barrier": that the reflex of fear would become overwhelming and the instinct of self-preservation decisive. Throughout the world, psychologists were wondering: Could man conquer his fear of height? Could he completely control himself and keep a grip on ancient and powerful instincts? Might it not happen that primitive reflexes—suppressed by one's upbringing and education, by one's will power and reason—would break their fetters and totally overwhelm a man?

The cosmonaut's field of vision would take in that tremendous height—that empty, boundless space. How frightening to lose, at that moment, his familiar footing and surroundings, that last fragment of earth, the spacecraft . . . Obviously, such a man would be subject to violent emotional reactions, to muscular rigidity, and illusions of falling . . .

Many people, of course, have experienced the fear of height in their childhood. A little child climbs a tree, looks down, and feels dizzy. Later on, when he has become an adolescent, his curiosity prompts him to look out of the window of an airplane, and he experiences spasms and vertigo. Even fearless steeplejacks have been known to feel a "gnawing in the stomach" when they first climbed up high.

And in space? In space, a man has no footing. There is no up or down, no pressure, no weight, nothing to go by . . . What happens to a man in the first moments of his encounter with open space? Shock? Paralysis? Trauma? Hallucination? The paroxysm of fright?

When a person, either at a great altitude or in the depths of the ocean, finds himself in a boundless, apparently empty expanse with nothing to orient him—or, conversely, when he is in a close, confined area—extreme emotional stresses come into play. He may experience the fear of falling, the fear of losing contact with his familiar surroundings, or the fear of losing his orientation points.

But man must overcome all these phobias. He must oppose spatial stress with conditioned "spatial boldness."

The space age has demanded of man not only physical perfection, courage, and daring, but also spatial boldness: the ability to react coolly to infinity of the universe *and* the narrow confines of the lock chamber.

In accordance with his training sequence—the spacecraft, the man, the surrounding space—Aleksei Leonov was so conditioned that he could bear up normally in the confined area of a simulator's command module, in an isolation chamber (the chamber of silence and solitude), and in a special spacesuit. These training sessions revealed that Aleksei Leonov could adapt himself to all kinds of conditions and space areas.

I remember well how he behaved as "master of the house" in the isolation chamber, where he had to spend day after day, week after week, all alone in a soundproof room totally isolated from the outer world. I often looked through the peephole into the cabin where the cosmonaut was living and working. He read, did setting-up exercises, prepared his meals, wrote letters, and became absorbed in painting pictures.

In his own day, Gherman Titov—who had smuggled a volume of Pushkin into the isolation chamber—learned *Eugene Onegin* by heart, and recited canto after canto of that "novel in verse" with the eloquence of an actor. As for Aleksei Leonov, he supplied himself with a sketchbook, paints, and drawing pencils; and in his spare time he made sketches.

Later on, Professor F. D. Gorbov studied them. He was trying to understand how prolonged isolation affected the psyche of a cosmonaut.

"It was rather warm in the isolation chamber," Leonov told me, "and maybe that was why I thought of the Russian winter and painted that winter with its snow-filled woods, white expanses, and thick Siberian *kerzhak* with hoarfrost on its branches. In Siberia, you know, we have the kind of *kerzhak* that would make any artist envy it for the pattern woven by Nature. I also painted a marine scene. I love the sea: there's something about it that I feel akin to. The picture I painted was of a sinking ship."

Leonov paused reflectively, rubbing his chin. "Yes, I love the sea very much: it holds a strong attraction for me . . . Then I did a sketch of Paganini. I had read a book about the great musician;

and I wanted to express, in a drawing, the violent emotions that tormented him and his passionate nature."

A psychologist who had been listening to Leonov's account began to smile: the latter's long imprisonment in the isolation chamber had had no effect on his psyche. But the psychologist also knew something else. He was familiar with the tragedy of solitude and silence men had experienced during long polar winters or during long undersea voyages in submarines. Both he and his colleagues were apprehensive of unforeseen things that might happen when a human being ventured into the "stellar ocean." So they went on conducting new tests.

The cartoons, caricatures, and serious sketches that Leonov drew while in the isolation chamber showed his stability. Neither the prolonged isolation nor the oppressive silence in the close confines of the chamber broke his spirits or traumatized him.

Still, the psychologists wanted to find out how Leonov would react to the boundlessness of the sky after his close confinement in the isolation chamber, the thermal chamber, and the decompression chamber. Accordingly, immediately after he left the chamber they took him out to the airport and sent him up in a plane. The earth was far below, invisible beneath the cloud cover. Leonov was ejected out of the plane into the "ocean of air," and plunged down toward the ground. Then his parachute opened above him. Calm and cheerful, he looked down at the earth and up at the sky, following the movement of the clouds. The doctors observing Leonov at the time of this abrupt transition from the confinement of the chamber to the boundlessness of the sky found no serious changes in his psychological state.

Shortly before *Voskhod*-2 was launched, Aleksei Leonov read a newspaper article by the Soviet physiologist Vasily Parin, vice president of the Academy of Medical Sciences, USSR, replying to a pessimistic article in the French newspaper, *L'Express*. The latter quoted statements from certain scientists to the effect that cosmonauts who had been in open space would go insane. It was with such statements that Vasily Parin had taken issue.

Leonov once told me: "I have noticed one particular trait in myself. Whatever I am about to do, I first visualize it very clearly and in detail—either when awake or in my dreams. Then I do it in actuality. One night, for instance, when I was at flying school, I visualized myself making a steep banking turn: I could see every detail of how I performed the maneuver. Later, when I had to perform it with a formidable instructor looking on, everything happened just as it had in my dream. And now I can see in my dreams how the rapidly receding earth will shift away from beneath my feet. It's like what you see in the newsreels, when they show a spinning globe of the earth on the screen. Next I'm flying, and I see the earth. I see seas and oceans. Their hues vary: now blue, now gray, now green. And the different continents: Africa is brownish-yellow, Europe is green, and the Antarctic is white . . ."

Here are a few excerpts from Leonov's diary, quoted with his permission:

> Five March, 1960.
> I am a cosmonaut. I have been accepted for the cosmonaut team.

The pages of the diary are covered with sketches, cartoons, caricatures of Leonov's comrades, and notations. In essence it is a lively, amusing life story of the cosmonaut team and Leonov himself. There are sketches of him in parachute and flight training; in the isolation chamber and on the centrifuge; and finally, in a spacesuit, as he was on his way to the launch pad as a backup.

Leonov would see his friends off when they were launched into space and greet them on their return. He would go to Red Square and join in the applause for his friends. Meantime, he and Pavel Belyayev were strenuously training for an unusual experiment.

One entry in the diary reads:

> Today I was in the TBK [thermal decompression chamber].
> It was the first time I have been in a deep vacuum. Space came closer . . .

Conditioning in the TBK marked a new stage in cosmonaut training: a man was being trained for a "flight" in open space, where he would not be protected by the skin of the spacecraft.

In a special laboratory, behind a low, extensible partition, technicians helped Belyayev and Leonov into their white, flexible spacesuits. On their space helmets were four bright red letters: CCCP

(USSR). Belyayev's expression, as he looked out through his visor, was calm and rather stern. Leonov smiled and seemed to be winking at someone.

The technicians opened the big cover of the TBK, revealing—in a very bright light—the command module of a spacecraft, with a contour seat for the crew and an air lock. I watched the friends get into their seats. Then the cover of the TBK was closed. From that time on, the two figures in their spacesuits could be observed only on a television screen.

Through the loudspeaker came the words: "This is Diamond . . . This is Diamond . . ."

Belyayev and Leonov had chosen the name of the hardest stone as their radio call sign.

"This is Diamond . . . This is Diamond . . ." Leonov was now making ready to step into the dangerous, terrifying deep vacuum of space artificially created on earth.

The instruments showed that there was virtually no barometric pressure in the TBK. A vacuum had been created under terrestrial conditions.

Normal barometric pressure, at sea level, is about 30 inches of mercury. A human being becomes accustomed to this pressure, beginning in childhood, and does not notice it any more than the fact that he, along with the earth, is being spun around at great speed. But as one gets farther away from the earth's surface, the pressure drops sharply, and this change has a baneful effect on the human organism.

The upper limit of that part of the atmosphere in which human life can be sustained without artificial pressurization is about 13,000 feet. At a height of 56,000 feet, even a well-conditioned person can exist for no more than fifteen seconds. With every increase in altitude, the pressure drops, and there is a disruption of that life-giving process whereby the blood is enriched with oxygen and freed of excessive quantities of carbon dioxide. The cells in the cerebral cortex begin to experience a lack of oxygen; there is marked inhibition of the activity of the higher centers of the brain, paralyzed by excessive amounts of carbon dioxide and nitrogen; and both blood circulation and respiration stop. Moreover, with the human body at its ordinary temperature of 98.6° Fahrenheit the blood begins to boil . . .

In open space, man can survive only in a spacesuit. This is no ordinary suit. It is, so to speak, an entire "apartment" worn like clothing. This apartment draped around a man's body is provided with heat and illumination, sewage disposal and a telephone, ventilation, and a supply of oxygen.

The designers of the spacesuit had to solve many very complex problems in order reliably to protect the wearer against the deadly vacuum of space and its catastrophic temperatures. It used to be thought that the temperature in vicinal space was near to absolute zero, or −459.6° Fahrenheit. But after the launches of the first geophysical rockets—and especially after the flights of the first artificial earth satellites—notions of the temperatures in space were radically revised. We now know that at great altitudes, the temperature of gas particles reached 2,732–3,632° Fahrenheit. However, because of the great dispersion of matter in space these temperatures do not represent a danger for the cosmonaut. A more critical problem was to protect the cosmonaut against the action of direct solar rays, which every minute impart 20 kilocalories to each square meter of surface exposed to them. This is enough heat to boil a quarter liter of water in that time. In the shadow of the earth, on the other hand, the body temperature could drop to −212° Fahrenheit, and even lower—as has been shown by measurements made on Sputniks. Therefore, the spacesuit had to be designed so as to protect the cosmonaut against both heat and cold.

Such was the spacesuit—one designed to be worn by a man taking a space walk—that Leonov was wearing when he took his place in the thermal decompression chamber. With the help of the spacecraft commander, Belyayev, Leonov crawled through the air lock from the simulator cabin into a room representing the vacuum of space.

As he egressed from the spacecraft into this "terrestrial space," Leonov—true to his artistic and poetic temperament—began to deliver an amazing fictional "broadcast": "I am outside [the atmosphere] of the earth . . . I am swimming in space . . . I can see the earth . . . I can see the beautiful Volga . . . I see brilliant stars against a dark sky . . ."

After a brief pause, he added: "The next thing for me will be to repeat this broadcast from space."

That day came.

Voskhod-2 was launched at 10:00 A.M. on 18 March 1965—after a heavy blizzard—and was put into an orbit close to the one aimed for. Its period of revolution around the earth was 90 minutes. Its perigee was 173.5 kilometers, and its apogee 497.7 kilometers.

At 11:30, when the spaceship was in its second orbit, a unique operation began. Slowly revolving, the earth was swinging through the abyss of space, as its oceans and continents provided a background for one of the most amazing events of the second half of the twentieth century. Pavel Belyayev, commander of *Voskhod-2* —imperturbable and punctual as always—helped Aleksei Leonov strap on his shoulders (over his spacesuit) a flat white pack containing an automatic life-support system. Both cosmonauts pulled down the visors of the space helmets and put on their space gloves. They equalized the pressure in the cabin and in the air lock. Then the two of them opened the hatch, and Leonov peered into the illuminated air lock.

"Well, go ahead, Aleksei!" Belyayev said simply.

Leonov swam headfirst into the lock chamber. Belyayev, who was watching him closely, kept repeating: "Don't hurry . . . Take it easy . . ."

Now Leonov had almost completely disappeared inside the air lock, with only his legs—in high, gray boots—still in the cabin. Belyayev checked to see that none of the bootlaces had come untied. Then he closed the hatch behind Leonov.

"Let's get to work," he said in an even voice.

"I'm ready, Pavel. I'm ready," Leonov answered. One could sense the enthusiasm in his voice. He was eager to peer out of the air lock into space and to swim in the starry abyss. His muscular body felt an urgent need for quick movements—for leaping, diving, and turning, as in a swimming pool.

But *Voskhod-2*'s commander was strict and precise: he would tolerate no departures from the schedule. He talked to Ground Control, getting the chief designer's instructions and advice. Then, closely watching the hand on his chronometer, he kept saying: "Take it easy, Aleksei . . . Be patient. Take it easy . . ."

In the air lock, Leonov checked his spacesuit to make sure it was airtight, and his space helmet to see whether it was properly closed and its dark visor filter in the correct position. "This is Diamond . . . This is Diamond," he radioed. "Everything is in order . . . Everything is in order. I feel fine."

"I'm opening the hatch," said Belyayev.

The egress hatch opened, and the air lock was flooded with sunlight of a kind no man had ever seen before: blinding, scorching, and yet exhilarating. Leonov squinted. He had known in advance that the sunlight would be unusually bright, and in the laboratory he had tested visor filters under a brightness almost equal to that of the sun. And yet the sun astounded him.

When he had got somewhat used to the blinding light, he moved toward the opened egress hatch, keeping his hands on the walls of the lock chamber. The dark sky with its brilliant stars came into view—as though he were looking up at it from the bottom of a well.

Barely poking his head up out of the narrow well and grasping the edges of the exit hatch, Leonov looked into the darkness of space. The moment had come: the moment of greatest tension not only for Leonov and Belyayev but for the scientists, doctors, designers, and instructors—all those who had trained this man for his space walk and were now following the experiment from the ground.

"Everything is going normally . . ." Belyayev said, with no change in the tone of his calm, matter-of-fact voice. He knew that the most trying test a man can undergo—the testing of his psyche—was about to take place.

Leonov pulled himself up until his chest was on a level with the hatch and looked around at the abyss. It was a first encounter with the universe, eye-to-eye, face-to-face. The boundlessness of this new realm, the vividness of the hues, the sharpness of the contrast between the inky blackness and the blinding radiance of the stars, the extraordinary feeling of lightness, the amazing abundance of light and warmth—all these things overwhelmed Leonov's impressionable soul.

As he emerged from the air lock, he kept a grip on the edge of the hatch with one of his space-gloved hands. He and the spacecraft were flying above the earth at a speed of 28,000 kilometers per hour. With bated breath, stiff with fright, we on earth watched the television to see what would come next.

"I can see the Caucasus," we heard Leonov say.

He saw the indigo blue of the Black Sea. He saw the cuplike shape of Tsemesskaya Bay, and nearby Novorossiisk, the white buildings of the sanatoriums at Sochi, the green fields of the Kuban. He looked down at the earth, hanging on to the edge of the hatch. He was taking his time—but not because he was hesitant.

To the contrary, Leonov was eager for quick action—for cutting loose from the spacecraft immediately. But he was restrained by the imperturbable commander, Belyayev, who was closely following his schedule, and all instructions from the ground.

According to the program, Leonov was to remove the cover from a movie camera affixed to the outside of the spacecraft. This he proceeded to do. Then his jocular voice came over the air waves: "Shall I send it into a new orbit?"

Leonov's joking tone of voice, and the mischievous gesture he made as he heaved the cover down toward earth and then watched it, had a reassuring effect on everyone watching him at the time.

The edge of the hatch, to which he was still clinging, was Leonov's last point of contact. Unhurriedly, he first removed one hand, then the other, then both at once—and floated off some eight inches from the spaceship, before rapidly coming back to the hatch. Only then did he really push off from the spacecraft—to the full length of the 17½-foot lifeline connecting to *Voskhod-2*.

He swam.

He soared.

He flew.

From Moscow, wire services and representatives of the press, radio, and television on all continents quickly broadcasted biographical details on the man who was now taking a space walk. He was thirty years old. He was a Russian from Siberia, and a Communist. He was a pilot and parachutist. He was married and had a four-year-old daughter named Vika (Victoria). He was fond of painting . . .

I should like to add a few touches to this description conveyed by the media. Aleksei Leonov's friends at Star Town called him "Sun-Blessed" because of his sandy hair, his golden-brown freckles, and his sunny disposition. No one had ever seen him depressed or in a malevolent, unsociable, or grim mood. He had the ability to get through everything easily and cheerfully—and, in his own words, "to hoist the scarlet sails of romanticism and dreams."[1]

And so Aleksei Leonov, pushing with both hands, swam off from the spacecraft to the full length of his lifeline. He had the feeling

[1] *Scarlet Sails* is the title of a very romantic story by Aleksandr Grinevsky (1880–1932), which has become a modern classic in the Soviet Union.—Translator

that the spaceship was bouncing away in the opposite direction. Meantime, inside the command module, Pavel Belyayev was distinctly aware of everything that Leonov was doing: he felt it when Leonov pushed against the craft and clutched at it; and he heard a kind of clang when Leonov's boot scraped against the side of *Voskhod-2*.

When he had swum away from the spacecraft, Leonov looked back at it admiringly. He found it a really very handsome thing: majestic, splendid, and marvelous.

Leonov had begun his experiment when *Voskhod-2* was flying over the Black Sea. The sea and its mountainous littoral were clearly visible. The sky was cloudless, and there was no haze or mist covering the earth: the weather had turned out to be perfect. As he flew on, Leonov could see first the silvery, snow-capped peaks of the Caucasus, then the broad expanse of the Volga, still ice-bound. The cosmonaut felt a thrilling sensation of amazing lightness and freedom—of being totally unconfined. This world with no points of support stretched out endlessly. The first man to swim in the ocean of space was so exhilarated that he turned a somersault and spun himself like a top. He was so taken up with these intricate pirouettes that he didn't even notice he was flying over the Ural Mountains.

Everything was amazing and extraordinary. He could throw out his arms and lie on his back, while distinctly aware that there was no support under him. He could turn head over heels without feeling any muscular tension.

Within Leonov himself, a struggle was going on between the artist and the engineer. The artist in him insisted on observing the colors of space, gazing in rapture at the unique luminescences, the rare spectrum of tones and hues. He was fascinated by the coloration of the boundary between space and the earth—a boundary which, with its two spectra, was clearly discernible. At those times when the spacecraft was emerging from the dark side of the earth into the sunlight, and vice versa, everything changed—everything produced its own miracles and surprises. When going from the bright side, there would be a shift in the spectrum from white through light blue and dark blue to violet. When emerging from darkness to the bright side, warm colors like red and yellow would be added to the cooler tones of the spectrum.

The sun, the stars, the earth—all had an unusual appearance.

Everything seemed strange and different from the earthling's usual notions. This wonderland beckoned to the artist in Leonov: it delighted him, and stirred his imagination. But the artist was opposed by Leonov the scientist, whose job it was to observe that same sky and sun, the stars and the earth, calmly and unwaveringly—to see them not in the marvelous glow and diversity of colors, but in that nakedness which reveals the nature of phenomena and processes. Leonov the engineer had been instructed to find out whether it was possible to work in space, so that one day cosmonauts might do welding, assemble docks for interplanetary ships, building "islands in the sky"—intermediate stations, space terminals—and make repairs on the outer hulls of spacecraft.

Leonov's "swim" in open space—which lasted about ten minutes—was still in progress. Now *Voskhod-2* was passing over Sakhalin. Through the mist he could see the Pacific Ocean. Operation EVA was approaching its end.

Throughout the experiment, Leonov's movements had been filmed by a movie camera installed on the outer hull of *Voskhod-2*. Now, according to the schedule, he was to remove the camera from its bracket and bring it with him into the air lock. He unfastened it from the bracket and tried to push it into the lock chamber. But at this point something unforeseen occurred: the camera "didn't want" to go in through the hatch. Not only did it refuse to obey Leonov—it interfered with his own attempts to get back inside the spacecraft.

Once again, self-controlled and persistent, he tried to push the camera into the air lock. It became wedged between the sides of the lock and his body, obstructing him to such a degree that a dangerous situation was created.

What should he do? Should he throw away the camera and the priceless film? If he did, the world would never be able to watch the man who had become the first living celestial body—a kind of satellite of the spacecraft—as he swam and soared in open space.

Leonov knew how valuable the film was, and he could not bear the thought of throwing the camera away and coming back aboard the spaceship without it. After pondering ways and means of overcoming the camera, Leonov gathered his strength[2] and managed

[2] He later reported that he was "rather tired" by this time.—Translator

to maneuver it in through the hatch. Then he himself crawled in after it.

"Well done!" Belyayev exclaimed, when Leonov was back aboard. Then he promptly reported to Ground Control: "The mission involving the cosmonaut's extravehicular activity and his return to the spacecraft has been fully carried out."

In the course of his "space swim" he had reached a point 17½ feet (the full length of the lifeline) distance from the exit hatch.

Five steps from the spaceship into open space. But every journey begins with the first step.

Mankind had seen with its own eyes the proof that another kind of existence was possible: beyond the earth, in a new habitat.

In the course of *Voskhod-2*'s daylong flight, Belyayev and Leonov had flown 717,260 kilometers. Now the time had come to make their landing.

Pavel Belyayev was bringing a spacecraft down under manual control for the first time, owing to certain abnormalities in the functioning of the solar orientation system. He flew *Voskhod-2* around the earth in one additional circuit. Then he and Leonov manually oriented the spacecraft and switched on the TDU—the retroengines.

This was a moment of considerable anxiety for them, since any error in orientation would mean that the spacecraft might go flying off beyond the earth's atmosphere, never to return. *Voskhod-2* plunged into the dense layers of the atmosphere.

The antennas on the outside of the spacecraft were fused by the heat. The liquefied metal, enveloped in terrifying crimson flames, spread over the heat-resistant glass of the viewport. Then came an explosion, and a hatch blew open; a jolt, and the spacecraft was dangling from the shrouds of a parachute.

At 12:02 P.M. on 19 March, *Voskhod-2* touched down in the general area of Perm—in the thick, snow-filled taiga (forest) of the Urals. The parachute was caught in the treetops. The manual re-entry had resulted in a considerable over-shoot.

The cosmonauts climbed out of their spacecraft. They made radio contact with the search party, giving their longitude and latitude. Then they built a campfire, pitched a tent. Soon hunters arrived on the scene, forest rangers made their way through the snow to them, and helicopters flew in. The copters dropped rope ladders, and doctors, cameramen, and instructors climbed down. Campfires began to blaze merrily, and people started cutting down trees to make a landing pad for the helicopters.

The cosmonauts were first taken to Perm and then to Moscow, where they were given a state reception, plus the highest awards of the motherland—and were probingly questioned by scientists and reporters.

When I asked Sergei Pavlovich Korolev to comment on the flight of *Voskhod-2*, he said: "Yuri Gagarin's flight opened the era of space navigation. Pavel Belyayev and Aleksei Leonov have solved another—and no less important—problem. Their flight showed that man can live in open space. That he can leave the spacecraft, no longer feeling confined by its bulkheads, and can work wherever he may have to. And he will in fact have to do construction work and welding on orbiting stations, make repairs on rockets and space-craft, and the stations themselves—if this becomes necessary."

"And now? What's next?" I asked Korolev.

"A new spacecraft. A new program. New flights."

"When will the spacecraft be launched?"

"When it is built."

"Which of the cosmonauts will fly it?"

"I consider Volodya Komarov well-skilled for testing space-craft," Korolev replied. "As you know, a spaceship must first of all be tested. I should also tell you that I have my eye on a very promising fellow, Georgy Beregovoi. During the war he was made a Hero of the Soviet Union. After the war he became a test pilot. Then he joined the space program at my suggestion. Komarov and Beregovoi are first-rate test pilots . . . As for the spacecraft, things are well under way."

The new spaceship was being built. Meantime, automatic satel-lites were effecting diverse complex studies of cosmic space and the celestial bodies of the solar system.

Automatic

Space Vehicles

Together with the launching of manned spacecraft, the USSR was systematically launching automatic satellites, interplanetary stations, and other automatic space vehicles. I have already discussed the *Kosmos* series of satellites. In May 1963, by means of the instruments on one such satellite (*Kosmos*-17), it was possible to study the dependence of cosmic rays on the level of activity during the period of the quiet sun. This satellite also provided data on cosmic radiation at altitudes of from 600 to 800 kilometers, and on the spatial distribution of charged particles.

Artificial earth satellites have assumed an important place in modern-day weather forecasting. The first meteorological satellite was *Kosmos*-23 (13 December 1963). The weather satellites *Kosmos*-26 (18 March 1964) and *Kosmos*-49 (24 October 1964) effected the first global magnetic survey of 75 per cent of the earth's surface, from a height of about 300 kilometers. *Kosmos*-51 (10 December 1964) made it possible to study the luminescence of the stellar sky in the ultraviolet and visible bands of the spectrum.

In order to establish manned orbiting stations in space, it was necessary to "teach" vehicles to carry out maneuvers and then to dock.

The maneuverable space vehicles *Polyot*-1 and *Polyot*-2 were put into orbit around the earth on 1 November 1963 and 12 April 1964, respectively.[1] They were equipped with rocket-engine systems for stabilizing flight and effecting extensive maneuvers in circum-terrestrial space. The experiment was successful. Scientists and designers obtained valuable data for the subsequent design of new systems for guiding the flight of space vehicles and for the future assembly of permanent orbiting stations.

As the scientific exploration of space expanded, the need for a huge "flying laboratory" became increasingly urgent. It would be particularly important in studying the primary particles of high- and low-energy cosmic rays. To this end, the *Proton* series of scientific space stations was built in the USSR.

The first scientific space station of this series, *Proton*-1, was put into earth orbit on 16 July 1965, by means of a powerful new booster. *Proton*-1 weighed 15,840 pounds.

Proton-2 went into orbit in November 1965. It was followed by *Proton*-3 in July 1966 and *Proton*-4 in November 1968. *Proton*-4 weighed about seventeen tons, at that time the world's largest automatic space laboratory.

Space had begun to serve the needs of human beings—to help them in their everyday, practical activity. Weather satellites and communications satellites—postmen in orbit—made their appearance. As we know, the twentieth century is the age of communications—of information. The flow of information used by mankind from one day to the next became so great that it required the development of new systems of communication. As it happened, the most useful systems were those operating on the basis of artificial earth satellites. The satellites of the *Molniya*-1 (Lightning-1) series were designed in the USSR to provide such a system.

Beginning 23 April 1965, a series of *Molniya*-1 active-repeater comsats—whose purpose was the creation of a long-range communications system—was put into orbit around the earth. Then a ground network of "Orbit" television receiving and transmitting stations was established over the vast territory of the USSR. Today, TV broadcasts from Moscow are simultaneously viewed by the in-

[1] *Polyot,* or *Polët,* means "flight."—Translator

habitants of the capital and by millions of people in Siberia, the Soviet Far East, and Central Asia.

Probes sent toward and to the moon have occupied a special place in the program of exploring space by means of automatic vehicles. I have already told how, on 2 January 1959, a booster rocket imparted the second cosmic velocity to the probe *Luna-1*, passed within some 6,000 kilometers of the moon, and became the first artificial satellite of the sun.

On 14 September 1959, *Luna-2* reached the moon and impacted near the eastern edge of the Sea of Rains, by the crater Autolycus. As we have seen, *Luna-3*, launched on 4 October 1959, photographed the other side of the moon.

As it turned out, however, there was still an unphotographed segment of the unseen side of the moon. This "blank space" on the lunar surface was photographed by the probe called *Zond-3* (Probe-3). As it flew past the moon on 20 June 1965, it photographed both the visible and invisible sides of the lunar surface.

The automatic station *Luna-9* was launched on 31 January 1966 and made a soft landing on the moon at 2145 hours and 30 seconds (Moscow time) on 3 February 1966, impacting near the Ocean of Storms, west of the Reiner and Marino craters. On 4 February, at a command from earth, *Luna-9* began the first television survey of the lunar landscape.

But *Luna-9* did more than transmit a panorama of the lunar surface. Its instruments made measurements and then relayed the information that the radioactivity on the moon's surface did not exceed the norms which human beings could tolerate. This indicated that man could work on the moon.

Experience had shown, however, that not all studies of the moon and circumlunar space could be made from the moon's surface. Studies of the density of meteoric substances near the moon, the intensity of radiation, and the magnetic and gravitational fields of the moon could be made only by means of a station orbiting the moon over a long period of time. This necessitated the building of an artificial moon satellite. And on 3 April 1966, *Luna-10*, which weighed 539 pounds, became the first artificial moon satellite.

Luna-10 was operative for fifty-six days—almost two months. During that time it made 460 circuits around the moon, and transmitted a huge amount of scientific information to earth.

Close upon the heels of *Luna-10* came the launching of new

lunar satellites: *Luna*-11 (24 August) and *Luna*-12 (22 October). *Luna*-12 made close-up photographs of the lunar surface.

Luna-13, which had the same television equipment for transmitting lunar panoramas as *Luna*-9, was launched on 21 December 1966. The duration of its flight was some three and one half days. It made a soft landing near the western edge of the Ocean of Storms, some 300 kilometers from where *Luna*-9 had impacted. *Luna*-13 transmitted to earth five close-ups of the lunar landscape, taken under different angles of the sun's rays. Then a special "mechanical hand" installed on *Luna*-13 reached out to the extent of five feet, carrying with it a mechanical probe-penetrometer and radiation densitometer. A microrocket was ignited: a stream of gas and flame shot vertically upward, and a titanium point penetrated the top layer of the lunar soil. The density of the topsoil proved to be about 0.8 gram per cubic centimeter. A chunk of this kind of soil—similar to the pumice we have on earth—would not sink in one of our rivers or seas. The effective temperature of the lunar soil was measured by means of radiation sensors. The use of gas-discharge counters, which registered cosmic corpuscular radiation, made it possible to determine the lunar surface's capacity to reflect cosmic rays. There was no doubt that man could live and work in the unusual lunar environment.

The next important problem was to learn how to recover a probe after it had made a circuit around the moon. This problem was solved with vehicles of the *Zond* type. In September 1968 *Zond*-5, after following an earth–moon–earth trajectory, became the first probe to re-enter the earth's atmosphere. It re-entered with a speed close to the second cosmic velocity and, following a ballistic trajectory, splashed down at the planned point in the Indian Ocean. The very complex engineering problem of recovering a probe from the vicinity of the moon, had at last been solved.

The next, and even more important, stage was the flight of *Zond*-6. On 17 November 1968, having flown past the moon and photographed it, *Zond*-6 effected a guided, aerodynamic re-entry and touched down at a predetermined point in the Soviet Union. The vehicle carried a life cargo—turtles—who returned to earth after making a trip around the moon. The significance of the *Zond*-6 shot was that a vehicle which had looped around the moon had effected a guided re-entry.

Zond-7 was launched on 8 August 1969. It, too, made a pass around the moon. Then, after extensive scientific tests and experiments had been completed, it effected a guided re-entry into the earth's atmosphere and a soft landing at a preselected site in the Soviet Union. Aerodynamic lift was utilized in the re-entry. After double "immersion" of the payload in the earth's atmosphere, aerodynamic braking reduced its speed from the second cosmic velocity to 656 feet per second.

Soviet scientists were also investigating other celestial bodies besides the moon. On 12 February 1961, the Soviet probe *Venera-1* was sent on its way—the first Venus probe to be launched. It weighed 1,415.7 pounds and was launched from a heavy Sputnik in earth-parking orbit. *Venera-1* was to serve as a "pathfinder" to the nearest planet. The flight program also included the investigation of cosmic rays, magnetic fields, interplanetary gases, meteoric particles, and solar radiation. It was important to ascertain the possibility of establishing long-range communications and of guiding space probes.

Communication with the probe was maintained until 27 February 1961, when it was 23 million kilometers from the earth. For that day, this was a record in long-range communications.

On 1 March 1966, *Venera-3* reached Venus and on its surface planted a pennant bearing the Soviet State Seal.

Venera-4 headed for Venus on 12 June 1967. In the course of more than four months it covered about 350 million kilometers. Radio contact with *Venera-4* was made 114 times.

On 18 October 1967, two meteors built on the earth blazed fiery arcs in the cloudy skies of Venus. They were the "orbital section" and the re-entry section of *Venera-4*, which was coated with heat-resistant material. The capsule's radio transmitters and instruments operated throughout the ninety-three minutes of its descent through the thick layers of the planet's atmosphere, supplying information on Venus.

The twin probes *Venera-5* and *Venera-6* were built in 1968. They were launched in January 1969, for the purpose of making simultaneous studies of the atmosphere of Venus above two different regions of that planet. In May 1969 the two probes reached Venus, one on the heels of the other. Wrapped in a flaming sheath of plasma, the capsules engaged the Venusian atmosphere in "single combat." The effects of aerodynamic braking were utilized in their descent through the atmosphere.

The basic mission of *Venera*-5 and *Venera*-6 was to continue the study of the chemical analysis and parameters of the Venusian atmosphere initiated in October 1967 by *Venera*-4. *Venera*-5 and *Venera*-6 completed their mission successfully.

The foregoing is a sketchy—and by no means complete—survey of the extensive space explorations effected by probes. But let us now return to the flights of the cosmonauts.

The Soyuz
Program

Both the *Vostok* program and the *Voskhod* program had been completed. Having served their purposes, the *Vostok* and *Voskhod* spacecraft were put on exhibit at museums and displays. Meantime, Soviet scientists had developed a new space program labeled "*Soyuz*" (Union).

The new, multipurpose, manned spacecraft *Soyuz* had been designed with a view to implementing this program. It was the intent of the scientists and design engineers that these spacecraft have a wider range of technical potential, that they carry out a series of investigations of circumterrestrial space, and that they serve as a basis for preparatory work with a view to assembling orbiting stations.

The creation of an earth-orbiting station had ceased to be a dream and become an urgent practical problem. According to the estimates of the scientists and design engineers, the employment of one and the same spacecraft for various purposes should—in the final analysis—make it easier and cheaper to build new space stations in orbit.

123. Vladimir Shatalov, twice Hero of the Soviet Union. As the commander of a spaceship, he made two flights into the cosmos. Shatalov took part in the world's first space-station experiment.

124. Baikonur Cosmodrome, 13 October 1969. The space crew of the *Soyuz*-8: Vladimir Shatalov and Aleksei Yeliseyev at the launching pad.

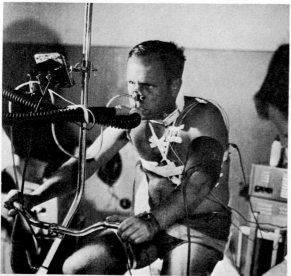

125. Viktor Gorbatko gets a medical check-up before the flight of *Soyuz*-7, launched on 12 October 1969, 1:45 P.M. Moscow time. The other crew members were Anatoly Filipchenko, commander, and Vladislav Volkov, engineer.

(ABOVE, LEFT)
126. Star Town, where Soviet cosmonauts live and work, is located in a picturesque Moscow suburb. This photo was taken just before the arrival of American astronaut Frank Borman and his family in July 1969.

(ABOVE, RIGHT)
127. Baikonur Cosmodrome, 12 October 1969. Cosmonauts Vladislav Volkov, Anatoly Filipchenko, and Viktor Gorbatko are on their way to the *Soyuz*-7 spacecraft.

(RIGHT)
128. The Baikonur Cosmodrome, 13 October 1969. *Soyuz*-8 before liftoff.

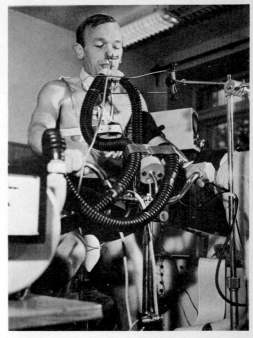

130. A thorough physical check-up includes data on blood pressure, pulse rate, gas exchange, cardiogram.

In photo: A physician checks Aleksei Yeliseyev while he is working out on a special device simulating a bicycle.

129. Baikonur Cosmodrome, 13 October 1969. The space crew of the *Soyuz*-8 before liftoff.

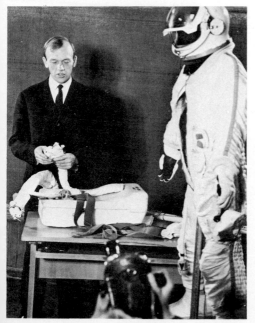

131. Cosmonaut Aleksei Yeliseyev, engineer, twice Hero of the Soviet Union, preparing for his flight in *Soyuz*-5. With *Soyuz*-4, his craft participated in the first docking of two manned spaceships. Star Town, 1969.

132. The cosmonaut's cabin of the *Soyuz* series makes it possible to create normal conditions for the crew's work and rest during flight.

In photo: Engineer Aleksei Yeliseyev in the cabin of the *Soyuz*-5 during the flight.

(ABOVE)

133. Frank Borman and his family in the Soviet Union in July 1969. Borman's wife, Susan, is placing flowers at the memorial slab in the Kremlin wall where the ashes of Yuri Gagarin are kept.

134. Cosmonaut Anatoly Filipchenko is painstakingly studying all the systems of the ship before his flight on *Soyuz-7*.

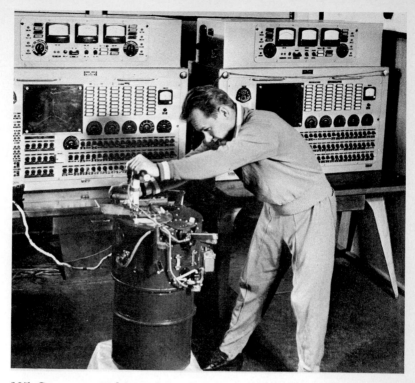

135. Cosmonaut Valery Kubasov is trying out the Vulcan, an automatic machine for welding in a vacuum and state of weightlessness. (PUBLISHED FOR THE FIRST TIME IN 1971.)

136. Anatoly Filipchenko during preflight training in the cabin of the *Soyuz*-6 in September 1969.

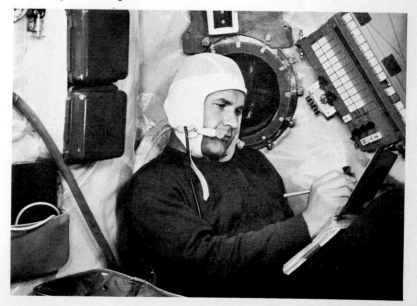

137. Engineer Kubasov is called "the first cosmic welder" by his fellow cosmonauts. He did welding experiments in space during the *Soyuz*-6 flight on 16 October 1969.

138. Engineer Vitaly Sevastyanov, Doctor of Science (Technology), and Colonel Andriyan Nikolayev, a cosmonaut, before training on a mock-up of a spacecraft that simulates normal flight and emergency situations.

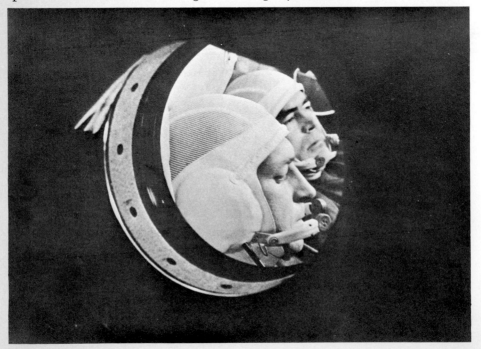

139. Engineer Vitaly Sevastyanov and Adriyan Nikolayev, commander of the *Soyuz*-9 spaceship, preparing for cosmic flights.

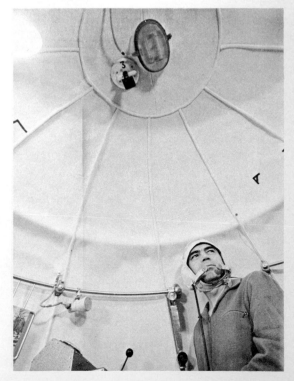

140. Colonel Andriyan Nikolayev in the *Soyuz* spaceship.

141. Engineer Vitaly Sevastyanov during navigational training.

142. Cosmonauts Andriyan Nikolayev and Vitaly
Sevastyanov, the crew of the *Soyuz*-9 spaceship, during
weightlessness training on a jet aircraft, 1970.
(PUBLISHED FOR THE FIRST TIME IN 1971.)

As it turned out, the new, manned spacecraft *Soyuz* met these requirements.

But, to everyone's deep regret, Korolev did not witness the flight of this new spacecraft. Academician Sergei Pavlovich Korolev—leading Soviet scientist, member of the Praesidium of the Academy of Sciences, USSR, Communist, twice honored as a Hero of Socialist Labor, and winner of a Lenin Prize—died suddenly in Moscow on 14 January 1966, in his sixtieth year.

In the person of Korolev, Soviet and world science had lost an outstanding scientist in the field of rocketry and space science: the designer of the first artificial earth satellites, and the first spacecraft—which had opened the era of man's conquest of space.

Grieving cosmonauts stood by the coffin of the beloved scientist and designer. They accompanied it to Red Square and brought flowers to the niche in the Kremlin wall where the urn with the great scientist's ashes was placed. For a long time they stood there by the niche, covered by a black marble slab, as if they could not believe the words inscribed on it:

Sergei Pavlovich
KOROLEV

30   14
19   06   19   66
XII   I

Korolev had often said: "Whatever the obstacles on his path, man will make his way to the stars." His work was carried on by his friends and co-workers, including prominent Soviet scientists and design engineers, workers in the aerospace industry, and cosmonauts. These men completed construction of the new spacecraft, *Soyuz.*

Before his death, Korolev had picked the men who were to test-fly the new spaceship: Komarov and Beregovoi.

Komarov was chosen for the first flight.

Before leaving home to set out on his second space flight, Komarov—already dressed for his trip—went up to his wife carrying a teddy bear. They lived in a sunlit, spacious apartment—on the top floor of a tall building—whose windows looked out upon the sky. From there, as from the bridge of a ship, they looked out upon woods and fields.

Dawn was breaking, and its first rays were dispersing the mist. Komarov looked at his wife, who was holding his suitcase. He ran a finger along her eyebrows, and gently kissed her on the eyes. She leaned on his chest; and both of them watched, wordlessly, as the glow of dawn came through the venetian blinds. The sky brightened, and the light-blue woods turned to gold.

Komarov straightened up: "It's time to go." He threw his leather jacket over his shoulders and went to the door with a military stride.

On 23 April 1967, at 3:35 P.M., the new spacecraft *Soyuz-1* was put into orbit. It was piloted by Vladimir Komarov, colonel of the engineer corps.

On 24 April, after completing his schedule of tests, Komarov received instructions to land. The spacecraft successfully negotiated the most difficult and critical phase—that of braking in the dense layers of the atmosphere—and the first cosmic velocity had been entirely damped out. But at an altitude of seven kilometers, when the main parachute cupola opened, its shroud lines became tangled, with the result that *Soyuz-1* impacted at a high speed, causing Komarov's death.

Star Town and the whole nation was in mourning.

At the interment, the cosmonaut team stood silently at the Kremlin wall in which the urn containing the ashes of Komarov had been immured.

Yuri Gagarin looked grim. Grief was in his eyes, and sorrow showed in the lines of his face. When I spoke to him, I had the impression that he had not heard my words or my question. But then he began to talk—forcefully, decisively, and passionately—clenching his fists: "Mankind never gains anything gratuitously. There has never been a bloodless victory over nature. We have just begun to explore space in the vicinity of earth. But who can deny that our earthlings' discoveries have been paid for by the lives of remarkable people—the heroes of various countries, the bold sons of mankind?"

Later, in a long article, Gagarin developed this idea. He wrote:

The Norwegian Amundsen; the Englishman Scott; the American De Long; the Frenchman La Pérouse; and our hero of the Arctic Georgy Sedov, together with the tireless explorer Aleksei Fedchenko: how long it is—this dramatic list of the explorers of our planet! Men have perished. But new ships have left their moorings, new aircraft have taxied to the takeoff strip, and new teams have gone off into the forest and the desert.

But is it only explorers who have suffered this fate? Haven't physicists given their lives for the sake of knowledge? Haven't doctors sacrificed themselves for the sake of others? And test pilots?

Nothing will stop us. The road to the stars is steep and dangerous. But we're not afraid. Every one of us cosmonauts is ready to carry on the work of Vladimir Komarov—our good friend, and a remarkable man.

Who would be daring enough to test-fly the *Soyuz?*

The assignment was taken on by Georgy Beregovoi.

I went to see him on the day of Komarov's funeral. Beregovoi was gloomy and untalkative. On the table before him lay the newspaper with Yuri Gagarin's article, "The Steep Roads up into Space." Beregovoi had underlined the sentence: "There never has been a bloodless victory over nature."

"Yuri is right!" he exclaimed. "Space is cruel. But that won't stop us."

A few words about Georgy Beregovoi—a man with an amazing life story. He was born in the Donbass—the iron- and coal-producing region. As a boy he became interested in model airplanes. He qualified as an amateur pilot when still very young, and then went to military flying school. He got his wings just as the war was beginning, and went straight from school to the front. There, he flew ground attack aircraft in General Kamanin's division. He distinguished himself in combat and was named a Hero of the Soviet Union.

On several occasions, he was shot down and had to bail out. Wounded and exhausted, he would make his way through the enemy lines. Then he would go back into combat and keep flying until his plane was destroyed by enemy bullets and shells. Once again, he would bail out and start on the long trek back—through snow-filled forests and via roundabout paths through almost impassable swamps . . .

After the war he became a test pilot. When he was already

over forty years old, Beregovoi took a new, bold step: he decided
to join the cosmonaut team.

Although his decision had been carefully thought out, it provoked objections from his friends and family. His friends told him:
"You're a Hero of the Soviet Union—a war hero. You're an Honored
Test Pilot of the USSR, and a colonel. You have a lot of experience,
and aviation needs you. What more do you want? Just stick to
aviation, and remember that the laws of aerodynamics are different
from the laws of celestial mechanics. At your age, it doesn't make
sense to begin a whole new education . . ."

Beregovoi listened to his friends but rejected their arguments.
And in 1963, after weighing everything carefully, he submitted a
request to be put on the cosmonaut team.

The authoritative medical commission ruled that Beregovoi was
fit to serve on the cosmonaut team, and before long he was being
welcomed to Star Town by Yuri Gagarin. At the time he was the
oldest of all the cosmonauts, including both pilots and non-pilots.

When Beregovoi reported in to Star Town, Komarov, Feoktistov,
and Yegorov were already in the stage of familiarization work with
the three-seat *Voskhod*-1. Beregovoi, too, began to work with this
spacecraft.

On the day when *Voskhod*-1 was launched, Beregovoi watched
the liftoff of the three cosmonauts and wondered: "When will my
turn come" It was known that the flight of *Voskhod*-2 was already
scheduled, but the crew had not yet been selected.

The flight of *Voskhod*-1, with its space crew of three, went off
beautifully. Soon a Wall of Fame was erected along the main
drive of Star Town, honoring the names of the heroes of space
travel: Yuri Gagarin, Gherman Titov, Andriyan Nikolayev, Pavel
Popovich, Valentina Tereshkova, Valery Bykovsky, Vladimir Komarov, Konstantin Feoktistov, and Boris Yegorov. I often used to
pause in front of that wall of gray marble, read the names inscribed in letters of gold, and wonder who would be next.

When the flight of Belyayev and Leonov went off successfully,
their names were added to those already glittering on the wall.

By way of preparation for his flight, Beregovoi was trained on
special stands and simulators. He was whirled on the centrifuge,
he made parachute jumps, he kept his balance in the unstable seat
of the "striped rotator," and sweated profusely in the ovenlike
thermal chamber. In the airborne "zero gravity swimming pool"

he swam very well. But it turned out that Beregovoi could not swim in water.

Once this fact had come to light, he had to set about mastering all styles of swimming and learning how to dive from the board all in a very short time. I saw how zealously Beregovoi worked at mastering this new discipline. After all, it's not easy to learn to swim at the age of forty-four.

When the prototype of the new *Soyuz* spacecraft had been assembled at Star Town, Beregovoi looked it over with great curiosity. Then he got into the command module and stretched out on the long seat to see whether it was comfortable. "It's fine," he said.

Beregovoi was continuing the testing begun by Komarov. The experience was not new to him. When one of his fellow test pilots was killed, he had continued his work and completed the test-flying of the new aircraft.

Beregovoi worked on an extensive program of scientific and technical experiments that he was to carry out, in particular, effecting a rendezvous between *Soyuz* and another pilotless craft put into orbit earlier. In the course of the flight he would also have to maneuver *Soyuz* manually, then make a soft landing.

Beregovoi explained to me that *Soyuz'* aerodynamic re-entry trajectory would make it possible considerably to increase the accuracy of the touchdown and to reduce to three or four G's the forces acting on the cosmonaut. He recalled that with a ballistic re-entry the loads were as high as eight or ten G's.

Beregovoi told me matter-of-factly: "On spacecraft of *Vostok* type, the capsule was designed to accommodate only one cosmonaut. Moreover, the duration of the flight was limited, although Valery Bykovsky, in *Vostok*-5, set a world record for duration of flight: 119 hours. In general," he concluded, "*Vostok* was a fine craft, and it made history. For that matter, both *Vostok* and *Voskhod* were fine; but *Soyuz* is better. It is a regular 'flying apartment'; or rather, a 'flying laboratory.' There's a lot of room—room to work in and room for resting."

Everything was going along well. During the winter Beregovoi trained in the simulator, flew aircraft, and studied *Soyuz* in detail at the plant. And then, like a thunderbolt out of the blue, a catastrophe occurred. The day of 27 March 1968 proved a fatal one.

That morning, Yuri Gagarin had jotted down his agenda for the day on a leaf of his calendar:

1. 1000—training flights.
2. 1700—editorial board of the magazine *Ogonyok* [round table]. I am to speak.
3. 1930—meeting with foreign delegations. Central Committee of the Young Communists' League.

Left lying on the calendar was his identification card as a corresponding member of the Children's Astronautics Association—valid until the year 1999.

On the morning of 27 March, at the scheduled time, Yuri Gagarin took off on a training flight. He was accompanied by an experienced flying instructor, Hero of the Soviet Union Vladimir Seregin. Gagarin's love of flying was almost compulsive: he couldn't live without it. At this time, he was dreaming of a new space flight and preparing for it.

The jet trainer climbed into the sky. The flight had begun normally. Gagarin felt good. But what happened next—in the sky above the wooded region around the town of Vladimir—is extremely difficult to describe. The MIG-15, veering off course, went into a steep dive. Smashing through birches and pines, the plane plunged into the ground.

The horrifying news shook the nation and the whole world. Was it possible to believe that Gagarin was dead? The tragic death of the "Columbus of Space" was beyond one's capacity for realization. Korolev's words came to mind: "Yuri is the personification of the eternal youth of the Russian people." Millions of people gazed at photographs of Gagarin—and remembered his lively, impetuous temperament—that of a very courageous man.

I visited the spot where Gagarin was killed, and I shall never forget that path through the woods, the trees knocked down by the plane, and the murky-green, stagnant water in the little pond that had formed in the swampy terrain where the plane had crashed . . . Scattered around it, on the spongy ground, were fragments of the plane's duraluminum fuselage and its wings.

The cosmonauts were grief-stricken and wept. They recalled Gagarin's flight; how he commanded their detachment; how he taught others and learned himself.

Moscow bade farewell to the first cosmonuat, who had perished so tragically.

I remember that Beregovoi came to Red Square and stood for a long time in front of the Kremlin wall gazing at the names inscribed in letters of gold: Korolev . . . Komarov . . . Gagarin . . . Seregin . . .

As the two of us were walking across the square, Beregovoi said almost sharply: "We won't retreat!" And he recalled what Gagarin had written after Komarov's death: "Nothing will stop us. The road to the stars is steep and dangerous. But we're not afraid."

I looked at Beregovoi's grim, sorrowful face and thought of the emotional stress he was under. How brave a man had to be, after so many tragedies and shattering experiences, to go to the launch pad and test a new spacecraft in flight!

Beregovoi threw himself into training for his flight. Late in the summer of 1968, when his training was completed, he was granted a furlough. He could have gone to the seashore in the Crimea or the Caucasus, or to Lake Issyk-Kul in Turkestan. But what he preferred above all was an automboile trip.

He and his wife, Lydia, spent a long time deciding where they should go. They leafed through tourist guidebooks and studied road maps. Finally Beregovoi suggested to his wife that they visit the sites of the air strips from which his unit had operated during the war. She agreed, since it was only natural she should want to see the areas where her husband had been in combat. Also, as a teacher of history, she wanted to take advantage of the trip to find out more about the Great Patriotic War.

I was fortunate enough to accompany the Beregovois and was struck by how calm he was at the wheel of his Volga. He was wearing a light suit, white panama hat, and sunglasses, and hummed a scarcely audible tune.

After visiting Khimki, where the defenders of Moscow are commemorated by gigantic steel antitank "hedgehog," we made a stop near Klin. "Our airstrip was right over there—not far from the road," Beregovoi said.

We set off across the fields toward the site of the airstrip. The path through the grain field led to a grove, behind which was a village. Beregovoi frowned and got out his map. This was the right place, but no airstrip could be seen.

"This is where we used to take off from," he said. "And there was a landmark. But now people are living here . . ."

He looked around for the landmark, but couldn't find it. "More than twenty years have gone by," he said at length. "Actually, you know, it's a good thing there's no longer an airstrip here."

At the Tchaikovsky Museum in Klin, the Beregovois walked in the garden listening to the great composer's Fourth Piano Concerto. "I and my plane helped to defend this house," Beregovoi said to his wife, in a low voice. "Our airstrip was over there . . ."

A day later it turned out that we had already covered 1,000 kilometers, and apparently the trip was only beginning. We turned off the main road and drove to the green heights of the Pushkin Hills. At the Svyatogorsk Monastery, we went up the stone steps to Pushkin's grave and stood for a long time by the marble obelisk.

Beregovoi pointed into the distance and said to his wife: "There was an air field over there."

Leaving the Svyatogorsk Monastery, we went for a walk in the preserve of "Pushkin country" in the shady woods of Mikhailovskoye.[1] We spent the day at Mikhailovskoye; and that evening, as we sat around a campfire on the bank of the Sorota River, Beregovoi told us some war stories:

"The ack-ack slashed into my plane, and I crashed into the trees. I crawled down out of the cockpit. After I'd stretched out on the ground for a bit and felt stronger, I looked at my map. I was dumbfounded: it was 150 kilometers back to our own lines! I spent five days fighting my way through the woods and swamps. . . .

"Then there was the thing that happened in the Kursk Bulge, near Yakovlevka. We got hit; and my gunner, Petr Ananyev, was wounded. 'Jump!' I shouted at him. 'But what about you, sir?' he asked. 'It's an order: jump! I'll follow you.' The cockpit was full of smoke, and Ananyev's boots and pack were ablaze.

"We came down in no man's land, and the Germans opened fire on us. But just then, from out of nowhere, a Russian jalopy showed up. The driver—a daredevil master sergeant from a tank

[1] Mikhailovskoye was a small estate inherited by Pushkin's mother, where the poet wrote some of his most important works, and where he spent the last years (1824–26) of his banishment from St. Petersburg under virtual house arrest.— Translator

battalion by the name of Vasily Rytsin—had driven through the exploding shells right up to the plane. He dragged us out, half-alive, put us in the jalopy, and hauled us away. Thanks to Rytsin, I was saved. I owe my life to him."

The moon had risen above the Pushkin Hills. A cool breeze was blowing from the river. The branches on the campfire were crackling. Beregovoi turned them over, fanned the acrid smoke away from his face and went on with his war stories.

I noticed that even when talking about the most horrifying things, he smiled, so as not to frighten his listeners. And instead of making much of his own experiences, he tended to laugh them off, as if to say, "War is war." Yet he remembered the names of gunners, radiomen, mechanics, machinists, fellow pilots, and the commanders of units and formations.

The campfire died down. It was time to go to bed. We'd be on the road again in the morning.

Beregovoi suggested that the two of us take a short walk. "It's so beautiful . . . Yuri would have admired it . . . Gagarin loved nature . . ."

We walked through the tall grass to the river, saying nothing, until Beregovoi suddenly exclaimed: "Do you think I might not make the flight?"

It turned out that he had been thinking about the flight the whole time. Whether he was reminiscing about the war, driving his car, sitting down to eat, or looking at "the sights," whatever he was doing, he kept thinking about the impending launch, about space, mentally seeing himself in the cabin of *Soyuz*. It must have required great strength of will not to betray his preoccupation with thoughts that were life and breath to him; that never left his mind, whether he was driving or making a halt, whether it was daytime or nighttime . . .

After a trip of some 3,500 kilometers, Beregovoi and his wife returned to Star Town. During what was left of his furlough, he helped his son prepare for his exams at the institute, worked on his car, and went to the theater with Lydia. One day in late September I went with him to the Kursk Station, where he was to meet his daughter, Lyuda, who had spent the summer at Artek.[2] And there at the station, I made a discovery: it turned out that Bere-

[2] The name of a "Pioneer" camp on the Black Sea.—Translator

govoi *was* capable of anxiety, after all. He kept wondering aloud how Lyuda was, whether her train wasn't perhaps late.

When the train pulled in, we could see Lyuda standing at an open window. She was waving and shouting something. Beregovoi dashed into the car and embraced his daughter—a slender girl tanned by the sun of the Crimea. His eyes shone with happiness.

"At Artek we have a space exhibit!" Lyuda blurted out. "Gagarin founded it, and some of his things are on display there. Some real instruments and a spacesuit! We have them there at Artek!"

Beregovoi smiled gently as he listened to his daughter. She did not yet know that her daddy would soon by flying off to the cosmodrome.

"This Is Argon!"

It was 26 October 1968. In the Co-ordinating Data-Processing Center, mathematicians were bent over columns of figures. One after another, electric figures flashed on screens, they were counting off fractions of seconds. On other panels, larger and brighter figures showed the time remaining before liftoff. The green and red indicator lights on the electronic computers—which were processing a vast flow of information—flashed on and off. The ground tracking and communications stations were in operation.

Over the air waves we heard: "This is Dawn . . . This is Dawn . . . Argon! Argon! How are you feeling?"

"Argon" was Beregovoi's call sign.

Firing switch to "Launch" . . . Liftoff!

And the boundless steppe, in the rain and mist, was suddenly far below him.

"The liftoff was smooth—even gentle," Beregovoi reported. "Now here come the G-loads . . . But everything is normal. Everything is fine."

In the main room of the CDPC, a huge map of the world was projected on a screen, showing the spacecraft's itinerary, traced out by one luminous orbit after another. In this same room was a blue globe around which a model spacecraft "flew," giving a three-dimensional notion of the earth-orbiting flight. Meantime, in front of the instrument panel in *Soyuz*-3, a miniature globe was revolving. The synchronous reciprocal action of these two globes— one on the spaceship and one in the CDPC—indicated the cosmonaut's position relative to the earth's surface.

There was close communication between the huge room of the CDPC and the command module of the spacecraft. We had the impression that Beregovoi was right there in the room, among us. Or rather, that all the maps, charts, globes, and flashing displays, together with the long polished table, the operations officer's console, the director's post, and the mathematicians' table, were contained in the roomy cabin of the spacecraft and were in orbit.

Beregovoi looked at us from the television screen and reported his observations in a businesslike tone. Then, as we watched him, he made a notation in the logbook and got busy with his instruments.

The program called for the two spacecraft, *Soyuz*-2 and *Soyuz*-3, to rendezvous and perform various maneuvers. Automatic systems were used in the radar search phase and in bringing the two spacecraft to within 656 feet of each other. The computers guided *Soyuz*-3 toward the "target"—the pilotless *Soyuz*-2. The rest of the approach and maneuvering was done by manual control. Beregovoi operated the maneuvering thrusters by means of on-board computers and other mechanisms of space navigation.

To all intents and purposes, Beregovoi was the first to effect orbital rendezvous and maneuver manually. When this basic part of the flight plan had been carried out, *Soyuz*-3 and *Soyuz*-2 drew apart to a distance of 565 kilometers, so that another approach could be made.

At this point, Beregovoi made a television broadcast from space. Millions of people heard his description of *Soyuz*-3, of space, and the stars. Thanks to his portable television camera, TV viewers could peer through the viewports of the spacecraft and get a look at our greenish planet with its expanse of ocean, the cloud cap over the North Pole, and the dark-hued continents.

"This is Argon . . . This is Argon . . ." Beregovoi's voice, as he gave his call sign, could be heard in the different rooms of the CDPC and at the tracking and communications stations. "This is Argon."

Beregovoi spent four working days in space. During that time, *Soyuz*-3 made sixty-four circuits around the earth.

Beregovoi's experience as a test pilot—the fact that he was accustomed to making various observations while in flight—was very helpful to him, on this space flight, in accurately carrying out a highly complex and crowded program of technical, biomedical, and scientific experiments. He repeatedly maneuvered *Soyuz*-3, using various methods of orientation; effected two rendezvous with the pilotless *Soyuz*-2; and completed a whole series of tests of the spacecraft's systems. In addition, he made observations of the stellar sky, the earth, and other heavenly bodies; detected the storm centers of typhoons and cyclones on the earth's surface; made reports to earth on fires in forests and jungles; studied the brightness of the earth's surface; photographed its cloud cover and snow cover; and photographed its horizon in a daylight and twilight.

At one point, when Beregovoi had transmitted still another "bundle" of observations, one of the scientists at the CDPC exclaimed—both in jest and seriously: "Well, by this time Georgy has given the institutes and laboratories enough to keep them busy for a whole year!"

So far, the flight had gone very well. But what about the re-entry?

I was tense. I kept thinking of that tragedy I would never forget for the rest of my life. And what about Beregovoi? How was he feeling right now?

In the CDPC everyone was watching the TV screen. Beregovoi's facial expression was calm and confident. In bringing *Soyuz*-3 down, he would take advantage of aerodynamic lift. For this purpose, the spacecraft would first be properly oriented in space. Then the retrorockets would be fired, imparting the needed braking impulse to the spaceship. Next, the command module would separate from the rest of the vehicle and, by means of re-entry maneuvering thrusts, be positioned for proper re-entry into the thick layers of the atmosphere. In the last phase, the parachute system would go into operation; then, just before touchdown, the soft-landing retrorockets would be switched on. According to the calculations, Beregovoi would land near the city of Karaganda.

I kept my eyes fixed on the bright screen. The white spot representing *Soyuz*-3 was skittering across the map toward the preselected area on the territory of the Soviet Union. One after another, the commands rang out. Over the radio came reports that the computers had completed their assigned tasks. My heart was pounding, and my mouth was dry . . .

High above the earth, the command module with the cosmonaut inside, was slicing through the gaseous envelope of our planet like a fiery meteorite—heated up by atmospheric friction and surrounded by raging flames.

The retrorockets were fired when *Soyuz*-3 was above the Atlantic Ocean. Then it was over Africa. Then over the Caspian Sea . . .

The parachute system went into operation . . .

Then the soft-landing retrorockets were fired . . .

And that was it.

The scientists, the ballistics mathematicians, the engineering estimators—everyone who for the past four days had been working in the tracking and communications stations, the observatories, and the CDPC—congratulated one another on the success.

"Beregovoi has touched down at the preselected site," the search party reported. "Everything is fine . . ."

The blizzard which had been raging over the steppe all night quieted down toward morning, and the search party had reached the touchdown point in good time. Scarcely had the spacecraft set down on earth, with its huge red-and-white parachute billowing, than someone's face appeared at the viewport. Beregovoi opened the egress hatch and was almost blinded by the glaring whiteness of the snow-covered steppe. Then, near a dark-hued haystack, he noticed a boy on a donkey—waving his fur cap and shouting something. In a matter of moments, *Soyuz*-3 was encircled by searchers—by kolkhoz farmers.

This was the earth. This was home.

At Vnukovo, the red carpet was spread out on the concrete, and artillery pieces were brought out to fire the salute. Thousands of red banners with Beregovoi's likeness on them were being waved by people of all ages who had hurried to welcome the cosmonaut on Lenin Prospekt.

When the ceremonies in the capital were over, the first cosmonaut with the rank of general—Major General of Aviation Georgy Beregovoi, flier-cosmonaut of the USSR, twice honored with the title Hero of the Soviet Union—returned to Star Town. The black limousine stopped at the end of a red carpet—a continuation, as it were, of the famous red carpet at Vnukovo.

Cosmonauts, pioneers, and school children holding bouquets were standing on the steps of the Palace of Culture. Beregovoi got out of the car. Here he was at home. And it was here that I first saw him really become emotional.

For that matter, he made no attempt to hide his feelings. Plainly, he didn't know what to do—whether to walk the red carpet with a military gait or run over to his friends and embrace them . . . He hesitated for a moment, then impetuously headed for the crowd. He embraced and kissed his friends, shook the hands reached out toward him from all sides, and seemed never to realize how he ended up on the speakers' rostrum in the Palace of Culture.

The crowd overflowing the hall greeted him with an ovation. He thanked his instructors, his cosmonaut friends, and all those who had helped him with friendly advice and scientific counsel. Then he paused, looking out over the rows of happy people in a holiday mood.

"We are all indebted to Yuri Gagarin," he said. "Gagarin was the first. We followed him."

At that moment, everyone in the hall remembered Gagarin's keen eyes and brilliant smile. One had the feeling that, at any moment, he would come into the hall, laughing . . . But he didn't come in.

In a choked voice, Beregovoi said: "Valya Gagarin is here among us."

Then he gathered up all the flowers from the table on the speakers' platform and, clutching them to his chest, stepped down from the stage. Everyone stood up. A strange silence came over the hall. Beregovoi went along the aisle to the rear. Shy and trembling, Valentina Gagarin got up to greet him. As she looked at him, her expression was sorrowful.

Everyone in the hall was silent—thinking of the man who had been here so often, who had spoken from the rostrum, greeted foreign guests, and shared his memories with young people.

Beregovoi tendered the flowers to Valya Gagarin. She began to weep. And the fearless flier, who had seen death many times, had tears in his own eyes.

Without saying a word, he returned to the stage, mounted the rostrum, and began to tell about his flight, the rendezvous with the pilotless *Soyuz-2*, and the maneuvers in orbit.

In concluding his speech, he said: "My heartiest thanks to the designers—and to the scientists, engineers, and workers who built the new spacecraft, *Soyuz*. It's a fine ship!"

Then he looked at Vladimir Shatalov, Boris Volynov, Aleksei Yeliseyev, and Evgeny Khrunov, who were in the audience. And as though passing the space baton on to them, he added: "We have among us, the men who are going to carry out the new program on this spacecraft. Gentlemen, I wish you success."

Launch
After Launch

The scientists and designers had envisaged the *Soyuz* spaceship as a part of a future orbital station. Two *Soyuzes* could be linked up or "docked," thereby creating the first experimental station in orbit. This was the idea behind the decision—made in January 1969—to carry out a very complex experiment: to launch two spacecraft, and effect manual docking in orbit.

After lengthy consideration of the candidates for making up the crews of the two *Soyuzes*, the "Big Four" were chosen: Boris Volynov, Vladimir Shatalov, Evgeny Khrunov, and Aleksei Yeliseyev.

This foursome included both veterans and newcomers. Boris Volynov and Evgeny Khrunov were certainly veterans. They had joined the cosmonaut team along with Yuri Gagarin and Gherman Titov. In the years since, they had gone through all kinds of training sessions and had served as backups on several occasions.

Yuri Gagarin had a good understanding of the mental state of a man like Volynov, who had often been someone else's backup. And by way of consolation, he once told him: "Boris, you know that the longer the flight, the more complex it is. You have been trained for the most complex flight, and you'll get it. Remember what I told you."

And Korolev had promised Volynov: "We'll give you a very special mission. You're strong, and you'll bear up. Okay?"

"I'll do my best," Volynov replied.

Later, Volynov served as Beregovoi's backup. This enabled him to make a very careful study of the *Soyuz* spacecraft.

When he had seen Beregovoi off, Volynov came back to Star Town and occupied himself with the most commonplace kind of work. He was calm and businesslike. During a brief interval of his spare time, I took a walk with Volynov along the drives of Star Town. We struck up a conversation about serving as backup. And Volynov remarked philosophically: "You have to learn how to wait. Going to the launch pad as a backup strengthens your will—it helps you to train better for your own liftoff. And I believe my own liftoff will come. Serving as a backup is a good kind of training for cosmonauts."

I listened to Boris Volynov and wondered about his staunch character. He was a Siberian, and this in itself meant a lot. Anyone born in Siberia has imbibed the Siberian strength along with his mother's milk. In early childhood, he becomes familiar with boundless expanses and huge forests—with mountain peaks and the rushing of torrents down the cliffs.

Volynov was born in Irkutsk, on the banks of the torrential Angara River, on 18 December 1934—right in the middle of a blizzard. His father died when he was very young; and he and his mother—Dr. Evgeniya Volynova—moved to the mining region of Siberia, the Kuzbass. In the city of Prokopyevsk—in the center of the Kuzbass—Dr. Volynova built up a good practice as a well-liked physician. Her patients included workers from all the mines.

Boris Volynov was graduated from high school in Prokopyevsk. One of his schoolmates was Tamara, who later became his wife. They grew up together, became friends, fell in love, and founded a well-knit family.

After getting his wings at the Volgograd Military Aviation School, Volynov served with various Air Force units. Then, in 1960, he joined the cosmonaut team. While performing his duties on the cosmonaut team, he completed course work at the Zhukovsky Air Force Engineering Academy. Meantime his wife, Tamara, had become a metallurgical engineer and had gone to work at a machine-building plant near Moscow. When Boris was preparing for his exams, she—as an experienced engineer—helped him with his calculations and blueprints.

The second veteran among the "Big Four" was Evgeny Khrunov. He was born on 10 September 1933, in a village near Tula, south of Moscow. After finishing seven-year school, he entered an agricultural technical school. But he had been interested in flying since early childhood, and in 1953 he enrolled at a flying school. Later he became a military pilot, and in 1960 he joined the cosmonaut team.

Khrunov might well serve as a model of simplicity and that kind of modesty which can reach the point of shyness. He is reserved, self-effacing, and always preoccupied with something. He was Leonov's backup.

I well remember a birthday party given for Khrunov. His wife, Svetlana, his son, Valery, and their friends and neighbors had prepared a festive table. When the guests had assembled, they all drank a toast to "the eternal backup." Khrunov did not feel offended. He merely spread his hands in helpless gesture, as if to say, "Well, what can a man do? That's the way it has to be."

Aleksei Leonov raised his goblet of champagne and made a little speech about Khrunov, his backup. "He's a man of strong convictions, and a first-rate flier. If he says he's ready, you can bet that he is. He always means just what he says."

When the guests had congratulated Khrunov and everyone had talked for a while, he invited them into his study, where a movie screen had been set up. His son, Valery, switched off the lights, Khrunov started the projector, and the "family show" began.

We saw Valery taking his first steps and watched him running and playing with other children. And we saw some shots of the south country, taken in Sochi and the Crimea, where the cosmonauts were vacationing. One sequence I remember particularly well. Wearing aqualungs, Khrunov, Volynov, Nikolayev, and Popovich came out of the sea. They took off their masks and frolicked about on the beach for a little while. Then they sat down on the stones. A moment later, oblivious of the scorching sun, they were drawing patterns in the sand—tracing out orbits and a diagram for the manual docking of two spacecraft.

Among those viewing the film was a newcomer, Aleksei Yeliseyev.

He had joined the cosmonaut team in 1966—six years later than Yuri Gagarin, Gherman Titov, and Evgeny Khrunov. With his wife, Larisa, and his daughter Lena, Yeliseyev watched with evident pleasure the shots of him water-skiing that Khrunov had taken. Looking darkly tanned in his swimming trunks, with outstretched hands grasping the "reins" from the motor boat, Yeliseyev skimmed along the blue water past the steep cliffs on the shore.

The young Yeliseyev was greatly influenced by the books on Tsiolkovsky that he read, and his own reflections about the man who had opened up the road to the stars. He developed an interest in aviation, and then in cosmonautics.

The Yeliseyev family moved to Moscow, where the future cosmonaut's mother, Valentina, took her doctor's degree and became a professor. (She is on the staff of the Institute of Physical Chemistry, Academy of Sciences, USSR.) Valentina was helpful to her son when he came to choose his own profession. After high school, Aleksei Yeliseyev entered the Bauman Higher Technical College in Moscow. When he was graduated, he went to work at a design bureau. In 1967 he earned the degree of Doctor of Technical Sciences.

When S. P. Korolev heard of the young scientist's desire to join the cosmonaut team, he gave him enthusiastic support. The chief designer was convinced that as many scientists, doctors, and design engineers as possible should be sent on space flights.

In the dual flight of *Soyuz*-4 and *Soyuz*-5, Evgeny Khrunov and Aleksei Yeliseyev had a very important task to perform: to transfer from one spacecraft to the other through open space. There was good reason why Aleksei Leonov was a most welcome guest at Khrunov's birthday party. The future "swimmers" in open space had become friends with the man who had first stepped into the "ocean of air." It was not simply that they profited from his advice. It was on the basis of Leonov's drawings that they studied space, the future docking operation, and the transfer in orbit.

According to the program, the two spacecraft, when they had docked, would become an experimental space station. After docking, Khrunov and Yeliseyev would transfer from one ship to the other, thereby demonstrating that in the future, people could do such things in open space as work on the assembly of manned stations, do welding, repair spacecraft, and fuel rockets.

Before attempting manual docking, an experiment was carried out with automatic devices. In October 1967, for the first time in the world, two Sputniks—*Kosmos*-188 and *Kosmos*-186—were automatically docked in orbit.

Both Sputniks were equipped with coupling units and special automatic approach control systems. After being put into orbit, they carried out several complex maneuvers—reciprocal radar search, approach, and link-up—and were then firmly docked. Subsequently they were undocked and de-orbited.

This successful experiment opened up broad prospects for the in-orbit assembly of large space stations capable of carrying out complex and varied investigations of space and the planets.

The computers had paved the way for the cosmonauts.

Vladimir Shatalov and Boris Volynov were named as commanders of the spaceships.

Vladimir Shatalov was born on 8 December 1927, in Petropavlovsk, a city in southwestern Siberia, but he spent his childhood and youth in Leningrad. The young Shatalov liked to build model airplanes, and experts in this field recommended him for admission to a special Air Force school. He completed ground school training, and (later) flight training at the flying school in Kacha. In 1956 he was graduated with distinction from the Red Banner Air Force Academy. In 1963 he joined the cosmonaut team.

Shatalov—fair-haired, powerfully built, and handsome—soon became known on the cosmonaut team as an excellent engineer and a cool-headed, tireless investigator. He was named commander of the so-called active spacecraft.

Here a word of explanation may be in order. Of the two spaceships put into orbit for docking, one would be equipped with a special rod-like coupling unit. This is the "active" spacecraft. After rendezvous, when the two spaceships were next to each other, the "active" spacecraft would insert its coupling rod into the adapter unit of the other *Soyuz,* thereby docking with it.

At Star Town, special, complex simulators were built—life-size, electrically operated mock-ups of the *Soyuz* modules that reproduced various conditions of space flight. I was fortunate enough to spend some time in these simulators with Shatalov and Volynov. I watched them as they took their places on the contour seats—together with Khrunov and Yeliseyev—and then went through the training procedures.

Manual docking requires a good seaman's eye, a firm hand, a cool head, and patience . . . I watched Shatalov. He was closely attentive to his work. There in the simulator, he seemed to feel he was in the command module of the spacecraft itself. And, indeed, an illusion of space flight had been created by means of cinematography. When he looked out of the viewport, stars twinkled, the moon shone, and the sun rose . . .

In the course of this extraordinary experiment it would be necessary for the "active" spacecraft to locate the other one in the boundlessness of space, then rendezvous and dock with it. It should be borne in mind that at this time the two spacecraft would be orbiting with a velocity of eight kilometers per second.

I watched Shatalov as he went over to manual control and brought his "spaceship" closer to the other "spaceship." Now the distance between them was only 492 feet . . . Through the optical sighting device, the coupling ring and winking navigational lights of the other simulator were already visible. Then came the long-awaited signal: "Docking completed."

All this, of course, took place in a laboratory, using simulators. But I was left with the impression that I had witnessed a real docking in orbit.

I was equally impressed by the training sessions in the TBK (thermal decompression chamber), in which the conditions of space vacuum had been reproduced. Before the session, I watched the cosmonauts get into special spacesuits equipped with flat packs containing their life-support systems. As I looked at the silvery spacesuits, it occurred to me that tailoring had now taken on a cosmic character—had in fact become a matter of designing complex engineering installations. The outer, protective coating of the spacesuit reflects the hot rays of the sun and creates a moderate temperature on the surface of the spacesuit. Other layers protect the wearer against the deadly space vacuum and assure the complete airtightness of the whole suit. And the heat-insulation layer serves as a kind of overcoat, protecting the cosmonaut against the penetration of solar heat—or the "cold" of the space environment.

While on a visit to the plant where the spacesuits are made, I took a look under these various layers and saw what they concealed: electric wiring, cables, valves, and entire systems of ventilation, heating, lighting, sanitation, and oxygen supply. At that same plant I tried on an experiment space helmet, complete with face plate and big light-filtering goggles. Inside the space helmet were a microphone and a telephone. I plugged them in and talked to the designer.

Space helmets of this kind were designed for Khrunov and Yeliseyev, since they would have to leave the craft and go into open space. Also, special flat packs stuffed with life-support systems had been made for them so as to supply oxygen during their extravehicular activity.

In their white spacesuits, with the life-support packs strapped to their legs,[1] Khrunov and Yeliseyev entered the thermal decompression chamber. When they were inside, the heavy hatch was closed. On the TV screen, I saw the cosmonauts take their places on the contour seats. The instruments showed that a vacuum—a mortally dangerous, airless space—had been created in the chamber.

While in this vacuum, the cosmonauts performed various tasks and tested their spacesuits.

At length, all the different kinds of training sessions were completed. And in freezing-cold weather, right after New Year's Day, preparations for the dual launch of the carrier rockets were begun at the cosmodrome.

By the morning of 14 January 1969, one of the boosters was in position on the launch pad—looming up among the work towers and through the thin clouds formed by the evaporation of the propellant.

Shatalov rode up to the top deck and raised both hands above his head by way of greeting. Then, helped by the technicians, he crawled through the hatch into the orbital section. When he had checked out the equipment there, he crawled down through another hatch into the cabin (command module). At this point, both hatches were hermetically sealed.

Shatalov took his place in the cabin, securing himself in the contour seat by means of the restraining straps. Then he reported: "Everything is in order."

Soyuz-4 lifted off at 10:39 A.M. The work towers and the um-

[1] These small life-support packs or "boxes" could be attached to any part of the cosmonaut's body.—Translator

bilical tower were pulled back. From under the rocket, blinding
flame burst with a deafening roar. The rocket was still being
held in the embrace of the clamps, until the required amount of
thrust was built up. But a moment later the clamps had burned off,
and Shatalov was reporting that he felt normal, and the spacecraft's systems were functioning normally.

In Star Town, as in millions of apartments all over the country,
people were keeping track of this flight that had just begun. Then,
only one day later, the world got the news that another spacecraft—
Soyuz-5—had been launched, with three cosmonauts on board:
Volynov, Yeliseyev, and Khrunov.

When *Soyuz*-5 had been successfully put into orbit, it was time
for the second phase of the flight: the rendezvous and manual
docking of the two *Soyuzes*. The spacecraft commanders, Shatalov
and Volynov, performed a series of maneuvers by manual control,
bringing the two spaceships closer together from a distance of
more than a thousand kilometers. But when the distance had
been reduced to only a few kilometers, automatic approach control
systems went into operation.

The following is Vladimir Shatalov's account of how the first
manual docking was effected:

> The two spacecraft carried out radar search procedure,
> located each other, and started to rendezvous. The automatic
> approach control systems brought them to within 300 feet of
> each other. At this point, I went over to manual control, and
> Boris Volynov did the same. The problem was to make sure
> that the docking units of both spacecraft were properly oriented
> toward each other. Throughout this time I was manually con-
> trolling the appropriate thrusters. With the control stick on the
> left-hand side I regulated the craft's linear velocity—slowing it
> down or speeding it up—and damped out the lateral velocity.
> When we were over the shores of Africa—some seven or eight
> thousand kilometers from the borders of the Soviet Union—we
> approached to within 130 feet of each other and started to
> hover. At this range, Boris Volynov and I performed several
> maneuvers.

All this time, a three-way conversation was going on among
Shatalov, Volynov, and Ground Control.

143. The *Soyuz*-9 spaceship being installed on the launching pad.

144. The *Soyuz*-9 spaceship before the takeoff on 1 June 1970.

145. Before the takeoff, Cosmonauts Andriyan Nikolayev and Vitaly Sevastyanov are saying good-by to earth, their friends, and all those who helped them to prepare for the flight.

146. Flight Engineer Vitaly Sevastyanov and Commander Andriyan Nikolayev aboard the *Soyuz*-9 spaceship, 1 June 1970.

147. The press conference with Soviet journalists after the flight of *Soyuz*-9. Andriyan Nikolayev and Vitaly Sevastyanov.

148. Lunokhod-1 model during testing on the terrestrial "lunodrome."

149. A part of the photo taken on the moon with the right camera-telephotometer of Lunokhod-1 on 9 December 1970. Clearly seen is a track left by Lunokhod-1.

150. Rocket carrier with the spaceship *Soyuz*-10 on its launching stand.

151. Baikonur, 6 June 1971. Rocket carrier with the spaceship *Soyuz*-11 before launching.

152. Crew of the *Soyuz*-11. Left to right: Vladislav N. Volkov, flight engineer, Georgy T. Dobrovolsky, commander, and Viktor I. Patsayev, test engineer, in the spaceship cabin. They died in a tragic accident during re-entry on 30 June 1971.

153. *Salyut* piloted station in the assembly shop.

Shatalov: Everything is normal. Everything is going normally. Range 130 feet. Speed near to zero. Approach begun.

Ground Control: Roger. I'm watching you.

Volynov: Roger, Amur. Roger. Dawn, Dawn, this is Baikal. Read you loud and clear. Range 130. The spacecraft is responding perfectly. But for some reason my "Docking" light is off and my "Contact" light is on.

Ground Control: All correct. That's the way it should be.

Shatalov: Request permission to begin docking.

Ground Control: Permission granted . . . This is Dawn. If possible, give us a brief account of what you're doing.

Shatalov: Roger. I now have Baikal on my screen. Velocity 0.82 feet per second. We'll proceed. Panels clearly visible.

Ground Control: Fine. Everything is normal.

Khrunov (*breaking in*): Beautiful! Very beautiful! Just magnificent! Amur is flying like a bird from a fairy tale! She's coming up like an aircraft—approaching like an aircraft!

Khrunov was interrupted by the calm voice of Volynov: "Everything is fine. Everything is fine. Waiting for contact."

High above the earth, far from their homeland, the two spaceships, like two fantastic birds, with the panels of their solar batteries outspread, were coming close together. One more second and the rod of the "active" spacecraft would be inserted into the adapter cone of the "passive" *Soyuz.*

Shatalov: I'm moving in. Everything normal. Contact. Linkup. Firm docking.

Ground Control: We can see it clearly. Every detail is visible. Everything is fine. Right on the nose!

Then Shatalov's jovial, joyful voice rang out: "Welcome, Baikal! The docking went off splendidly. The spacecraft are matched. Fastening is being continued. No relative motion between the spaceships."

On both spacecraft, the "Mechanical Contact" and "Coupling" lights flashed on. The spaceships linked up on equalized planes;

the switch catches went into operation; the electrical plugs were connected; and then the "Docking Completed" light flashed on.

An experimental space station with a crew of four had been docked.

When the space station had begun to function, the cosmonauts got ready to carry out the second part of the program: the transfer from one spacecraft to the other.

Khrunov and Yeliseyev decided they wouldn't be empty-handed when they came to call on Shatalov. Taking advantage of the fact that their own spacecraft had been launched a full day after Shatalov's, they had brought with them mail addressed to Shatalov, newspapers with articles about the flight, and photographs published in honor of his liftoff.

Carrying this mail, the photographs, and a movie camera, Khrunov and Yeliseyev got ready to transfer to the other spacecraft. Boris Volynov helped his friends get into their spacesuits and gave them a friendly hug.

Up to that time, no one had ever put on a spacesuit under zero gravity conditions. When they were suited, the cosmonauts began to check their communications, locking devices, and fasteners, to make sure that their spacesuits, space helmets, boots, and gloves were absolutely airtight. All this time they were floating about in the service module.

At length, Volynov embraced his friends once again, waved good-by to them, and crawled back through the now open hatch into the command module. Once there, he got back into the pilot's seat.

When Volynov had "swum" through the hatch, Khrunov and Yeliseyev again checked to see whether their spacesuits were airtight and their life-support systems were working. Then they reported they were ready to go out.

After his return to earth, Khrunov told me about his egress into open space:

"According to instructions, I was to be the first to leave the orbital section of Soyuz-5. I remembered Aleksei Leonov's advice: 'The main thing is not to get impatient. Think things over ten times, and wiggle your finger. Then think things over twelve times, and wiggle your hand. Each move you make creates heat within the spacesuit. If you make abrupt, hasty motions, your body heats up inside the spacesuit. This badly hampers activity, and may even cause a loss of the cosmonaut's working capacity.' I did what Leonov advised. First of all I thought, then I acted. The spacecraft commander, Boris Volynov, made sure that the air-lock system was functioning perfectly and that we cosmonauts were in good shape. Then, at the scheduled time, he gave the command to move out.

"The hatch opened, and a stream of sunlight burst in. The sun was unbearably bright and scorching. Only the thick, filtering visor saved my eyes. I saw the earth, the horizon, and the black sky and had the same feeling I had experienced before my first parachute jumps. And I'll freely admit I felt all the anxiety of an athlete at the starting line. But I overcame that anxiety. I became completely absorbed in my work and thought only of carrying out my assignment.

"I emerged from the spacecraft without difficulty, and looked around. I was amazed by the marvelous, magnificent spectacle of two spacecraft linked together high above the earth. I could make out every tiny detail on their surfaces. They glittered brilliantly as they reflected the sunlight. Right in front of my eyes was *Soyuz*-4, looking very much like an aircraft. The big, long spacecraft was like a fuselage, and the solar panels were like wings.

"When I had taken a good, long look at this wonderful sight—a glittering spacecraft against the background of the earth and the dark sky—I began to move. I went toward the docking unit of *Soyuz*-5. Attached to its outer surface was a camera which had filmed the rendezvous and docking of the spaceships.

"I had learned the rule that Leonov had kept pounding into me: if you move too abruptly away from the spacecraft, you'll start spinning around one axis, or you'll even be rotating around several axes and so lose your spatial orientation. Therefore, you have to calculate and think hard about the degree of effort, the angle of departure, and what the consequences will be.

"What do we mean when we say a man took a 'space *walk*'? For us earthlings, the concept of displacement—of motion—is usually associated with the notion of walking. But under conditions of weightlessness, a person can't 'walk' over the surface of a spacecraft in the usual sense of that verb: there is no actual support under his feet, and nothing pressing to the surface. Way back when we were training in the 'zero-gravity pool' in the cabin of the TU-104 jet airliner, we found out that the best way to move in open space—to 'walk' along the spacecraft from one point to another—was on your hands. Special rigid rails were designed for this purpose.

"And so . . . I grasped one such rail and, going hand over hand, moved toward the camera. Now I was to perform my first work procedure: to remove the camera from its support and turn off its electric power supply. Holding on to the rail with one hand, I used the other to remove the camera and disconnected the electric power supply system. Then, using the same method of hand-walking along the rail, I moved along the surface of the newly assembled orbiting station to the foreward compartment of *Soyuz*-4.

"While I was getting out of the hatch of our ship, Yeliseyev was keeping close behind me. Then he, too, dove into open space, making use of the rails, just as I had done. We made observations of the earth's horizon, checked the operation of the altitude-control jets, and kept in communication with the spacecraft commanders. Then I went into the orbital compartment of *Soyuz*, and from its hatch I watched my friend's progress, keeping in constant communication with him. At a signal from the commander, Yeliseyev went into the orbital compartment. We closed the hatch, cut in the pressure feed, creating normal pressure, and helped each other to take off our spacesuits.

"Then Shatalov came swimming in toward us through the hatch. We all hugged and kissed each other, talking fast and not making much sense. Shatalov thanked us for the mail we had brought him and held up the newspapers and letters for the TV audience to see.

"We decided that the occasion called for a toast; but when we uncorked the bottle, the contents gushed out and sprayed the bulkhead of the compartment. 'The ship is raising the toast for us!' Shatalov joked.

"Now the situation aboard the spaceships had changed. On the ship where there had been three of us, Volynov remained alone; and on the one that Shatalov had been flying by himself, noisy gaiety reigned—because there were three of us."

Joined together, the two *Soyuz* spacecraft formed one big space station. It could perform the same maneuvers as its component craft could separately: orient itself in space, stabilize itself, and change the parameters of its orbit.

At 6:40 P.M. Khrunov and Yeliseyev, now feeling at home in their new working areas, went into the orbital compartment for a rest, while Shatalov rested in the command module. The commander of *Soyuz*-5, alone in his own craft, completed his work schedule and then went into the orbital compartment. There, he radioed a "Good night!" to everyone, and promptly fell asleep. The two spacecraft orbiting the earth had become bedrooms for the cosmonauts, who were exhausted from the stress of the day.

The next day, 17 January 1969, both spaceships touched down at the preselected sites—*Soyuz*-4 forty kilometers northwest of Karaganda, and *Soyuz*-5 200 kilometers southwest of Kustanai.

The achievements? At my request they were summed up by pilot-cosmonaut Konstantin Feoktistov: "The most important achievements of the flight were the successful performance of maneuvers, radar search and contact, approach, link-up, and docking of the spacecraft. It is important to note that docking assured the unity of the entire complex in terms of mechanical systems, power supply, and communications. The driving pulses sent to the verniers and attitude-control jets, were now transmitted throughout the station, and it responsively changed its position in space. Also, the fact that the station had a unified power supply made it easier to concentrate and redistribute electric power in accordance with the cosmonauts' needs. Then, too, with the engines of the two *Soyuzes* forming a single system, the station's capacity for maneuvering, correcting its orbit, and controlling its attitude was substantially increased. On the whole, it is important to note that we have now had operative in space, for the first time, a regular space complex including four individual living areas with an over-all volume of 635.6 cubic feet. The fact that there was so much elbowroom in the compartments had a beneficial effect on the cosmonauts' working capacity and the way they felt.

"The automatic docking of *Kosmos*-186 and *Kosmos*-188 in October 1967 and that of *Kosmos*-212 and *Kosmos*-213 in April 1968 served as the basis for the development that logically followed: the experiment in creating the first manned space station.

"It should be emphasized that principles of automatic maneuvering were sketched out as early as November 1963, and then elaborated in April 1964, when the world's first maneuverable satel-

lites—*Polyot*-1 and *Polyot*-2—were launched. They were equipped
with special apparatus and engine systems making it possible to
change the attitude and plane of the orbit while in flight.

"Another very important achievement of the dual flight,"
Feoktistov continued, "was the transfer, through open space, of
two cosmonauts from one spaceship to another. This experiment
has laid the groundwork for carrying out such extravehicular activities as building orbiting stations, delivering loads to them, and
relieving one crew with another.

"It is quite evident that we are approaching a phase when man
will actively work in space. The hull of a spacecraft will no longer
constitute a barrier for him. The creation of orbiting stations and
laboratories—the highroad of man's penetration into space—is ever
more clearly coming into view."

A Space Flight
into the Future

Today, the investigation of the universe has become a practical
problem of the same order as the investigation and development
of the Antarctic. Speculations about civilizations elsewhere than
on earth—heretofore abstract, not to say fantastic—have become
matters of practical concern.

The second half of the twentieth century is an era of speed,
of the restructuring of life on a global scale, of fantastic discoveries,
and of the rapid obsolescence of what was new only yesterday.

The effect of change is especially striking in Star Town. Today,
when you say to a new arrival, "You're living in a house built on
a spot where there used to be lots of mushrooms . . ." the newcomer just shrugs and looks at you with a rather disdainful smile,
as if to say: "What mushrooms and berries is this old geezer talking
about?" Star Town now has apartment houses, asphalt streets,
stores, an athletic complex, a cultural center, a school, and its own
post office. There is no room for mushrooms here any more.

In the more than ten years of its existence, Star Town has
changed a lot and witnessed many events of various kinds. It seems
only a short time ago, for instance, when Andriyan Nikolayev

saw Valentina Tereshkova off from Star Town for her flight, then tenderly greeted her upon her return to earth; when they fell in love and founded the first "space family."

I attended the wedding of Andriyan and Valentina at the "Marriage Hall" in Moscow. The orchestra was playing, the room was flooded with blinding light from the TV and movie cameras, and the air was full of the scent of flowers. Then the bride and groom entered the crowded hall, accompanied by their cosmonaut friends. Valentina was wearing a white bridal gown, Andriyan a severe black suit. They tried to conceal their excitement as they listened to the heartfelt speech that was part of the ceremony and heard everyone wish them happiness. They signed the marriage register and exchanged gold rings. When it was all over, they went out and got into the honeymoon car that was taking them to a state reception in honor of the space newlyweds.

In due course, a child was born into this cosmonaut family—a daughter named Elena. Today she is a young girl—black-eyed, merry, and fond of dancing.

Andriyan Nikolayev has been graduated with distinction from the Zhukovsky Air Force Academy of Engineering. His wife, Valentina Nikolayeva-Tereshkova, has also taken a degree. She defended her thesis brilliantly and was graduated with distinction. The audience at this ceremony applauded her loudly. When the applause had died down, Nikolayev, rather embarrassed, went over to his wife and kissed her in front of everyone—blushing furiously. Then Georgy Beregovoi congratulated Valentina on behalf of all the cosmonauts and gave her a firm handshake.

Outwardly, life at Star Town goes on at an even pace. Every morning the scientists, technicians, instructors, and engineers form a broad stream of humanity as they go to work. In the laboratories, the simulators, the gymnasium, the stadium, and on the hockey field work begins right on the minute, both winter and summer. At the TSPK—the Yu. A. Gagarin Center for Cosmonaut Training— every activity is called work: gymnastic exercises, tasting "space food," making parachute jumps into a forest or body of water, being whirled around on the "striped rotator" to the point of vertigo, workouts in the zero-gravity pool aboard an aircraft in flight, and the painstaking calculation of orbits . . .

The Gagarin Cosmonaut Training Center has been visited by a wide variety of people interested in the life and work of the

Soviet cosmonauts: scientists and reporters, political figures and philosophers, film stars and writers. Not a day goes by but what the cosmonauts meet guests from foreign countries. But the meeting that created an especially great impression and became a real event was that with the American astronaut Frank Borman. Preparations for his visit to Star Town included an exhibit of photographs dealing with the life and space flights of that intrepid explorer of space and the display of placards reading "Welcome!"

Frank Borman's name became a household word after his flight in *Gemini*-7 in late 1965, and especially after his successful fly-by of the moon in *Apollo*-8 in December 1968. Borman, his wife, and their two sons had come to Moscow as guests of the Union of Soviet Societies of Friendship and the Institute of Soviet-American Relations.

It was in the full heat of summer—on Saturday, 5 July 1969— that Star Town extended its friendly welcome to the American astronaut. At the entrance to the Palace of Culture he was greeted by Marshal of Aviation P. S. Kutakhov, Commander in Chief of the USSR Air Force, Colonel General of Aviation N. P. Kamanin, and the entire cosmonaut detachment. Valentina Nikolayeva-Tereshkova presented a bouquet of flowers and played hostess to the American astronaut's wife and children.

Accompanied by the Soviet cosmonauts, Borman walked through the crowded hall up to the stage. After a speech of welcome by Marshal Kutakhov, the guest gave a talk in which he discussed his space flights—especially the flight of *Apollo*-8 around the moon —and the system of training American astronauts.

Borman paid close attention to the remarks offered by the future flier-cosmonauts then in training for a large-scale flight on three *Soyuz* spacecraft. The program for this flight called for an over-all crew of seven cosmonauts. Two of them, already famous, were seated next to Frank Borman on the stage: Hero of the Soviet Union Vladimir Shatalov and Aleksei Yeliseyev. The other five, still-unknown cosmonauts—Georgy Shonin, Valery Kubasov, Anatoly Filipchenko, Vladislav Volkov, and Viktor Gorbatko—were sitting in the audience with their wives.

On the subject of future orbiting stations, Borman remarked: "Then we astronauts will become celestial cabdrivers, hauling the personnel of those stations when it's time to change shifts. Such stations will be able to strengthen international scientific co-operation, since in fact scientists from various countries will be working in them."

At one point, Borman was asked: "What was your most vivid impression in space?" And the audience applauded loudly when he replied: "The earth as seen from moon orbit. I saw a light blue sphere on which I had left everything dear to my heart. And I thought how small our old mother earth really is, and how we had to take care of her . . ."

As a souvenir of their meeting, Georgy Beregovoi and Pavel Popovich gave Frank Borman a model of the *Vostok* spacecraft in which Yuri Gagarin had made his historic flight. They also presented him with some books and the cosmonauts' memorial badge. For his part, Borman gave them a copy of the film of his flight around the moon in *Apollo*-8. Before presenting it to the cosmonauts, he conducted a showing of the film, accompanied by witty and incisive comments.

After the ceremonies, Gherman Titov, who was accompanying Borman on his trip through the Soviet Union, invited his guest to visit Yuri Gagarin's study. The American astronaut was closely attentive as he looked over the room where the Columbus of Space had worked. By way of commemoration, he wrote a comment in the guest book for honored visitors to the museum.

The send-off for Frank Borman at the Sheremetievo Airport was memorable. Among those who had come to see him off were Colonel General Kamanin, and the flier-cosmonauts Gherman Titov, Georgy Beregovoi, and Konstantin Feoktistov. When I asked Borman to say a few words of farewell, he said: "We American astronauts will never forget that Soviet people were the pathfinders in space. Everything you have done so far has been done successfully, and with great skill."

The Intrepid
Seven

Soviet and American cosmonauts agree that the decisive role in the mastery of space will be played by those orbiting stations. Man is destined to live beyond the earth. There he will find his future. And there he will find the solution to many problems never solved on earth.

One of the causes compelling man to break out beyond the limits of the earth, lies within himself: in his tireless striving to understand the unknown—in the creative drive imparted to him by Nature. But of course there are other important reasons: demographic, social, biological, psychological, etc. With each passing year, Tsiolkovsky's "Program for the Cosmos" acquires even greater significance.

Following the highroad of man's penetration into space, Soviet scientists, designers, engineers, and cosmonauts decided to take one more step toward the creation of orbiting stations. They decided to launch three spacecraft and, in the course of their group flight, to perfect a very complex combined communications system and carry out the maneuvering and rendezvous of the spaceships, along with a series of scientific experiments.

The reader is already acquainted with Vladimir Shatalov and

Aleksei Yeliseyev, who took part in the dual flight made in January. In the course of that experiment, Shatalov performed so well that he was named commander of the crew of seven for the group flight of *Soyuz*-6, *Soyuz*-7, and *Soyuz*-8.

During an interview I had with Shatalov in Star Town, he admitted: "I'm very eager to make another flight. The fact is that when I'm in orbit for the second time, I'll be more able to make thorough observations, to analyze what I've seen, to realize what to expect, and keep cool in the face of emergencies. And I'm sure Yeliseyev is also looking forward to another flight. A second flight would be very useful to him as a scientist."

I of course asked Shatalov, as commander of the seven-man team, about the basic goals of the new group flight. Here is what he told me:

"All seven of us will check out and test the on-board systems and the improved design of the *Soyuz*. We'll have to refine the systems of manual control, attitude control, and stabilization of the spacecraft in orbit. Also, we'll have to check out the autonomous systems of navigation. For the first time, three spacecraft will be in orbit at the same time. They will all carry out procedures of reciprocal maneuvering and approach. Under such conditions, very great importance attaches to the problem of perfecting communications among all three spacecraft and the computer centers on the ground. These centers are located all over the country. But the time will come when we're beyond the radio horizon, and direct contact with the ground will be cut off. Then we'll get help from the radio stations on tracking ships, which will already be in position at sea.

"Incidentally," Shatalov remarked, "the big tracking ship *Cosmonaut Vladimir Komarov* will be in position near Montreal, and will serve as a unique kind of relay station: earth–tracking ship–spacecraft–earth."

During our talk, Shatalov and I had been standing at the entrance of Star Town's planetarium. The commander of the seven-man cosmonaut team glanced at his watch. "Aleksei Yeliseyev will be along in a moment," he said. "We have a lesson coming up in the planetarium."

Aleksei Yeliseyev arrived on the dot, and I went in with the two cosmonauts. Inside the planetarium, the lights slowly went out, and stars twinkled in the "sky." The instructor moved the narrow beam of his searchlight along the display and asked the cosmonauts about the constellations. In the semidarkness of the auditorium I watched the faces of the two men who had already been up in space and were preparing for another launch. Shatalov and Yeliseyev were hard at their work. They answered the questions and then put questions of their own to the instructor. Meantime, they were carefully taking notes, as students should.

When the lesson was over and we had left the planetarium, I asked Shatalov what new results his second flight would yield. He answered laconically: "Everything is new. Everything is interesting. Everything is important."

As we walked along, Yeliseyev tore off the branch of a spruce tree, kneaded it in his hands, then held it against his cheek, passing the needle-shaped leaves along his skin.

Then, weighing every word, he said: "The investigation of space has only just begun. Actually, we have done no more than open our eyes. We'll have to spend a long time studying and analyzing phenomena and facts before we reach a complete understanding of the laws of space—an understanding of its effect on terrestrial phenomena. Of course we have learned a lot in the past few years. But we still have to learn infinitely more. The creation of the first experimental station in orbit, and the transfer from one spacecraft to another, showed that we now have good grounds for considering that the construction—or, more accurately, the assembly—of stations of any desired size is feasible.

"This new flight is important in the sense that it will involve the launching of three spacecraft. All three of them will carry out maneuvers and rendezvous. This simultaneous work may give rise to unforeseen difficulties which will have to be overcome. And in overcoming them, we bring closer the time when orbiting stations are created."

On the path along which we were walking, we met up with Georgy Shonin and Valery Kubasov, hurrying toward the planetarium. These two made up the crew of *Soyuz*-6.

Georgy Shonin was one of the veterans on the cosmonaut team. He was born on 2 August 1935 in the town of Rovenki, in the Ukraine, and spent his childhood years in Balta, not far from Odessa. He early developed an interest in aviation, went to flying school, and later became a fighter pilot. In 1960 he joined the cosmonaut team, along with Yuri Gagarin. Dark-eyed, reserved, and tactful, Shonin earned the respect of the other cosmonauts. On several occasions he had teamed up with Boris Volynov in training sessions; and he was Volynov's backup for the January flight.

Valery Kubasov was born on 7 January 1935 in Vyazniki, northeast of Moscow. After high school he entered the Sergo Ordzhonikidze Aviation Institute in Moscow, then went to work at a design office. While there, he took a degree as Candidate of Technical Sciences.

Kubasov has published a number of scientific papers, e.g., "The Correction of Interplanetary Trajectories Using Impulses of Radial Heliocentric Velocity." In this paper Kubasov analyzed methods of correcting interplanetary trajectories on the theory that the impulses of velocity acted along a line between the vehicle and the sun. The young scientist's paper attracted the attention of S. P. Korolev.

While talking with Kubasov, the chief designer remarked that there would soon be a need for engineers on spacecraft. He said the time was not far off when scientists from various fields would be put to work on earth-orbiting flights. Korolev always kept thinking about "populating" space with scientists. And when he met this powerfully built young man—a scientist and sports enthusiast who was eager to make a space flight—he did everything possible to help him get on the cosmonaut team. In the person of Kubasov —a rugged athlete and gifted scientist—he recognized a true candidate for space flight.

In describing the ideal testing-engineer for space flights, Korolev emphasized his character traits. His decision to become a cosmonaut must not be based on youthful fervor or romanticism for its own sake. The program would not accept such a man. Patriotism, valor, modesty, the ability to make an instantaneous decision with a cool head, an iron will, know-how, and warmth toward other people—such were the decisive traits. Anyone lacking them could not be a cosmonaut. Kubasov remembered Korolev's advice and requirements, and did everything possible to justify the latter's trust in him.

For the group flight, Kubasov was given the assignment of doing the first welding job in space. For this experiment, a special welding unit called "Vulcan" had been designed. Vulcan's designer was an outstanding specialist in the field of welding and a scientist with a worldwide reputation: Academician Boris Paton, president of the Ukrainian Academy of Sciences.

Kubasov met Academician Paton, and the two of them analyzed the results of the tests made on the ground.

I went to Kiev and asked Paton to tell me about the projected welding operations in space.

"The present state of space investigation," he told me, "opens up likely prospects for the creation of permanent orbiting stations with crews alternating shifts. But the practical implementation of these and other schemes is impossible without extensive welding operations in space itself. The deep vacuum, weightlessness, the wide range in temperatures from the intensive heat of the sun to the freezing cold in shadow—the mere list of these factors shows what specific difficulties must be overcome by welders in space. And space also places other demands on the welding equipment: it must be highly reliable, functioning accurately and impeccably under the harsh conditions of space."

In his description of the Vulcan welding outfit, Paton pointed out that because of purely technical complications, it was difficult to reproduce, on earth, the simultaneous action of all those factors operative in space. Therefore, he said, the tests of Vulcan had been conducted stage by stage. First, the basic principles in the designing of small, highly reliable welding units for each of the welding methods being tested were worked out in ordinary vacuum chambers. Then the tests were conducted in aircraft, under conditions of weightlessness and under other conditions.

I was at the airport when Kubasov made in-flight tests of Vulcan under conditions of weightlessness. In the zero-gravity pool I noticed a squat green cylinder somewhat resembling a round refrigerator. Its weight did not exceed 110 pounds. Accompanied by designers, trouble-shooting engineers, and fliers, Kubasov carried out the program of in-flight tests on Vulcan. The young scientist was pleased with the results and was hopeful that the welding in space would go off successfully.

The crew of *Soyuz*-7 consisted of three cosmonauts. Anatoly Filipchenko was named commander. Filipchenko was born on 26 February 1928 in the village of Davydovka, near Voronezh. His first job was as a lathe operator. But he became interested in flying, and went to an Air Force flying school. He was graduated with distinction, and served with various Air Force units. While on duty with the Air Force, he completed a correspondence course and was graduated from the Air Force Academy.

The flight engineer for *Soyuz*-7 was Vladislav Volkov, and the research engineer was Viktor Gorbatko.

Vladislav Volkov, who for some reason was called "Vadim" by the other cosmonauts, was born on 23 November 1935 in Moscow. His father, Nikolai, was an aeronautical engineer, and his mother, Olga, worked at aircraft plants for many years.

Young Volkov became a student at the Moscow Aviation Institute. While still a student, he qualified as a parachutist and a pilot. He was also interested in soccer and hockey. In fact, his skillful performance on the ice and the field was soon well reported by the press.

The other engineer on the crew of *Soyuz*-7, Viktor Gorbatko, was born on 3 December 1934 in a village in the Caucasus, but spent his childhood in the Kuban. After high school, he completed a course at an Air Force ground school, then got his wings at the Bataisk Air Force School. He served in an air regiment along with Evgeny Khrunov. Inasmuch as both were first-rate pilots, they were recommended for the cosmonaut team.

At Star Town, Gorbatko and Khrunov became even closer friends. Both were named as backups for Aleksei Leonov. Later—in January 1969—Gorbatko served as backup for Khrunov. But now his own turn had come.

All three crews had learned how to handle the *Soyuz* spacecraft, completed a series of complex training sessions, and passed their exams. Then they set off for the cosmodrome.

Preparations for the launch of *Soyuz*-6 were begun on the cold, rainy morning of 11 October 1969, with strong whirlwinds raging across the steppe.

Georgy Shonin and Valery Kubasov lifted off at 2:10 P.M. *Soyuz*-6 was put into orbit with an apogee of 223 kilometers and a perigee of 186 kilometers.

At 1:45 P.M. on 12 October 1969, less than a day later, the second spacecraft—*Soyuz*-7—was launched. I have already mentioned its crew: the commander was Anatoly Filipchenko, the flight engineer was Vladislav Volkov, and the research engineer was Viktor Gorbatko. *Soyuz*-7 went into an orbit with an apogee of 226 kilometers and a perigee of 207 kilometers.

The flagship of this space squadron—the third spacecraft, *Soyuz*-8

—was launched one day later: at 1:29 P.M. on 13 October. Vladimir Shatalov and Aleksei Yeliseyev were making their second space flight on this craft. The parameters of its orbit were apogee, 223 kilometers; perigee, 205 kilometers.

Three spaceships were in orbit above the earth. Never before had such a large group of spacemen been in orbit.

The crews established two-way communications and went to work at their assigned tasks. In this group flight, the organization of communications among the three spacecraft was of special importance. Along with the ground communication points, the network included radio stations and the tracking ships of the Academy of Sciences, USSR, positioned at various points in the hydrosphere: the *Cosmonaut Vladimir Komarov,* the *Morzhovets,* the *Nevel,* the *Bezhitsa,* the *Dolinsk,* the *Ristna,* the *Kegostrov,* and the *Borovichi.* Their radio stations were constantly receiving and processing information from the spaceships, and maintaining constant contact with the crews.

The precise organization of communications and the co-ordination of the work of the three crews, the ground centers, and the thousands of specialists assured the success of the experiment.

The crews of the three spacecraft made joint observations of vicinal space, perfected interspaceship communications and guidance of the group flight, and tested those instruments and devices required for autonomous navigation.

When they had carried out their maneuvers, the spaceships rendezvoused. The crews made observations of the other spaceships, took photographs, and used movie cameras to determine the visibility of objects at various distances. They also investigated the possibility of exchanging information by means of light indexes and visual optical devices.

In the course of the flight, each crew carried out a great many observations and experiments. These included observations of value to geologists and cartographers, oceanologists and meteorologists— e.g., observations on the development of cyclones, the movement of storm fronts, and other processes in the earth's atmosphere. They conducted medicobiological investigations for the further study of how factors in space flight affect the human organism. Using various functional probes and psychological tests, they determined the state of the human organism and the level of human working capacity in flight. They also solved problems of group psychology, ascertaining the conditions requisite for harmonious group activity.

The cosmonauts ate breakfast, lunch, and dinner. Their menu included liver pâté, chicken, bread, and preserved fruits. The differing tastes of the cosmonauts had been taken into account, and they could make changes in the menu as they wished. Thus the lunch eaten by Shonin and Kubasov included dried fish, pâté, chicken, bread, and prunes, while the crew of *Soyuz*-7 had puréed meat, veal, bread, and buns. But these slight differences in taste had no effect on the cosmonauts' work. The crews' common goal and mutual understanding gave them a good esprit de corps, and they worked in harmony, helping and encouraging one another with advice and jokes.

On 15 October the crews conducted many maneuvers in orbit. *Soyuz*-6 and *Soyuz*-8 took turns approaching to within several hundred yards of *Soyuz*-7. All approach maneuvers were made manually through on-board automatic navigational devices.

On 16 October the crew of *Soyuz*-6 began the welding operation. The unique Vulcan welding outfit was located in the orbital compartment, with the control panel in the cosmonauts' cabin. While the spacecraft was in its seventy-seventh orbit, Shonin depressurized the orbital compartment, creating a deep vacuum. Then flight engineer Valery Kubasov, using the remote control switches, turned on the welding unit. He first did some automatic welding, using a short arc under low pressure. Then he switched on the automatic equipment for welding with an electron beam and a consumable electrode. A special indicator panel on the control board enabled the cosmonaut-operator to follow the work of Vulcan. Data on the welding were transmitted to the earth and recorded on instruments.

I asked Academician Paton to comment on the operation of the Vulcan unit in space flight.

He replied: "The operation of Vulcan showed that a stable process of welding metals by means of melting is feasible under the conditions of vicinal space. The miniaturized welding units tested in the experiment proved highly reliable and efficient. The basic designs used in building them can serve as the basis for designing special welding units for performing specific engineering procedures in space.

"This experiment in welding in orbit had opened a new page

in the exploration of space. An engineering procedure involving the heating and melting of metal has been performed in space for the first time. The age of space metallurgy has dawned."

At 12:52 P.M. on 16 October, having completed their flight, Georgy Shonin and Valery Kubasov touched down in the frozen, barren steppe 180 kilometers northwest of Karaganda. It was cold and a ground wind was blowing when the cosmonauts emerged from the hatch. After weightlessness, G-forces, and everything else they had experienced, it was pleasant to feel land under their feet. It may have been cold and covered with snow, but it was earth!

Some kolkhoz herdsmen, members of the search party, and a cameraman rushed toward them. They embraced the cosmonauts, and peppered them with questions. A helicopter was already hovering noisily overhead; nearby, horses were neighing; and everyone was talking excitedly.

Soyuz-7 and *Soyuz*-8 continued orbiting after Shonin and Kubasov had landed. One day later, on 17 October at 12:26, *Soyuz*-7 touched down 155 kilometers northwest of Karaganda, and the three cosmonauts soon stepped out on the snow.

Volkov, a fun-loving individual, was in his usual form—singing, laughing, and hugging the people who had arrived on the scene. Filipchenko, the commander of the spacecraft, looked it over carefully and checked the equipment. Gorbatko, rather embarrassed, was giving his first autographs—on cigarette packages. The wind was whipping stinging sleet and snow through the air, and a white haze hung over the steppe. But how good it looked to the cosmonauts, who had just returned from space, with its bright stars and fantastic glows on the horizon!

At 12:10 P.M. on 18 October the flagship, *Soyuz*-8, set down 145 kilometers north of Karaganda.

Shatalov and Yeliseyev were unshaven and weary but happy as they stepped out of their craft. For the second time, they had lived through all the vicissitudes of a space flight and return to earth.

Shatalov was overjoyed because the three spacecraft had landed so close together. It was a great success for those who made this accurate touchdown possible. "They set down like airplanes!" Shatalov proudly told the reporters.

The reporters noted that despite the bad weather, with a bliz-

zard raging over the steppe, the flagship had touched down right
on target—as had the other two.

Moscow joyously welcomed the cosmonauts at Vnukovo Airport.
I noticed that the long red carpet was twice as wide as the one along
which Yuri Gagarin had walked in 1961. Then, he was alone. Now
there were seven cosmonauts.

The flagship of Aeroflot—a huge Ilyushin-62—flew in and touched
down. While bands played and guns fired salutes, the cosmonauts
were welcomed by the leaders of the Party and the Government
and by thousands of Muscovites. All the way from Vnukovo to
the Kremlin, people sang, bands played, and girls scattered flowers
on the limousines. At a ceremonial reception in the Kremlin's
Palace of Congresses, the cosmonauts were awarded high honors,
with Shatalov and Yeliseyev receiving the title of Hero of the
Soviet Union for the second time.

When the ceremonies in the Kremlin and Star Town were over,
daily work was resumed. Later, I asked Shatalov to tell me about
the flight in greater detail, and give me his ideas about the future of
cosmonautics.

Here is what he told me: "We made a flight into the future—and
the future belongs to orbiting space stations. We will have to make
extensive investigations of vicinal space. It is especially important to
study the effect of prolonged weightlessness on human beings."

In that same autumn of 1969, another important event took place.
By way of returning Frank Borman's visit to the Soviet Union and
Star Town, Georgy Beregovoi and Konstantin Feoktistov went to
the United States. They visited many American cities, met President
Nixon and the American astronauts, with whom they found many
areas of agreement. They acquainted themselves with the simulator
used for the moon flights, and went on an excursion to the fabulous
park called Disneyland.

When Beregovoi and Feoktistov returned to Moscow, I met with
them and listened attentively to their account of their interesting
and useful trip. They told me about the American astronauts and
lunar trainer, and how they had looked through a microscope at the
lunar dust brought back to the earth by Neil Armstrong and Edwin
Aldrin.

A few months later, on 1 June 1970, Neil Armstrong paid a

visit to Star Town. The audacious, manly American astronaut was warmly welcomed by Colonel General of Aviation A. N. Yefimov, Deputy Commander in Chief of the Soviet Air Force. Speaking to an audience that overflowed the hall, Armstrong gave a most interesting account of his trip to the moon. Then he showed a film of the flight, with his personal commentary.

Greeting Armstrong on behalf of the Soviet cosmonauts—and of the scientists and engineers who had designed our space hardware —Georgy Beregovoi presented him with a model of the docked *Soyuz* spaceships. Flier-cosmonaut Valentina Nikolayeva-Tereshkova gave our guest a bouquet and a badge commemorating his visit to Star Town.

Then came a moment one can hardly describe unemotionally. Neil Armstrong told us that on the moon's surface he had placed medals in honor of those cosmonauts who had perished—including Yuri Gagarin and Vladimir Komarov.

At Armstrong's request, Valentina Gagarina and Valentina Komarova—the widows of the Soviet cosmonauts who had lost their lives —came up on the stage. Armstrong embraced them and, with tears in his eyes, gave them duplicates of the medals he had left on the moon. Another set of duplicates was presented to Star Town.

Silence reigned in the auditorium, as memory summoned up the features of those who had perished in the battle for space.

After the ceremonies, Armstrong visited Yuri Gagarin's study. In the guest book he wrote of Gagarin: "He called us all into space."

Late that evening, Georgy Beregovoi invited Armstrong to his home. As they were enjoying a convivial dinner, Beregovoi said: "Neil, two of our boys are about to lift off. Would you like to watch it?"

With great interest, Armstrong viewed the televised launch of *Soyuz*-9, with Andriyan Nikolayev and Vitaly Sevastyanov on board. Immediately afterward, he sent them a friendly telegram: "Best wishes to the crew of *Soyuz*-9—Nikolayev and Sevastyanov—for successful completion of your mission and a happy landing!"

The crew of *Soyuz*-9 also received telegrams from two other American astronauts, Frank Borman and James Lovell, who held the world record for duration of flight. (They had spent fourteen days in space.) The American astronauts' interest in the flight of *Soyuz*-9 was expressive of the unanimously serious concern of scientists and designers with solving general problems of assuring prolonged manned flights in a condition of weightlessness.

The first person to talk about weightlessness as a really serious problem—and this happened decades ago—was Konstantin Tsiolkovsky.

Investigations of space made since then have fully confirmed Tsiolkovsky's view as to the great importance of zero gravity with respect to the human organism. How can man adapt himself to it? Is there a limit to the time he will be able to live and work in a weightless condition?

In the words of L. I. Brezhnev, General Secretary of the Central Committee of the Communist Party of the Soviet Union:

> The creation of long-lasting, manned orbiting space stations represents the high road for man's journey into space. These stations will become science's outposts in space—bases for solving many problems of a scientific and economic nature. From the romance of the first contact with an uncharted realm— from the bold challenge tossed at that unknown realm, with its dangers and threats—space flights, for all their danger and difficulty, are developing primarily into complex and responsible *work* in the cause of science: in the cause of humanity's real interests. Space for the good of people, space for the good of science, space for the good of the national economy. Such, in brief, is the substance of the Soviet space program—its philosophical credo.

From individual manned flights to permanent orbiting stations— such is the development envisaged for cosmonautics in the near future. The experience gained creating the first experimental space station from the manual docking of *Soyuz*-4 and *Soyuz*-5 while in orbit, showed that modern space engineering is ready to build orbiting stations and laboratories. But how long will people live on those stations?

This problem made it vital to study the effects on respiration, blood circulation, and the functioning of the vestibular apparatus —over a prolonged period.

Weightlessness was Problem Number One.

Crew compatibility in the course of a long flight was Problem Number Two. We all know that for two people to spend week after week together in one small room is very trying. Trifles can be exaggerated into annoyances, annoyances into quarrels. And the two cosmonauts were going to be confined in the cabin of that spacecraft, day and night, for a period of eighteen days. . . .

The crew for the long flight of *Soyuz*-9 consisted of the pilot, Colonel Andriyan Nikolayev, flier-cosmonaut and Hero of the Soviet Union, and the flight engineer, Candidate of Technical Sciences Vitaly Sevastyanov, a bright young scientist.

The reader has already heard about Andriyan Nikolayev's flight in *Vostok*-3 in 1962. On that dual flight with Pavel Popovich, who was piloting *Vostok*-4, Nilolayev remained in space for almost four days, during which time he made sixty-four circuits around the earth. On that occasion, he bore up well under zero gravity, and even came to enjoy it. From then, weightlessness became an obsession with him. He kept studying it under terrestrial conditions, in the zero gravity pool of aircraft in flight.

Vitaly Sevastyanov was six years younger than Nikolayev. He was born in the Urals region and spent his childhood in the seaside resort town of Sochi. He attended the Moscow Aviation Institute and took a doctorate. Then he joined the cosmonaut team, where he struck up a friendship with Nikolayev, although they were totally different in temperament. Nikolayev was a model of imperturbability, while Sevastyanov was always smiling, ready at any time to return a joke with a joke.

Soyuz-9 was launched on the night of 1 June 1970, when the steppe was scorching hot. This was the beginning of a flight which lasted eighteen days. During that time the spacecraft covered almost 12 million kilometers and made 286 orbits around the earth.

The cosmonauts carried out an extensive and complex program of scientific-technical investigations and experiments. They worked out refinements of the spacecraft's manual and automatic systems of guidance, attitude control, and stabilization. Also, they tested the automatic navigational devices under varying in-flight conditions.

Nikolayev and Sevastyanov quickly grew accustomed to weightlessness, ate four times a day, and did setting-up exercises. At "bedtime" they took off their flying suits and, wearing only sweatshirts and shorts, crawled into their sleeping bags and dropped off immediately. On one occasion Ground Control had to make use of a special on-board siren to awaken the sleeping space travellers.

The howl of the siren jolted them awake, and when they reported back to earth, their tone of voice was apologetic.

Positive results were yielded by the series of medicobiological experiments on the human organism aimed at better adaptation to zero G conditions. Especially helpful to the cosmonauts was the series of setting-up exercises, together with medication. For their physical training, they had expanders and special weighted suits. Their "space pharmacy" comprised various kinds of medication to combat weightlessness.

Then came the day when Falcon-1 and Falcon-2 (the radio call signs of the cosmonauts) were free to discontinue their technical experiments and do whatever they liked. (Active relaxation—the essence of which is a change in the nature of a person's purposeful activity—can be very effective.) The cosmonauts decided to relax by playing chess. A most unusual game—ground–space–ground—was begun. Nikolayev and Sevastyanov were using the light pieces. The dark pieces were being maneuvered (at Ground Control) by Colonel General Nikolai Kamanin and a flier-cosmonaut Viktor Gorbatko. The players in this unique game of chess spent four communications periods to make thirty-five moves. The game ended in a stalemate.

On the birthday of Nikolayev's daughter, Elena, she came to Ground Control accompained by her mother, Valentina Nikolayeva Tereshkova. Valentina and Lenochka talked over the radio to the girl's father—a deeply moving experience. They could see him on the huge TV screen, and it seemed that he and his friend Vitaly Sevastyanov were not in space but right there in the Gound Control room. The other cosmonauts listened to Lenochka's happy chirping, wished her a happy birthday and chatted with Valentina.

Among the complex scientific experiments and observations made by the crew of Soyuz-9, I should like to mention an unusual procedure carried out on 13 June 1970, during the 189th orbit. On that day, in its planned orbit, the manned spacecraft Soyuz-9, at an altitude of 240 kilometers, came into contact—at a preselected point above the western part of the Indian Ocean—with the weather satellite Meteor, orbiting at a height of 600 kilometers above the earth. Meantime, the Academician Shirshov, a scientific research ship of the Hydrometeorological Office, was in position on the surface of the ocean. An observation of one and the same spot was made from "three storys" and yielded valuable results for meteorologists.

The flight of *Soyuz*-9 demonstrated the excellent characteristics of this manned spacecraft and its life-support and communications systems. It enabled scientists to take a more optimistic view of the possibilities of men's living and working while on prolonged space flights, and of permanent orbiting stations. To a certain extent, it also solved the problem of psychological compatibility in a confined area. For all their differences in temperament, in the course of their eighteen days of living together in one compartment, Nikolayev and Sevastyanov demonstrated their friendship, solidarity, mutual understanding, and efficiency.

On 19 June 1970, after successful completion of the program for its eighteen-day flight, *Soyuz*-9 touched down with great accuracy 75 kilometers west of Karaganda. (It is worth recalling that eight years before Andriyan Nikolayev made his first landing in this same area—south of Karaganda.)

The re-entry section of *Soyuz*-9 came down precisely at the preselected site. From their helicopter, the members of the search party saw the main parachute open, and for eight minutes they flew alongside the descending spacecraft. The specialists noted how soft the landing was: the shock absorbers of the cosmonauts' contour couch were not even disturbed.

The four helicopters of the search party landed almost simultaneously with *Soyuz*-9. The cosmonauts' faces appeared in the viewports of the spacecraft. The hatch opened, and Nikolayev came out. He took off his headpiece and waved it in the air. As for Sevastyanov, on his way from the spacecraft to the helicopter, he bent down, grabbed a handful of soil, squeezed it in his fist, and shouted with heartfelt emotion: "Earth!"

The doctors examined the cosmonauts and reported that their health was immeasurably better than had been expected. The lift-off and the long flight in a zero-G condition had gone off successfully, and the cosmonauts had felt fine. But re-entry was another matter. After having adapted themselves to weightlessness, the cosmonauts were subjected to tremendous G-forces. And once back on earth, they felt the powerful effects of gravitation.

The State Commission decided to skip the traditional welcome at Vnukovo. The heroes of the space flight would be sent directly to

Star Town for a thorough medical examination and, if necessary, emergency treatment.

They reported they had the feeling that gravitation was pressing down on them and holding them to the earth. For this reason, an appropriate life regimen was prescribed for them.

Nevertheless, they were holding press conferences with reporters. From then on, they had conferences everyday—with scientists, design engineers, and doctors.

These conferences were held in a room with a glass partition. This precaution was taken in order to protect the cosmonauts—only recently de-orbited—against possible infectious diseases. (At this time, their weakened organisms were more susceptible to infection than under ordinary conditions on earth.) This unique "space symposium," which lasted for several days, was most valuable to the scientists and design engineers—not to mention the doctors.

Nikolayev and Sevastyanov were sitting behind the glass partition at a table equipped with microphones, telephones, and little fans. The questions and their answers were transmitted over the radio telephone. During the first few days the cosmonauts were somewhat slow to respond. They were pale, and their faces were furrowed with wrinkles. They tried to carry on a lively conversation and even make jokes; but they tired rapidly, and there were frequent lapses.

From one day to the next, however, they changed under our very eyes. Color returned to their cheeks, the wrinkles vanished, and their gestures and facial expressions became freer. As I listened to their precise answers, I was struck by their capacity to remember everything and by their sensitivity to natural phenomena. They went into raptures about cosmic dawns, the light from the sun, the glittering of the ocean, and the bright light from distant stars.

The period of readaptation—of becoming accustomed to the earth—drew to a close. And the cosmonauts, when I saw them during the last sessions in the conference room, were cheerful and pink-cheeked. Morever, their answers delighted the scientists, designers, doctors, and reporters.

I asked Vitaly Sevastyanov how they had solved, in flight, the problems of group psychological compatability. Nikolayev answered for him: "We worked well together. We took off. When we came back to earth they suggested we sleep in separate rooms. But we protested: we'd got used to each other, and become friends."

My next question was: "What is your opinion of the prospects for prolonged flights?"

Vitaly Sevastyanov's answer was: "Today there is hardly anyone who doubts that man can live and work under conditions of weightlessness. What's important now is to refine the system of readaptation—getting used to the earth again. This involves many unsolved problems, and opens up broad creative possibilities for the scientists."

After their final medical examination, the two cosmonauts were given a brief vacation. Then, on 3 July 1970, they were the guests of honor at a formal reception in the Georgiyevsky Hall of the Great Kremlin Palace. On that ceremonial occasion, Andriyan Nikolayev was awarded his second gold medal as Hero of the Soviet Union and informed that he had been promoted to the rank of Major General of Aviation. Sevastyanov was awarded the title of Flier-Cosmonaut of the USSR, and the gold star of a Hero of the Soviet Union.

The flight had been completed. But in many institutes and laboratories, intensive work went on. The great body of scientific information was processed; photographs and film clips were studied; and systems of life-support, manual, and automatic control were analyzed. In short, the entire spaceship that had made such a long flight through the ocean of air was thoroughly investigated. Another long stride had been taken toward orbiting stations.

Orbital Space
Station Salyut

Andriyan Nikolayev's and Vitaly Sevastyanov's flight aboard *Soyuz*-9 was of great importance to the further development of space flight and hastened the advent of the first manned orbital space station.

I have already mentioned that the Soviet space program has defined the orbital space station as the fundamental step in man's exploration of the cosmos. The idea of building such stations was first expressed by the great Russian scientist and inventor Konstantin Tsiolkovsky.

Enlarging upon the ideas of Tsiolkovsky, dreamers and scientists of different lands advanced many plans and proposals for "ethereal islands." Some suggested building space stations in the form of giant doughnuts, others proposed cisterns, still others spheres and cones. There were projects for stations in the form of triangles and rhombuses, like paper box-kites.

And now the fantasy had become reality. It stood before me in the assembly area of space station *Salyut*. I gasped and began to laugh. I had to laugh at myself. Decades ago when I had visited Tsiolkovsky and heard his stories of "ethereal islands", not only had I failed to believe in these dreams of genius, I had even found them absurd. How I laughed at myself now!

I inspected the station—and the thought came to me that the whole of human history is connected with the idea of home. Without a home man could not exist. Even the most incorrigible runaways and wanderers will sooner or later long for a warm hearth when they pass lighted windows. Domesticity is one of the greatest, holiest, and most indestructible qualities of human nature. Whereever man may be—whether it be in the high mountains or the snowy wastes of Antarctica, in trackless forests or burning deserts he will build himself a house. So it was thousands of years ago, and so it will ever be. A man builds himself a house where he is going to live. And if he is now building himself his first house in space—that means he is seriously getting ready to live there.

Let me introduce you to the space station *Salyut*. Outwardly it resembles a rocket perhaps because of the set-backs in its diameter. At the same time it looks like a plane, a strange plane with four wings that are actually the panels of its solar batteries.

Outwardly *Salyut* looks like . . . well, imagine a cone with a docking device set at the end; then a small cylinder about six and one half feet in diameter. The cylinder expands to ten feet and then thirteen. Next comes a spherical bottom and a cone: these are the fuel tanks and behind them the propulsion devices. With these the space station can be raised or lowered from one orbit to another and otherwise maneuvered in space.

The size of the space station is quite impressive: its length counting the booster carrier rocket is sixty-six feet, its maximum diameter in excess of thirteen feet, its volume about one hundred cubic meters and its weight over twenty-five metric tons.

I began my examination of the station with the docking apparatus and the tunnel through which the cosmonauts would pass on their way from the command module of their rocket into the working quarters of the *Salyut*. Here were several control panels and the astrophysical scientific apparatus. I went through a hatch and landed in the work compartment. In it were the cosmonauts's couches, scientific equipment, stores of food and water, various elements of the life-support system, and a control panel. The section looked like a one-room apartment and there was even a dining table for the future inhabitants. I sat down at the table, lifted the top, and looked at the utensils, the can-openers, the bin for discarded cans and tubes.

Next to the dining table I noticed a water tank. Tubes led from it to individual mouthpieces—one for each cosmonaut to drink from. The water, by the way, is not ordinary water; it is treated with silver. "Silver water" is less prone to spoilage and retains its "earthly" taste. In flight the tank will be replaced as needed and the crew kept supplied with fresh silver water.

Each day a man requires about seven hundred liters of air, two liters of water and approximately six hundred grams of assimilable nutritive substances. In space it is the same as on earth.

During the flight the cosmonauts will receive the necessary amounts of water. And what of the food?

Provision has been made on board for four hot meals daily. The entire supply is stored in refrigerators. There there are packages containing breakfasts, lunches, and dinners; on each is indicated a number and a time when it is to be eaten. The cosmonauts' rations include frankfurters, steak, ham, chicken, tongue, sausage meat, veal, sliced bacon. All of these foods have been sealed in metal cans, cut into small pieces, and tightly packed in brine or jelly. All of the foods that have been prepared for this flight differ from those that were prepared for previous space flights in their increased moisture content. This gives them additional juiciness and aroma. As a substitute for some of the pâtés there are also dairy foods: creamed cottage cheese, mixed with apple or black currant puree, and processed cheese.

Let us now take a look at their air supply.

In our daily life on earth we rarely give thought to the air that we breathe. To the scientists and engineers who designed the *Salyut* the problem of pure air was one of the most crucial ones. In breathing the human organism discharges into its environment carbonic acid, acetic acid, volatile oils, methane, hydrogen, acetone, carbon monoxide—in all over four hundred chemical compounds. Besides these, various fittings and non-metallic elements used in the construction can also constitute sources of toxic admixtures: plastics, adhesives, coatings, sealants, insulating materials, gaskets. An extremely fine aerosol of dust particles can pollute the air too, invading the respiratory passages of the cosmonauts and producing adverse effect on their health. When you add to this, dust particles from human hair and skin it will become clear that in addition to pollution of the air by chemical and biochemical substances in the hermetically sealed cabin of the orbital space station there will be further contamination by aerosol systems containing a significant concentration of toxic substances. In order to assure the cosmonauts of clean air and easy breathing, it was necessary to design an effective air regeneration system, a temperature control system, and, for the removal of airborne particles, a special dust filtration apparatus with powerful circulating fans. Working together these systems provide pure air of comfortable room temperature and humidity levels within the inhabited part of the orbital space station.

Men quite naturally will be interested in the question of how they shave. Back in the days of Andriyan Nikolayev's and Vitaly Sevastyanov's long flight on *Soyuz*-9, experiments were made with various types of shaving equipment including electric razors with special aspirators to suck up the whiskers and keep them from flying about the cabin or lodging in the respiratory tract of the cosmonauts. Nikolayev and Sevastyanov came to the conclusion that under conditions of weightlessness ordinary safety razors were the best when used with a special soap-free shaving cream.

My attention was drawn to the wet and dry napkins made of natural and artificial fibers. They were designed for personal hygiene—"washing" the hands and face and cleansing utensils.

At that time *Salyut* was still earth-bound, but everything aboard reminded one that it was destined for prolonged flight in zero gravity conditions. In the future man will become master of this mysterious and frightening absence of weight. Doctors of medicine will make use of it in the treatment of disease, and engineers and workers will take advantage of weightlessness to build vast, hitherto unknown industrial enterprises. For the present, the main thing is to find new ways of protecting people from the harmful effects of extraterrestrial conditions.

With this goal in view, Andriyan Nikolayev and Vitaly Sevastyanov tested various medical and pharmacological procedures and different types of physical exercises during their eighteen-day flight. In describing his flight, Nikolayev stressed that physical exercise was the decisive factor in maintaining his and Sevastyanov's full capacity for work during the flight and in their ability to readapt rather rapidly to conditions of normal gravity upon their return to earth. The results of their experiments and suggestions were incorporated into the design of space station *Salyut*. Aboard the *Salyut*-1 I saw a "gym": an exercise area with a set of expansion exercisers and special elastic costumes. I tried on one of these "penguin" stretch suits—it consists of layers of taut rubber—and I immediately felt a pull against my spine and tension throughout the skeletomuscular system. In conditions of weightlessness such tension will compensate for the absence of terrestrial gravitation.

In addition to the life support systems, space station *Salyut* contains a whole battery of scientific devices and instruments including the gamma telescope and the "Orion" complex of astrophysical equipment.

When I had completed my tour of space station *Salyut,* I was convinced that for the first time a "space house" and "space lab" had truly been built. Great pains had been taken to provide all that was necessary for the cosmonauts to live and work outside their native earth.

On 19 April 1971 a powerful launching vehicle boosted *Salyut* into the proper orbit. At apogee it was 220 kilometers above the surface of the earth, at perigee, 200. Ground-control centers verified the accuracy of its orbit and the proper functioning of all its systems. During the night of April 23 spacecraft *Soyuz*-10 speeded toward a rendezvous with the space station.

Aboard *Soyuz*-10 were two Soviet cosmonauts who are already familiar to the reader—Vladimir Shatalov and Aleksei Yeliseyev. Both were on their third trip into space. Accompanying them was test pilot-engineer Nikolai Rukavishnikov, who was experiencing all the drama of his first launch. Rukavishnikov comes from the city of Tomsk in Siberia. In his childhood and adolescent years he traveled all over the country with his parents. Both his mother and his stepfather worked on the survey and planning of new rail lines. The never-ending journeys with his family soon awakened in the young Nikolai the desire to explore the unknown and bravely confront the future. Upon the successful completion of his studies in the Moscow Institute of Engineering and Physics, Nikolai Rukavishnikov went to work in engineering design. In January 1967 he joined the cosmonaut team.

From the very first moments of their flight, the crew of *Soyuz*-10 set to work on their program of scientific and technical experiments and observations, which included docking with space station *Salyut*. After the necessary corrections in orbit and attitude, *Soyuz*-10 inched toward the orbiting space station under automatic control, and Vladimir Shatalov completed the docking maneuvers. For the first time a spacecraft and space station were docked in orbit. They remained joined for five hours and thirty minutes. During this period the crew checked out various systems on board, including the new docking device. The experiment confirmed the correctness of design decisions in the building of the orbital space station.

On 25 April, having successfully completed their program, the crew of *Soyuz*-10 returned to earth.

Salyut set to work, independent of ground control, on its scientific and technical assignments. Far from earth, in the deep night of space, the solitary, unoccupied station continued to fly. Not one person was on board, but at times it seemed as if cosmonauts were already living and working in their house in the sky, so rational was the response of *Salyut* to the complicated interrogation of the ground-control center. From the station came a steady stream of information about the functioning of the various systems, heat regulation, and power supply. All by itself the station locked in on the sun and, rotating slowly, kept its solar batteries trained in the proper direction for charging. It maintained contact with the ground and executed corrections in its orbit. All the while, like a living being, space station *Salyut* prepared itself for an encounter with a second space vehicle.

On 6 June 1971, six months after the launching of the orbital station, *Soyuz*-11 streaked toward a rendezvous. At the controls were Commander Georgy Dobrovolsky, flight engineer Vladislav Volkov, and Pilot Viktor Patsayev. After docking, it was their task to proceed into the station and conduct an extremely complex series of scientific investigations. The equipment of the exercise area, the comfortable arrangements for day-to-day living, the "penguin" suits, and many other details would permit the cosmonauts to adapt readily to conditions of weightlessness and later to re-adapt to conditions on earth.

On *Soyuz*-10 there had been only one "newcomer" to space, but this time the situation was just the reverse—both Commander Georgy Dobrovolsky and Pilot Viktor Patsayev were newcomers. It was Vladislav Volkov's second flight—he had made his first in 1969 in the joint flight of three spacecraft.

Vladislav Volkov was an outgoing man with the build of an athlete. His constant inclination to humor, his feeling for the right word, his enthusiasm for sports, his knowledge of song, his eagerness to be of help to his comrades have made him the most popular man on the cosmonaut team. At the cosmodrome, a few days before the launch, Volkov said to me: "It's finished! I just finished my book!" With a smile he added, "Flying is a lot easier than writing." Vladislav Volkov was speaking of a book that he had written for young people about his own life and space flight. I have read the manuscript—it teaches young people how to live, how to think about the future, how to face up to difficulties and hardships and stride boldly forward.

Georgy Dobrovolsky is from the south, from Odessa, where he was born in 1920. Odessa has the reputation of being the birthplace of wags, wits, and squabblers. And when Dobrovolsky says "I am an Odessa man" he means that he loves a wisecrack, a good joke, and people who like to enjoy life. Like many little boys growing up in Odessa, Dobrovolsky wanted to become a sailor. The Black Sea was right in front of him. He saw the boats and listened to the sailors and his head spun with dreams of voyages around the world. But Dobrovolsky did not become a sailor. Instead, he became involved with another ocean—the air. A bold and experienced flyer, Dobrovolsky successfully completed his studies at Red Banner Air Force Academy without interruption to his work as a pilot and subsequently joined the ranks of the cosmonauts.

Viktor Patsayev was just the opposite of Dobrovolsky and Volkov. He was unhurried, calm, rarely given to jokes and witticisms. He weighed his words carefully, and when he did speak, spoke in the clear, precise words of the engineer. Viktor Patsayev was born in 1933 in Kazakstan, in the city of Aktyubinsk. From Central Asia he moved to Penza, where in 1955 he was graduated from the Industrial Institute. Employed subsequently at the Central Aerological Observatory near Moscow, he demonstrated exceptional talent in devising miniaturized meteorological instruments. After the C.A.O., Patsayev worked in engineering design. A modest, quiet man, constantly occupied with his technical affairs, he nonetheless cherished a dream—he passionately wanted to fly in space. But Patsayev was no idle dreamer; he joined a flying club. He taught himself to fly light planes and then jets. In the flying club he became friendly with Vladislav Volkov. They flew together and shared friendly dreams of space flight.

The three friends lifted into orbit on 6 June 1971. On the very first day they made corrections in their orbit. As the spacecraft completed its second circuit of the earth, space station *Salyut* had, according to prior calculations, a lead of 4,000 kilometers and was flying in a higher orbit. With its greater speed, *Soyuz*-11 gradually gained on the station, hour by hour, circuit by circuit. In twenty hours this lead was cut to one tenth of the original distance, and at 6 A.M. on 7 June the spacecraft and station were a mere 400 kilometers apart.

Dobrovolsky started the altitudinal rockets. A slight shudder ran through the spacecraft. Flame shot from the nozzles of the rockets. The craft moved into a new orbit. By 7:26 it had almost overtaken the orbital station: it was now less than ten kilometers away. The automatic approach system began its operation. The two omnidirectional antennas of space station *Salyut,* like beacons, began to orient and guide the spacecraft in.

"Dawn, this is Amber, I have a sighting on it now, it is a small point," Georgy Dobrovolsky reported to Ground Control.

Six weeks earlier Aleksei Yeliseyev had also caught sight of space station *Salyut* in the window of his spacecraft. To him it had looked like a sparkling diamond against the black velvet of space. Now Dobrovolsky, Volkov, and Patsayev were also seeing this sparkling diamond.

Space station *Salyut* was now completing its 795th orbiting of the earth.

The stabilizer rockets began to function, and with a few short bursts the spacecraft turned around so as to present its docking mechanism toward space station *Salyut.*

Every minute they were getting closer.

Dobrovolsky radioed: "7:35. The distance is now one thousand meters."

The ship's small steering rocket fired. Jets of flame spurted from tiny nozzles.

The approach continued under automatic control until the two craft were within one hundred meters of one another. The last stages of the approach and docking took place under manual control, with Georgy Dobrovolsky at the controls. In a short while he radioed to ground control: "We are right on target, distance 60, speed 0.3, the upper and lower lights of the station are clearly visible."

They drew ever closer and closer. Another minute and the tip of the docking mechanism on *Soyuz*-11 entered the cone of space station *Salyut*. The hard mechanical docking of the two spacecraft took place and the linking of their hydraulic and electrical systems

After they had checked the seals and equalized the air pressure in the command section of the ship and the access tunnel, the cosmonauts received permission from ground control to open the hatch. Electrical switches were thrown. Viktor Patsayev crawled into the open metal tunnel. He had already been in the station and knew it well, but now it seemed both familiar and unfamiliar—without human presence, bathed in fantastic sunlight, it seemed strangely empty and deserted. Flight Engineer Vladislav Volkov crawled in behind Viktor Patsayev. He greeted the station merrily with a wave of his hand, as if it were a person and, sitting down on a chair, looked over the "living room." Finally they were joined by Commander Georgy Dobrovolsky. The friends hugged one another and congratulated themselves on their success. Then without delay they began the inspection of the compartments and the checking of the various systems, gauges, and apparatus.

Automatic space station *Salyut* had now become a manned one. People were now aboard. They made themselves at home, got things ready for work and shut down their own spacecraft. After that, *Soyuz*-11 began to draw power from the station, and the functioning of its on-board systems would be monitored by telemetry.

In the "space house" a new way of life began. For the first time in space, people sat down to eat at a real table, for the first time walked and rushed about as they do on earth, grew gardens, studied the stars through the gama-telescope, carried out a program of scientific and technical research and experimentation that surpassed in scope anything that had been hitherto undertaken.

Switching on the Orion astrophysical observatory, the station crew began to gather precious information about the stars. The Orion is a complex optico-electronic system. It was installed on the outer surface of the station and for that reason had been subjected for a rather prolonged period of time to the destructive effects of a vacuum, cosmic radiation, and sharply varying temperatures. It had not been damaged. Scientists and design engineers were given proof that it is possible to build complex astrophysical devices and systems that will be able to function outside earth orbiting stations.

Among the numerous experiments and studies conducted by the crew of space station *Salyut* we should mention their study of the phenomena of high-frequency electromagnetic resonance in transmitting antennas in the conditions of space flight. The experiments were conducted with the help of the "Era" multipurpose apparatus. Important, too, were their studies of radiation in circumterrestrial space. We all live in the presence of radiation that our sense organs are unable to detect. Radiocommunications, climate, weather, polar lights are all connected with this mysterious world of electromagnetic radiation. To understand it, to discover its secrets is one of the greatest tasks of contemporary science.

Of much interest to science are those studies that the crew conducted of the optical properties of the planetary atmosphere. At the World Meteorological Congress in Geneva, experts were discussing the question of what is now happening to the earth's atmosphere. What processes associated with the development of industry and the rapid growth of technology are at work and what are their effects on its properties? Scientists have determined that a change is taking place in the world's climate. It has perceptibly altered during the course of the last several generations. In the first half of the twentieth century a warming trend was noted, but since the 1940s a reverse trend seems to have set in. The study of the earth's atmosphere from space with the help of long-lived earth-orbiting space stations will vastly increase our knowledge about the climate of our planet and the effects of our activities upon it.

From the station came a flow of information of great value to geologists, meteorologists, ichthyologists, dam-builders, foresters, and fishermen. For large catches of fish one must have precise, specific information about currents and the movement of schools of fish. As the fishing industry develops, it will be necessary to send out several thousand research ships to locate and track the movement of schools of fish, something which could hardly be practical. Only earth-orbiting stations can replace these thousands of ships and swiftly transmit information about ocean conditions and the movement of fish. What is more, such stations will be able to advise the captains of vessels of courses to avoid storm zones and incipient hurricanes and typhoons. The crew of *Salyut* constantly observed and photographed various atmospheric formations, typhoons, cyclones, cloud covers, and characteristic geological formations of the earth's surface. This information is being put to use by specialists in many fields: geology, agriculture, land-reclamation, geodesy, and cartography. It will lead to increased accuracy in weather forecasting.

The medical and biological experiments that the cosmonauts carried out will contribute to many branches of scientific study. For example, one experiment involved the effect of the absence of gravity on the growth of higher plants. For this purpose a "space garden" was set up on board *Salyut*. A growing medium had been prepared on the upper level and seeds of cabbage, flax, and onion were placed in it. Scientists are well acquainted with the details of their growth under terrestrial conditions, but how would they behave in zero gravity? Russian flax was of particular interest to the scientists because it is especially sensitive to the earth's gravitational field. Onion was suitable for sophisticated genetic experiments, and cabbage, if all goes well in the experiments, might become an important source of nutrition for future cosmonauts during protracted flights.

Viktor Patsayev became the first "space gardener." Every evening with twenty squeezes of a rubber bulb he administered water to the plants from a special reservoir tank. The hydroponic method of cultivation was used. The seeds sprouted and the space garden turned green. An automatic camera recorded the growth of the plants in the extraordinary conditions of space.

Days went by. The number of orbits kept increasing: 10 . . . 50 . . . 100 . . . 200. Days spent on the station were crossed out: 5 . . . 15 . . . 17. The eighteenth day of life and work on *Salyut* was drawing near. I recalled that Andriyan Nikolayev and Vitaly Sevastyanov had spent just that number of days in zero-gravity conditions. Upon their return to earth they were unable to re-adapt immediately to earth conditions, and it took sometime before all the uncomfortable symptoms disappeared and the cosmonauts once again felt themselves to be earthlings. Might not this period constitute an outside limit to the length of time that man could survive in space?

No; the flight went on. Each day Dobrovolsky, Volkov, and Patsayev made their report from orbit—they were feeling fine, their capacity for work was undiminished, they were in high spirits and quite pleased with the observations and experiments that they had been able to carry out. Twenty days went by . . . twenty-two . . . and still the flight went on. Viktor Patsayev celebrated his birthday, one more sign that people could make themselves at home in space.

On the big screen at the CCC—the Co-ordinating Computer Center—I could see Dobrovolsky, Volkov, and Patsayev. They held conversations with scientists, reported on their condition. It seemed as if they were right there in the room, or rather as if all of us at the center were right there with them in the "living room" of *Salyut.* Such is the magic of the second half of the twentieth century. As I watched the cosmonauts at work, my thoughts wandered to other work going on in space, to the unmanned probes and orbiting devices, and above all to the *Lunokhod*-1, the first of the extraterrestrial wheeled vehicles. My imagination transported me from circumterrestrial orbit to the surface of the moon streaked with the tracks of this automatic, electrically powered vehicle.

Set down on the moon by automatic station *Luna*-17, the *Lunokhod* had been rambling about amid the craters of the Sea of Rains for over seven months. In solitary silence it has traversed many kilometers of terrain, and has slept out the long lunar nights in mysterious craters. Steering clear of rifts and stones, it has described a complicated route returning toward the station that delivered it.

I stared at the faces of the cosmonauts on the screen, listened to their reports, and rejoiced that they were now in the twenty-fourth day of their unprecedented flight and fully accomplishing their mission.

On 29 June 1971, at noon Moscow time, manned station *Salyut* had completed its 358th revolution about the earth. The cosmonauts had finished their program of activities and had received instructions to land.

The cosmonauts reactivated their spacecraft, transferred their scientific materials logs and exposed film to it, and resumed their places for return to earth. Having checked out all on-board systems, Dobrovolsky, Volkov, and Patsayev got the craft ready to undock from space station *Salyut.*

At 9:28 P.M. *Soyuz*-11 and orbital station *Salyut* undocked and proceeded separately on their flights. The crew of *Soyuz*-11 reported to ground that the undocking had gone off without incident and all systems were functioning normally.

Everything was in order. On the next day, 20 June, at 1:35 A.M., after the ship's attitude had been corrected, the braking rockets were fired. The burn went off as scheduled. When the rockets shut off, communication with the crew was interrupted. After aerodynamic braking in the atmosphere in conformity with the program, the parachute system was activated and then, just before touchdown, the soft landing rockets. The flight terminated in a smooth landing in the designated region. Helicopters of the search party landed almost immediately at the side of the spacecraft. Doctors hastened to the spacecraft and the hatch was opened. Cosmonauts Dobrovolsky, Volkov and Patsayev were in their places, but they were dead.

Later came the explanation: during the descent, about thirty minutes before touch-down, a rapid drop in the pressurization of the compartment had killed them suddenly. The drop had been caused by a leak in the spacecraft.

I made no attempt to hide it . . . I wept. There were tears in every eye I saw that day. Even the bravest and the manliest betrayed their grief. The grim news of the death of the brave crew of *Soyuz*-11 went straight to the heart of all humanity. They had been children of this earth and their fate had become a personal loss to all of us who live on this blue planet.

During those hours I stood by the teletype and read the messages of sympathy and condolence that poured in from all corners of the globe. I remember the message from Washington that James Low, assistant director of NASA, sent to the Academy of Sciences of the USSR: "The loss of the three astronauts is a terrible tragedy. I extend my deepest sympathies to their families and colleagues. We feel deep respect for their achievements in space, and our hearts go out to them in their loss." The director of the unmanned space center in Houston wired: "I am shocked and disheartened by this news. A completely unexpected conclusion to a flight that had gone so well. A great sorrow to the other astronauts and to all those who have worked so selflessly in the space program . . ."

All of Moscow came to bid farewell to the cosmonaut heroes. Thousands of people gathered in Red Square on a hot and humid day and there were delegations from every country. Their grief was profound and there were tears in their eyes . . . but in their eyes also there was the fire of resolution, an indomitable will to victory over the cruel forces of nature.

Almost everyone recalled the words of Yuri Gagarin, uttered on the day of Vladimir Komarov's tragic death: "Nothing can stop us!"

In the new there is always the unknown. In every sphere of activity the beginning is always the hardest thing, whether it be the first step or the first flight. The role of chance can never be completely excluded in the advance of technology. The firm and courageous words of the cosmonauts in their address to the nation are dear to the hearts of us all: "We know that our chosen path is fraught with difficulties and dangers, but we have never for a moment doubted the rightness of our choice and will always be ready to undertake the most difficult flights."

The selfsame thought was expressed in a memorial service in Red Square by Soviet cosmonaut and two times Hero of the Soviet Union Vladimir Shatalov. He said: "It is fitting that we proceed with the conquest of space."

Sorrow strengthens the strong. When the period of mourning was over I went to Star Town. I sensed an air of resolute activity. As ever, the white birches shimmered and flowers waved in the gardens, but the people seemed somehow more severe, more intense. In the cosmonauts' wall newspaper I read some lines rich in philosophical significance: "The conquest of space is a difficult journey, but it is one upon which mankind has already embarked. It is an inevitable step in the logic of world progress."

It is true. Men are ever more actively invading the cosmos, ever more intensively studying it and attempting to make it their home. The penetration of space is already understood to be not just an isolated experiment but a decision about the destiny and future of humanity. At last we have overcome the geocentrism that has dominated the mind of man for thousands of years. The people of the earth are becoming increasingly aware of limited space on our world and are coming to a clearer understanding of the fact that the earth is only a grain of sand in the immensity of the universe. Will this not forge a new spirit of unity among peoples as they confront the mysterious forces of the stars? Will it not fuse their strengths, talents, fantasies, and spiritual energies in a common struggle to master a new environment—the solar system? It can provide us with oceans of light and "mountains of grain" in the visionary words of Tsiolkovsky and yield man boundless power over nature.

The ascent to the cosmos is an irreversible process, the fruit of our entire history. Millions of years ago life emerged from the oceans and adapted itself to a new environment, to survival and development on dry land. In our very day man is emerging into a new environment—the cosmos. The road to this new environment is not an easy one, and along the way lurks much that is unknown. But a great goal can give birth to great strength. The entire history of humanity, however complex and contradictory it may have been, is living evidence of power and reason of human beings. It is important to remember that until very recent times only philosophers occupied themselves with the problem of the meaning of life and meditated upon the future of humanity. Today with the development of space exploration and the capability of radio and television to put it within reach of more than half of the world's population, millions and millions of people are thinking about man's role in the fate of the world and of the universe. It is making people loftier and better, urges them onward toward unity and social justice, peace and friendship.

As for the further course of space exploration, it may be stated with conviction that the 1970s will bring about the development and use of long-term manned orbital stations with rotating crews. From episodic experiments in space, science will progress to the regular and continuous gathering of information by scientists and specialists in orbiting laboratories. Once embarked on this course, space science and technology will mark great advances in their understanding of the nature of the universe, the origin of life, and the influence of solar activity on terrestrial processes and in the atmosphere of our planet.

Space is awesome, dangerous, infinite. The conquest of it is fraught with enormous difficulties. But so was the conquest of America, Siberia, the Arctic, and Antarctica. The whole history of mankind is living evidence of human power and reason.

I believe in Man. I believe in his wisdom and might. I believe in his future among the stars.

Man is headed for the stars.

ABOUT THE AUTHOR

Evgeny Riabchikov describes space flights as if he himself had made orbital flights around the earth. But he has never traveled in space, although he has often been in the pilot's compartment of such spacecraft as *Vostok, Voskhod,* and *Soyuz.* He has been in trainers at Zvezdnyy Gorodok (Star Town) during simulated flights, during which he was subjected to vibrations and the simulated scream and roar of the rocket engines. With the aid of film projectors, he saw what happens in an actual orbital flight. Through an optical apparatus he saw how the training craft "flies" into the shadow of the earth and then out of it, as the hues of the cosmic dawn brighten.

The author of this book has made many such "flights."

The beginnings of Evgeny Riabchikov's involvement with aeronautics—and later, with astronautics—go back to 1923, and to the old Russian city of Nizhny Novgorod (now Gorky) on the Volga. That year, the organizers of the famous Novgorod Fair had decided to make use of an airplane to lend éclat to its opening. On the day when the "real, genuine" airplane that he had heard about was to arrive, the barefoot little Evgeny set out at a run along a cowpath on the outskirts of the city. He had been quick to realize the need for bonfires on the field where the plane was supposed to land, so the pilot could judge the direction and force of the wind. "I can build bonfires even on water!" he boasted to the men in double-breasted suits who were anxiously pacing up and down on the airfield. They took a good look at the boy and believed him. Columns of thick, acrid smoke were soon rising toward the sky.

But the airplane did not come that day. The next morning Evgeny was the first one to rebuild the bonfires. But dangerous rivals soon appeared. The news of the plane's imminent landing on the pasture had spread through the city, and young and old alike were streaming toward the aerodrome. The other boys also wanted to light bonfires so that they could earn the right to be in the thick of events.

The plane finally arrived from Moscow. And it was on that day in 1923 that Evgeny Riabchikov first became interested in aviation.

As it happened, he never became a professional pilot; but he did become an aviation journalist and writer. So that he could get to know pilots and aircraft designers better, he learned to fly at the Central Flying Club and made numerous parachute jumps. As a journalist and passenger, he has flown a million kilometers. He has been on flights over the Arctic and the Antarctic and was a passenger on one of the first Soviet jet planes. He has been aloft in the gondolas of dirigibles and balloons and has been on hand at the start of famous flights.

In the USSR Evgeny Riabchikov is known as a popular writer, journalist, and radio and television commentator specializing in aviation and cosmonautics. He has written thirty-four books and made more than a thousand radio and television broadcasts. Space cinematography has figured importantly in his accomplishments. He has made a long series of films on the life, training, and flights of the cosmonauts.

On his sixtieth birthday, the cosmonauts presented him with a medal and a mock scroll certifying him as a member of their confraternity.

Aleksei Kazantsev
Copy editor of the Russian text of *Russians in Space*